Xiangzheng Deng

Modeling the Dynamics and Consequences of Land System Change

Xiangzheng Deng

Modeling the Dynamics and Consequences of Land System Change

With 76 figures, 7 of them in color

高等教育出版社
HIGHER EDUCATION PRESS

Springer

Author
Prof. Xiangzheng Deng
Institute of Geographic Sciences and Natural Resources Research,
Chinese Academy of Sciences
No.11A, Datun Road, Chaoyang, Beijing, 100101, China
E-mail: dengxz.ccap@igsnrr.ac.cn

ISBN 978-7-04-031489-2
Higher Education Press, Beijing

ISBN 978-3-642-15446-1 ISBN 978-3-642-15447-8 (eBook)
Springer Heidelberg Dordrecht London New York

Library of Congress Control Number: 2010933075

Printed on acid-free paper

Springer is part of Springer Science+Business Media (www.springer.com)

Preface

The dynamics and consequences of land system change have always been one of the central themes of global change research. A land system responds to human socioeconomic development while being directly influenced by human activities. As one of the most important research components in the sustainable development strategy currently advocated in human society, land system change has received much attention from the international communities. Although there are still some disputes about the mechanisms of global change induced by land system change, the allegation that land system change is an important starting point for the study of global change has been recogonized by both the physical and social science communities as well.

With the development of research on land use change and the establishment of the Global Land Project, researchers have increasingly realized the close relationships among natural environmental evolution, terrestrial ecosystem processes, human production activities and the dynamics of land system change. It is necessary to explore the interactions and associations among various factors in the land system from a systematic perspective to recognize the causes and effects of land system change. Land system change influences human survival and development from two aspects — matter and energy. There are direct or indirect connections between global environmental problems such as global warming, soil erosion, vegetation degradation and sharp declines in biodiversity and unreasonable land use patterns. The ecological and environmental effects of land system changes act on the human socioeconomic system and in turn become one of the main factors which influence and limit sustainable development. For example, cultivated land degradation, grassland desertification and deforestation caused by land use change have directly threatened the regional production and supply of products such as grain, animal products and timber.

Land system change is influenced by both the natural environmental conditions and human activities. The natural environmental conditions largely determine the direction of land system change. There are controlling effects of geographic factors such as altitude, aspect, slope, landform and soil types on land system change, while climatic conditions such as the accumulated temperature, precipitation and sunshine also influence the direction and speed of land system evolution. Furthermore, socioeconomic factors such as population increase, economic development, and technical progress and policy changes are also important driving factors for land system change.

Simulating the dynamics and consequences of land system change has been a breakthrough point and destination in research on land system change. As an interdisciplinary research, the simulation of the dynamics and consequences of land system change involves a wide range of disciplines, and it is necessary to consider the spatial and temporal scales simultaneously in the simulation process. This book discusses the principles and methods for simulating dynamic change in regional land systems and consequent effects, after identifying problems in existing models and methods, and develops a three-tier modeling approach involving the Computable General Equilibrium of Land Use Change (CGELUC), Dynamics of Land Systems (DLS) and Estimation System for Land Productivity (ESLP) models to solve the critical technical difficulties.

This book also reviews the current methods which have been used to simulate the dynamics and consequences of land system change, illustrates current thought, and explicitly introduces the principles, modules and functions, use, and data preparation processes underlying the models in detail. Finally, this book selects a case study area, simulates and analyzes the dynamics and consequences of land system change in that area to help readers better understand the basic operations and processes of the CGELUC, DLS and ESLP models.

Simulating the dynamics and consequences of land system change is still an evolving process, and the principles, models and methods are continuously changing and being examined, altered and improved. The three-tier model for simulating the dynamics and consequences of land system change used in this book is still in the development stage and there are imperfections in the systematic approach and integrity of the results contained in this book. The author only hopes to evoke valuable comments and hold extensive discussions with experts in related fields, both in China and abroad, to offer advice on how to improve modeling the dynamics and consequences of land system change.

Xiangzheng Deng
March 15, 2010

Acknowledgments

First, I am grateful for the contribution and financial support of China Book International and Higher Education Press. Particularly, I would like to express my thanks to Dr. Bingxiang Li and Dr. Lili Liu from Higher Education Press and the publishing editors from Springer who have been very patient and resourceful in helping me prepare the individual chapters and other materials for printing.

This book is based on a number of my studies which were funded by the Major State Basic Research Development Program in China (No. 2010CB950904), the National Natural Science Foundation of China (No. 70873118; No. 40801231; No. 41071343), the Key Project in the National Science & Technology Pillar Program of China (No. 2008BAK50B06; No. 2008BAC43B01; No. 2008BAC44B04) and the State Major Project for Water Pollution Control and Management of China (2009ZX07106-001-07). During my research and preparation of this book, a number of scholars and experts gave me helpful advice. My special appreciation is to Dr. Scott Rozelle, Dr. John Gibon, Dr. Emi Uchida, Dr. Jikun Huang, Dr. Jiyuan Liu and Dr. Xiubin Li for helping me with the ideas, methodologies and data. Also I would like to thank Qun'ou Jiang, Yingzhi Lin, Haiming Yan, Feng Wu, Wei Huang and Jifu Du for helping me to arrange the literature, draw illustrations, and revise model parameters.

Last, but not least, I am grateful to my family and colleagues in my group for their support and encouragement to pursue my research interests. It is their support and understanding that guaranteed the completion and publication of this book.

Contents

Chapter 1 Land System and Research Plans

The land system is a complex natural economic system consisting of the terrestrial part of the Earth's surface, all the environmental factors within an upper and lower range of the land, and some of the results of human production and living activities over the space (Lambin et al., 2003; Krausmann et al., 2003; Lin and Ho, 2003). The land system is the essential foundation of human survival and development (GLP, 2005). Land system change relates to the changes caused by humans on the land output by altering land use types. This is a complex process reproducing nature and the economy through the intervention of human activities, and inter-conversions between cultivated land, forestry area, grassland, water area, built-up and unused land are one of the important external manifestations of land system change (Nagendra et al., 2004; Deng, 2008; Verburg and Overmars, 2009).

There are three main reasons for land system change. First, the type and quantity of human demand for land outputs and services vary in different stages of socioeconomic development which results in a type of land system change known as endogenous conversion or active change (Heilig, 1997; GLP, 2005; Deng et al., 2008a). Second, the properties of the land can change due to nature and human activities; this is known as exogenous conversion or passive change. An example of exogenous change occurs when the aims of a social group change, forcing people to change land use patterns (Haberl et al., 2003). The third reason occurs when technical progress leads to land system change, which is known as technical change. As an important part of land use and land cover change (LUCC) research, land system change research is continually deepening due to advances in the global environmental change research (Turner II et al., 1994; Irwin and Geoghegan, 2001; Verburg et al., 2006).

The core plan of International Geosphere-Biosphere Program (IGBP) and International Human Dimension of Global Environmental Change Program (IHDP) was the LUCC plan, and in 2005 it achieved the assigned targets and registered great success. Since 2005, the Global Land Project (GLP) Science Plan has become the core of the IGBP and IHDP research plans (GLP, 2005; Rudel et al., 2005; Stehfest et al., 2007). The GLP puts emphasis on research into land system change and suggests that research on land system change should recognize various influencing factors and their effects from the perspective of system science, choose appropriate models as tools for understanding land system change, and reflect land system change at various spatial scales. Although great advances have been made in research on simulations of land system changes, there are still many areas that require improvements (Haberl et al., 2001; Gao and Deng, 2002; Pfaff and Sanchez-Azofeifa, 2004). Land system change is a dynamic process; therefore, to obtain valuable simulation results for decision-making, it is necessary to comprehensively consider the influence of various aspects including regional socioeconomic conditions, traditional cultures, natural conditions and historical land use conditions, and construct different scenarios of land system change to make more accurate predictions (Reenberg et al., 1998; Deng et al., 2008a).

Human socioeconomic activities play a significant role in various factors leading to land system change (Liu et al., 2003; Verburg et al., 2006). At longer time scales, land system change appears mainly due to changes in natural environmental conditions (Deng et al., 2002; Wang et al., 2005). Therefore, it is necessary to consider socioeconomic factors and natural environmental factors from a system perspective and depict the various directions of land system change by revealing the underlying mechanisms (Deng, 2008).

1.1 Land System

The land system is complex, consisting of natural factors including terrain, landform, soil, geological foundation, hydrology, climate and vegetation in particular region and past and present human land use activities and their consequent effects in the region; the land system is made up of biological and non-biological factors and their interactions (GLP, 2005; Deng, 2008).

1.1.1 Structure of the Land System

The land system is in a process of dynamic evolution. Depending on the degree to which humans have acted on the land system, scholars have categorized land systems as primeval land systems, semi-primeval land systems, semi-artificial land systems and artificial land systems. Research into land systems has mainly focused on land types, land uses, land assessments, land planning and management, and land carrying capacity (Deng, 2008; Deng et al., 2009).

1.1.1.1 Land Type

Land type is a consequence of artificial divisions based on regional differences and the following criteria and principles. Land type research includes the identification of individual morphological units and land gradation and classification (Deng et al., 2002). The identification of individual morphological units is based on a comprehensive understanding of the characteristics, regional distribution, regional differentiation and regional conjugation of various factors in the natural geographical environment of a particular region. Each individual morphological unit occupies a particular geographical space and may share common natural characteristics with other units, but may also differ significantly from other units. Land gradation and classification are used to generalize the properties of individual morphological units with logical methods to make them structural and systematic. Land gradation is used to determine the hierarchy of the individual morphological units, while land classification is used to generalize common morphological characteristics from the landscape for the individual morphological units (Deng et al, 2008b). Field survey data, satellite photographs and aerial photographs which can identify regional changes and the distribution characteristics of different units are the main information sources for land gradation and classification, and are the foundations of the current land system research (Islam and Weil, 2000; Lin and Ho, 2003; De La Rosa, 2005; Reynolds et al., 2007).

1.1.1.2 Land Use

Land use research mainly focuses on restraining factors related to land use, land use types, and the analysis of land use structure from the perspective of land systems (Veldkamp and Fresco, 1996; Liu et al., 2002a; Deng, 2003). The restraining factors related to land use include aspects such as natural, social, technical, economic and historical-cultural factors which have wide impacts on land system change (Chen et al., 2008). As a result of the two-way selection between land multi-suitability and diversification of human demands, the land use type is also an outcome of the interaction between the complexity of the natural environment and specialization of territorially divided production. The land use type is also related to the contradictory unity of the land as a complex natural and socioeconomic ecosystem for sustaining the self-balancing and virtuous cycles (Liu et al., 2002b). The land use structure refers to the mutual spatial position formed by comparative relationships between the various land use types and the relationships between spatial positions, which is determined by the natural environment (mainly the land surface configuration and the combination of water and heat), the spatial distribution of natural resources (soil, mines, ground and surface water, landscape, forest and grassland) and places for human residence and activities (DeFries et al., 2004). Land use research estimates the directions and approaches to land development by analyzing the status of the land system and diagnosing the driving factors of land use change.

1.1.1.3 Land Assessment

Land assessment is an important part of scientifically evaluating the land system to allow appropriate exploitation, use, changes and protection of the land (Verburg et al., 2000). Land assessment generally includes land suitability assessment, land use efficiency assessment and land productivity potential assessment. Land suitability assessment identifies all the possible land uses from the perspectives of the demand for different land use types in the area and the land quality (Huffman et al., 2000). Land use efficiency assessment focuses on the degree to which the productivity of the land meets society's needs, considering the productivity distribution, land input and output efficiency, ecological effects of land use and potential benefits of land protection (Liu et al., 2003; Deng et al., 2006). Land productivity potential assessment estimates the potential of the land to provide people with produce, which reflects the degree of land use and development (Yang and Li, 2000). Land assessment considers natural, social and economic properties associated with the land as a basis for determining specific assessment targets, and considers appropriate land use and reclamation from the perspective of the ecological, economic and social suitability and the possible effects of various land uses.

1.1.1.4 Land Planning and Management

Land planning and management involve determining objective conditions for the exploration and utilization of land and maximized ecological, economic and social benefits (MLRC, 2003). Land planning is generally used to determine future land use strategies based on the results of land planning models. Land management refers to the planning, organizing, controlling and monitoring activities around land use, which the government carries out under specific environmental conditions, using administrative means, laws, and economic techniques and polices (Deng et al., 2008b). Land planning acts directly on the processes of land use and change, while land management is an effective way to monitor and coordinate the status, structure and function of the land system (Rozelle and Rosegrant, 1997).

1.1.1.5 Land Carrying Capacity

The land carrying capacity, or the population carrying capacity of land, refers to the size of population that the land in certain region can support, and is a core part of land-population system research (Skole and Tucker, 1993; Huffman et al., 2000). Research on land carrying capacity can be carried out by measuring various aspects such as resources per capita, product consumption per capita and pollutant production per capita (DeFries et al., 2002). It is a simple and practical method to assess the land carrying capacity from the food production capacity and the food consumption standards under certain living conditions, which has been widely used (Rozelle and Rosegrant, 1997).

Land system research involves the following aspects: land type and natural zoning, land use and regional economies, land assessment, location analysis, land planning and management, regional policies, land carrying capacity and regional economic development.

1.1.2 Theory and Methodology of Land System Research

Land system research aims to optimize land use by studying the land system composition, development and regional differentiation. It identifies the natural features of the land and the suitability of the land for exploration. It also assesses the land productivity potential and productivity efficiency and directs land development, utilization and alteration in the process of understanding, utilizing and altering the land (Deng et al., 2006; Deng, 2008). The land system is closely associated with human survival and development, and all human activities on the land are under the influence of both natural and economic rules (GLP, 2005). Land system research considers the dual influences of the natural environment and socioeconomic conditions, and combines the land production ability and human demand. Land system research also studies the dynamic balance between production and demand and emphasizes the human-land relationship, providing scientific guidance to optimize the human-land system (Haberl et al., 2001). The theory and methodology to support land system research are consequences of the synthesis and intersection of modern science, involving various subjects, and various branches of natural and social sciences (Deng, 2008). The development of land system research theory is promoted by the territorial differentiation rules of various systems and theories including the natural environment, territorial complex theory, location theory, differential rent theory, fertile decline theory, biological evolutionism, community theory, ecological balance theory, law of value, planned economy theory, entropy theory, dissipative structure theory, and the theory of consideration of local conditions of the natural resource exploitation and utility (Acevedo and Restrepo, 2008). The development of cartography, geographic information system (GIS), remote sensing (RS) technology and the application of computer technologies in land system research have helped to advance land system theory and technologies (de Koning et al., 1998; Frolking et al., 1999; Seto and Kaufmann, 2003; Li and Yeh, 2004).

Previous land system research has inherited and developed land system research theories and methodologies from different subjects, which have developed from the study of the individual aspects of land to the study of the relationships between different components and now involves multi-directional research based on system science approaches. A comprehensive research system including the land and systematic theories of land system research has now been established (Zhu et al., 2005). According to current land system research, the structural-functional theory, the corresponding conversion analysis theory and the theory of land prices can be regarded as the core of land system science.

1.1.2.1 Structural-functional Theory

The principle that the land system structure determines the land system functions is one of the most widely used theories in land system research (Deng et al., 2008a). Land system structure analysis is an effective way to reveal the land system functions (Abbasi and Rasool, 2005). Land system research provides a scientific basis for the development of land according to local conditions and promoting land productivity by analyzing the land system structure (involving landscape composition, temporal succession structure and spatial composite structure). The land system structure includes the degree of homogeneity, regional differentiation of land types and their formation and development, exploring natural features, and the use and potential alteration of land (Fischer et al., 2001). A complete understanding of land system structures and functions allows research into individual land parcels to be converted into comprehensive regional comprehensive research (Lambin et al., 2000; Lambin et al., 2001).

Analysis of regional land system structures mainly includes three aspects: (i) the relationship between the land function and its location; (ii) the overlapping relationship of different functions, i.e., the diversification of land use; (iii) neighborhood effects. The analysis of the regional land system structure provides a basis for the land system status diagnosis and land assessment, and the results of the land assessment directly reflect the functions of the land system. Generally, high quality land has a high assessment grade, and wide land suitability has a greater potential productivity and therefore, higher land use efficiency.

1.1.2.2 Analytical Theory Based on Land Use Structure

Analytical theory based on land use structure is an important part of land system research (Rahman et al., 2007). Land is the most basic means of agricultural production, and the starting point for all primary production activities and many people's livelihoods. With the development of society, land system structures and various regional structures such as the industrial department structure, production distribution structure, production, marketing and consumption structure, natural environmental structure, administration and management structure and social cultural structure all change correspondingly. For example, the land resource structure directly influences the regional industrial department structure; the land type structure has direct impacts on the productivity distribution structure (especially agricultural productivity) (Verburg et al., 2000); the landscape composition and temporal succession structure constrain the environmental structure; the land use structure determines the production, marketing and consumption structure; and land planning reflects the administration and management structure and the sociocultural structure (Verburg, 2006).

The corresponding conversion analysis theory of land use structure based on land structure is the theoretical basis for coupling and optimizing various regional structures, promoting synergies among society, economic techniques and the environment and directing the appropriate use, exploitation and management of the land system.

1.1.2.3 Theory of Land Prices

An important part of land system research involves changing land use types based on the theory of land prices, promoting the appropriate use of land use economics and reinforcing land management and protection, allowing the regulatory function of the market to dominate (Annie et al., 2000). The social asset attributes of land determine that it has special use values. The use value of land is represented by the function of the land system and the land value reflects the properties of the land as commodities (de Koning et al., 1999). Land price is the currency of land value, which depends on land characteristics such as area, location, fertility and improvability (Krause, 2002). Land price is also influenced, either directly or indirectly, by investments, supply and demand, location (accessibility), polices and other social, economic and cultural factors (McIntyre and Lavorel, 2007). The land price can be improved, and land use efficiency can be maximized by optimizing the land use, continually improving the soil fertility, improving the land quality, constructing transportation networks, changing the infrastructure associated with land, increasing labor inputs, and realizing intensive land management. Additionally, land planning has also been shown to be an important factor affecting land price.

Overall, land system research has introduced aspects of "systems thinking" in regards to the characteristics of the land system such as concepts of wholeness, complexity, ordering, relatedness and dynamics. It has proposed basic principles including: the need for overall, comprehensive, connection and development viewpoints; developing and updating the methodologies of the land system research based on previous research; turning the "factor analysis method" into the "systems analysis method"; emphasizing the relationship between cognitive and practical processes of land development as well as the combination of qualitative analysis and quantitative study; and improving the rationality, objectivity, rigor, predictability and practicality of land system research by integrating the achievements of various subjects, such as mathematical methods (including probability theory, operational research, mathematical statistics and fuzzy mathematics), computer technology, the quantification and automation of RS technology, and GIS.

1.1.3 Procedures of Land System Research

Land system research should be carried out in a stepwise manner following the system engineering method, which has the following general characteristics. First, theory should be integrated with applications, i.e., land system should be researched into the unified processes of understanding, using, altering and protecting nature; and second, the research should consider the whole system comprehensively, i.e., land system research should study the land comprehensively using systems science, considering both the wholeness system and hierarchies, and consider overall interests of the land system.

Procedures of land system research can be reflected within a three-dimensional coordinate system containing knowledge, logic and time dimensions (Fig. 1.1). This procedure can be summarized as follows.

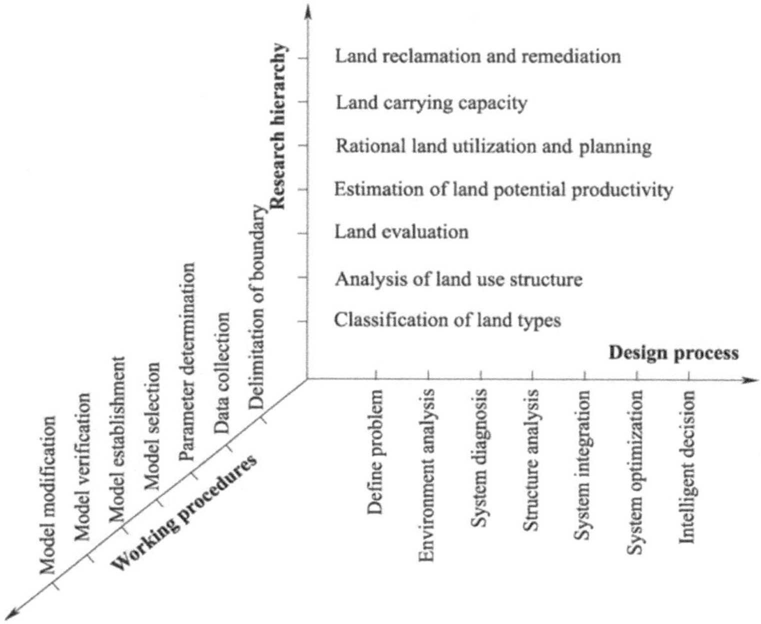

Fig. 1.1 Three-dimensional research procedure for land systems.

For the knowledge preparation, the practical background to the land system research should be understood, land system research theory and methodology should be mastered, and proper land research techniques should be selected. To develop research ideas, classification of the land type should be made first. Then the land assessment can be performed and the land carrying capacity analyzed, which allows the relationships among the natural resources, social environment and population development to be determined. The land use planning and management scheme should be formulated last. The research work involves several steps: first, delimit the boundaries of the research, i.e., determine the scope of the study area, carry out the investigation and field survey and finish the information collection; second, determine the parameters, choose and establish appropriate models according to the aim of the research; third, verify the accuracy of the models with a series of checks and tests including the theory test, empirical examination and practice test, and compare the dynamic monitoring data from the system with the simulation results; finally, modify the models and further perfect the research conclusion, and then submit the research results.

1.1.4 Model Architecture of a Land System

The land system is a very complex system involving numerous factors and components, research on which has not yet been standardized and normalized, and thus a complete model of the land system has yet to be proposed (GLP, 2005). The principle behind the current land system research methods is based on the philosophy of systems science, which establishes corresponding mathematical or non-mathematical models according to the research components and achieves the expected objectives with techniques such as GIS, and expressions such as tables and figures (Veldkamp and Fresco, 1996; Kerr et

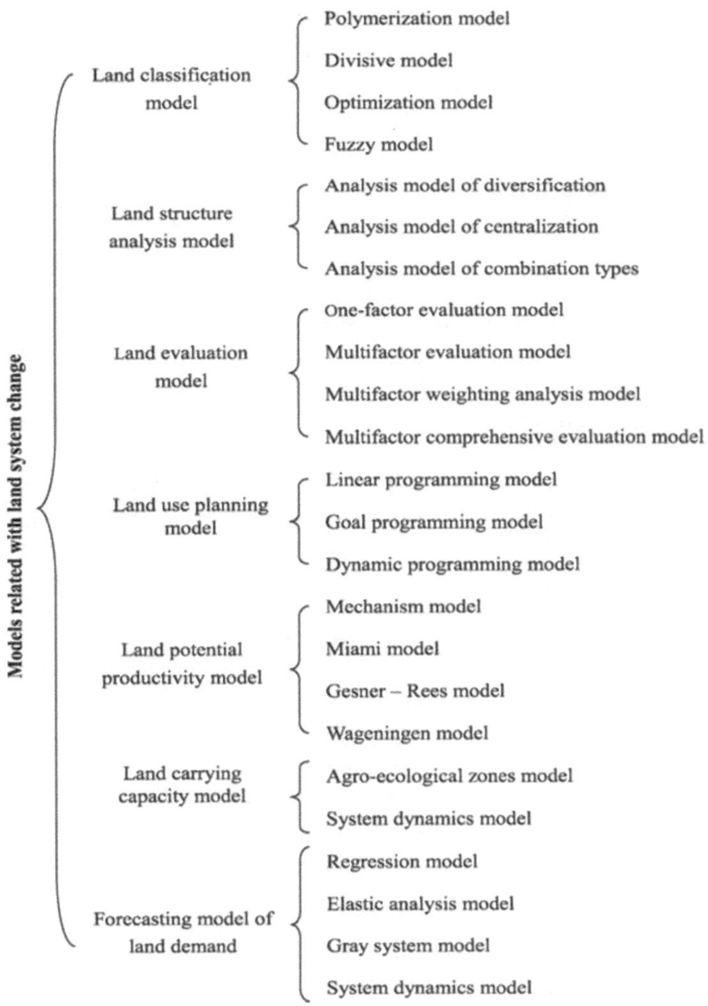

Fig. 1.2 Hierarchy of models related to land system change.

al., 2003). The modeling issues involved in this book refer to solvable modeling issues that can be abstracted to mathematical or analogue expressions.

Currently, researchers have designed a set of land system research models to solve practical problems depending on the needs of the research, and have proposed various outcomes as assistance to others. Based on this existing research, the land system research models can be categorized as land type models, land structure analysis models, land evaluation models, land use planning models, land productivity potential models, land population capacity supporting models and other prediction models (Veldkamp and Fresco, 1996; Pfaff, 1999; Veldkamp and Verburg, 2004). All of these model types have a system with a hierarchy, structure and functions (Fig. 1.2). The model system shown below was used to research the land system of the Tarim River Basin and a good research result was achieved (Zhao et al., 2006).

1.1.5 Approaches to Land System Research

Modern land system research has integrated multiple technologies and developed in the direction of integration, systematization, harmonization and intelligence. The combination of land system research and the latest achievements in GIS, RS, applied mathematics, computer and artificial intelligence has promoted the origination, development and continual update of these techniques (Verburg et al., 1999; Veldkamp and Verburg, 2004). The comprehensive study and application of new technologies has become the main development trend in land system research and has resulted in the development of related techniques. Examples of related techniques include the extraction of land information with RS to facilitate land investigations and land use monitoring, the development of land system research from qualitative to quantitative with mathematical advances, the realization of systematic simulations of expert knowledge, and the advance of land system research using the theory and methods of artificial intelligence.

The broad use and development of computer technology is one of the most important premises in the development of comprehensive new techniques for land system research (Veldkamp and Verburg, 2004). With the advent of information age, the support of computer technology has been necessary for both the internal development of techniques such as RS, applied mathematics and artificial intelligence, and the integration of these fields. Computer technology is the core technology for all new technologies in land system research.

The use of various technologies means that the main structural relationships within land system research show a certain hierarchy (Fig. 1.3). The GIS and modeling methods have been widely used in many research fields, and have been combined with computer technology to further improve the dominant spatial analysis function of GIS; as RS accuracy has been improved and combined with GIS and global positioning systems (GPS), accurate real-time monitoring of the system can be achieved (Li and Yeh, 2004). With these problems solved, the integrated development of RS databases, land databases and computer models can occur, which can further extend the functions of GIS and speed up the development of land system research (Liu et al., 2002b).

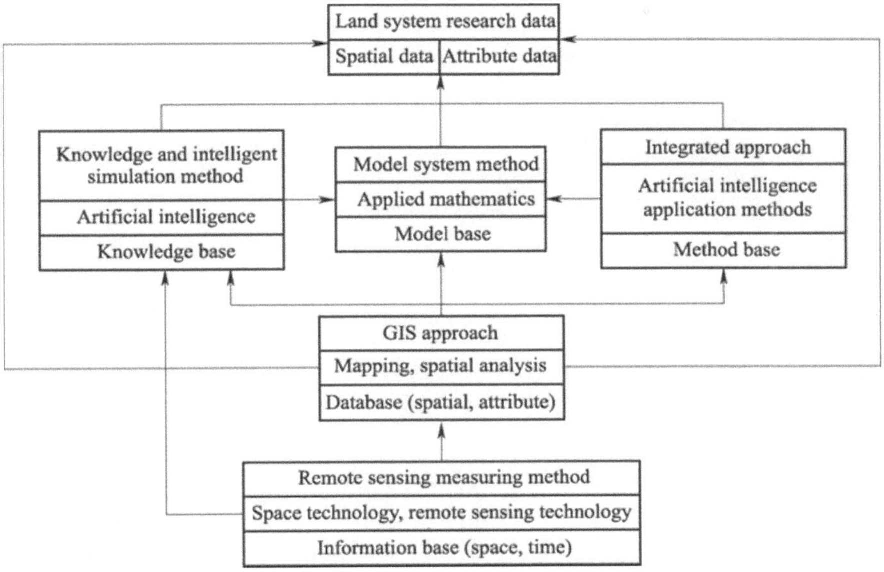

Fig. 1.3 Technical architecture of data and methods of land system change.

1.2 Research Plans and Achievements of the LUCC Plan

Land use change always leads to land cover change at a regional, national or global scale, which then causes a further series of environmental changes. Under this background, LUCC was proposed as an important subject for global land science research (Liu et al., 2005; Turner II et al., 2007; Verburg et al., 2010). Scholars in China and worldwide have carried out many studies on LUCC to discuss the processes, driving factors and environmental effects from multiple different perspectives in recent years (Zhang et al., 2003). This chapter mainly introduces the definitions, land use research topics, research progress and important results achieved to date.

1.2.1 Identification of Land Uses

Land use refers to the use of the land to acquire the required products or services (Turner II, 1995; Verburg et al., 2010). Agriculture and urbanization are all associated with different land uses. Cropping, forests, grassland, roads, buildings, soil, glaciers and watersheds are all classified as different land covers, and various changes including changes in biodiversity, actual or potential land productivity, soil quality, and runoff and deposition speed are land cover changes (Verburg et al., 2004). Land use and land cover are closely associated concepts but are different from each other; land use change is usually the cause of land cover change as well as the response to it. The interaction between land use change and land cover change is an interdisciplinary field involving both the natural and social sciences.

1.2.1.1 Land Use Pattern

A land use pattern describes the operational activities of land use and includes all types of farming, animal husbandry and human habitation. The effects of these land use patterns are cumulative and influence land cover at the global scale, involving various aspects of changes in atmospheric composition, biodiversity, soil conditions and runoff (Cai, 2000). These effects can be categorized into three types, modification, conversion and maintenance, depending on the processes involved (Burgi and Turner, 2002; Liu et al., 2003; Nagendra et al., 2004). Modification refers to changes in the internal conditions of one type of land cover, such as deforestation or cultivated land fertilization. Conversion means that one type of land cover is converted to another, such as a conversion from forest to farmland or grassland. Maintenance means the land cover is retained in a particular condition, such as a terraced field, with maintenance occurring on the associated structures, such as the renovation and trimming of an irrigating system.

It is necessary to integrate both natural and social sciences to study these effects because land cover change affects the physical world due to land use changes, but is determined by socioeconomic driving forces (Fig. 1.4). It can be seen that land use and land cover have formed a closely related and interactive system which is linked with the social driving force (Verburg and Overmars, 2009; Reenberg et al., 1998).

1.2.1.2 Research Background of Land Use Change

Since the early 20th century, human demand for food production has increased rapidly with rapid population growth and improved living conditions (Yang and Li, 2000; Deng et al., 2006). As a result, humans are exploiting natural resources at an unprecedented scale and speed. Since 1990 when worldwide economic development entered a completely new phase, land use change has become increasingly common due to industrialization and rapid urbanization (Reenberg et al., 1998; Lin and Ho, 2003). The subsequent food crisis, environmental pollution and loss of biodiversity have gradually be-

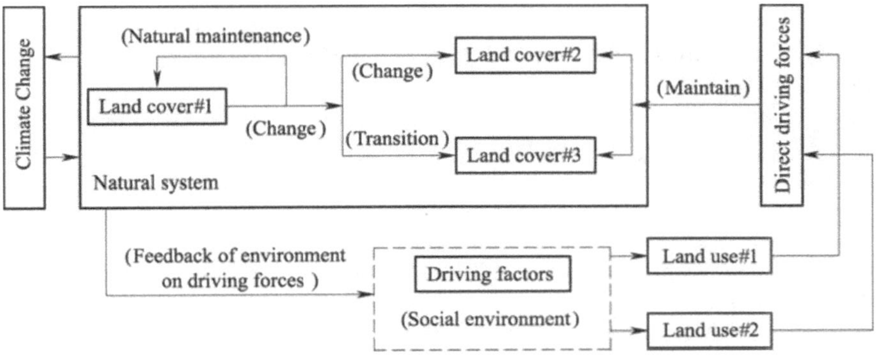

Fig. 1.4 Relationship between land use and land cover.

come globally important issues (Heilig, 1999). As the land is the basic means of production and the most important labor object, it has become the fundamental starting point for solving the environmental problems mentioned above and retaining sustainable land use (Tanrivermis, 2003; Veldkamp et al., 2004a). The effective management and sustainable use of land resources have become an important component and guarantee of economic growth and regional sustainable development (Tanrivermis, 2003).

LUCC has a great influence on changes in the Earth system and its components. In the late 20th century when studies of the interactions among the atmosphere, hydrosphere, lithosphere and biosphere were flourishing, LUCC was a typical representative of interdisciplinary studies, and became a core research topic in Earth system science (Miller et al., 2002). It has become important to understand the driving factors of LUCC in economic growth and its inner mechanisms and predict possible changes in the future, allowing for the optimization of land resource management strategies. With the development of LUCC research, attention shifted from the Earth's fluid system to human activities, the most important factors that have influenced meso-scale (several decades to several hundred years) changes in the Earth system. It became apparent that LUCC processes are not only the intersection between natural and human processes, but they also link regional sustainable development with global environmental change. The need to further develop LUCC research comes from this understanding.

LUCC are closely related to the living environment (Hietel et al., 2004). Considering the Earth as a life support system, biodiversity influences the living environment quality, and land productivity determines the quantity of living species, while other environmental changes including climate change and environment pollution also influence the living environment by land cover change, which shows the importance of land use change research.

1.2.1.3 Relationship between Land Use Change and Global Change

LUCC is the most important aspect in global environmental change research at both regional and global scales (Turner II et al., 1990; Haberl et al., 2001;

Rudel et al., 2005). Land cover supports the source and sink of much of the material and energy flows in the biosphere and geosphere, so LUCC mainly resulting from human activities has an important influence on the climate, biogeochemical cycle, hydrology and biodiversity in the Earth's system (Tang and Wang, 2009). Thus, LUCC research is an important aspect in global environmental change research. LUCC plays an important role in three important and high profile topics: global change; sustainable development; and biodiversity protection (Deng et al., 2008a).

Global environmental change includes both systematic changes and cumulative changes (Turner Ⅱ et al., 1994). Systematic change refers to real changes in the global bio-geochemical system, such as changes in the atmospheric composition, land cover patterns, carbon cycling and climate. Cumulative change refers to a phenomenon where the cumulative impact of massive regional change results in global environmental changes, such as vegetation deterioration, loss of biodiversity and soil erosion. LUCC affects global change mainly through cumulative changes. Although the impact of regional LUCC on Earth's system is negligible, where these changes occur repeatedly in both time and space, global effects may occur such as deforestation, chemical fertilizer application and the spread of urban areas. Due to the significance of LUCC in global change, the IGBP and IHDP jointly classified the LUCC plan as the core plan of global change research (Turner Ⅱ et al., 1994; Turner et al., 2003).

Global change has a profound impact on land use change in return mainly through climate change and regional environmental change (Fig. 1.5). Climate change can directly and indirectly influence land use change through fluctuations in temperature, precipitation and climate disasters. The impact

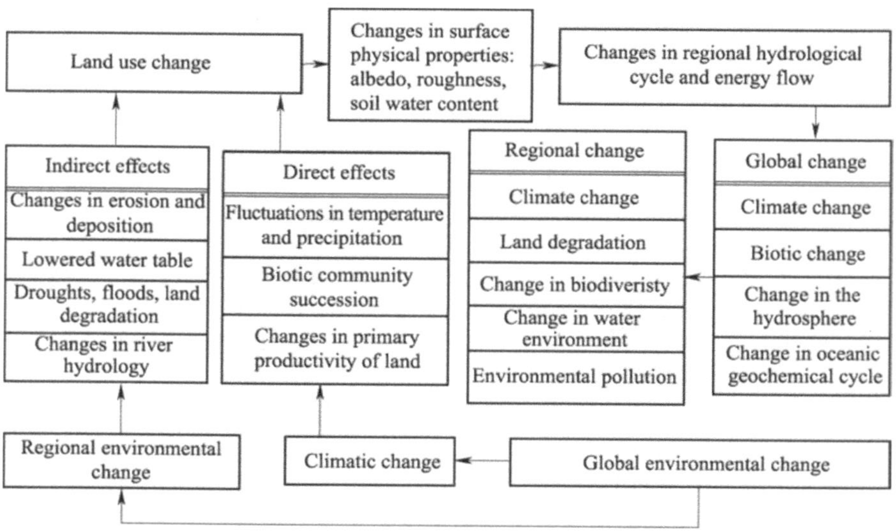

Fig. 1.5 Relationship between land use change and global environmental change.

of regional environmental change such as groundwater retreat and changes in river hydrology on LUCC is even more profound due to the typically regional characteristics.

1.2.1.4 Relationship between Land Use and Sustainable Development

LUCC is not only closely associated with human activities, but also directly or indirectly influenced by terrestrial and marine ecosystems, and predicts the future quantities of important material resources such as land and water (Turner II, 2010; Valbuena et al., 2010). Consequently, many of the sustainable development questions raised at the World Conference on Environment and Development were related to LUCC, which has been an important component in sustainable development research (Fig. 1.6).

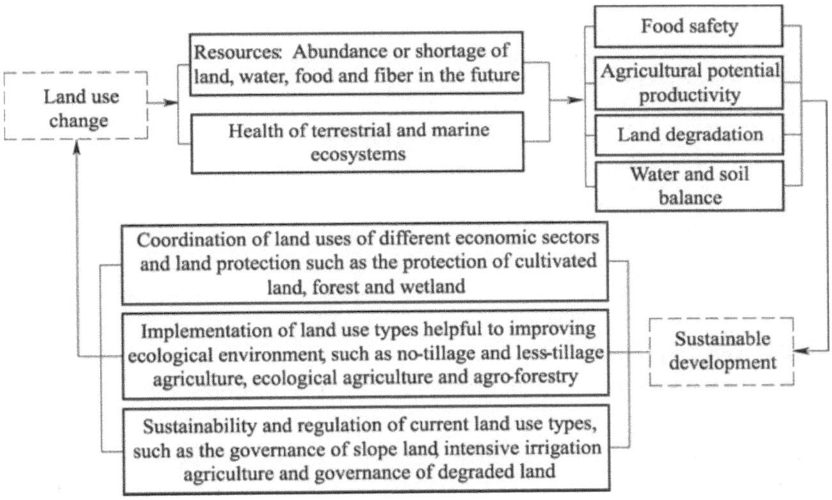

Fig. 1.6 Relationship between land use change and sustainable development.

LUCC and sustainable development interact with each other (Fig. 1.6). LUCC can change resources and the environment and may lead to regional or global problems which pose a challenge for sustainable development, while sustainable development limits LUCC by ensuring the reasonable use of the resources considering these problems (Tanrivermis, 2003; Haberl et al., 2004). From this perspective, sustainable development could be considered as the development direction for LUCC research, while LUCC provides sustainable development research with specific information and approaches.

1.2.1.5 Research Topics for Land Use

Core research topics

With an increasing understanding of the importance of LUCC in global environmental change research, the IGBP and IHDP developed and implemented a detailed LUCC research plan which considered the features of LUCC and the needs of global change research. The main components of LUCC research are as follows:

- How has human land use activity changed the land cover in the past 300 years?
- What are the main human factors that lead to land use change in different regions and under different historical conditions?
- How will land use influence the land cover in the next 50 to 100 years?
- How do various natural and human factors influence the sustainability of different land use patterns?
- How do climate change and global biogeochemical cycles interact with LUCC?

Key research fields

Based on the five scientific questions above, the LUCC plan further determined three key research fields of LUCC:

- Mechanism of changes in land cover
  Monitor the spatial and temporal processes of land cover change with RS techniques, and connect the changes with the driving factors. Construct empirical diagnostic models that can explain the mechanisms of spatial and temporal land cover changes and predict future measurable changes.
- Regional and global models
  Build macroscale LUCC dynamic mechanistic models which include all the economic components related to land use.
- Research framework
  The three key research fields of LUCC research interact with and complement each other, and together constitute the LUCC research framework (Fig. 1.7).

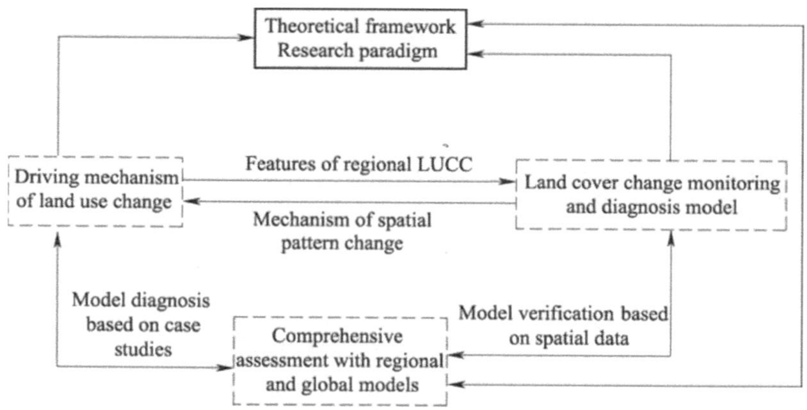

Fig. 1.7 Regional LUCC research framework.

1.2.1.6 Research Synthesis

There are two comprehensive areas of research that include all three key research fields of LUCC:

- Data collection and classification of land use and land cover, which includes the data source and quality and the design of a land use and land cover classification structure that can meet the needs of the three key research fields.
- Scale dynamics. The scale effect is an important aspect of LUCC research because different research scales can influence the overall understanding of LUCC.

1.2.1.7 Research Tasks

Establishing the LUCC research plan determined directions for LUCC research all over the world, and provided a foundation for international cooperation. With the guidance of the IGBP and IHDP, LUCC research has begun developing rapidly in major international organizations all over the world. In summary, LUCC research both in China and abroad is mainly focused on the following tasks:

- Establishment of an LUCC RS database;
- Research on a classification system for global changed land cover;
- Systematic research on regional LUCC and its economic driving forces;
- Research on the land use change analysis system based on simulation techniques and econometric methods;
- Prediction models and scale research for both regional and global LUCC;
- Research on the land use system and land quality index system based on land assessment;
- Research on models of regional differentiation and land use degree based on RS macrosurveys and land dynamic analysis.

1.2.2 Progress of Land Use Research

International research on land use change began formally after the "Agenda 21" document developed by the United Nations in 1992, although many countries had carried out research relevant to LUCC before that. Vernadsky (1926) began to research the main biogeochemical cycling on Earth in the mid-19th century. Other scholars (Vitousek et al., 1997) discussed changes in the Earth's surface caused by human activity. Sweden has undertaken dynamic monitoring of desertification and vegetation change in the Sahara Desert since 1972 and has carried out long-term research on LUCC in this region (Ahlcrona, 1988). The Ecological Society of America identified a priority research field for the last ten years of the 20th century in 1988, and proposed the Sustainable Biosphere Initiative Plan, which focused research on the effect of ecology on land resource management and protection of Earth's life support system (Seto et al., 2000).

1.2.2.1 Research Progress

LUCC became a focus area for global environmental change research in the 1990s due to the impact of two globally influential organizations, the IGBP and IHDP, which have been active in sponsoring comprehensive global research plans since 1990 (Turner II et al., 1995). The IGBP and IHDP developed the *Land Use and Land Cover Change Research Program* in 1995 and considered it to be a core program in global environmental change research, starting thematic studies of LUCC at various scales. The international project office of the LUCC program was established in Barcelona, Spain on October 11th, 1996, and its main task is to promote the development of international programs of research on LUCC driving mechanisms and strengthen support for the management and implementation of the current program, and to extend the current research on LUCC and foster international cooperation (Turner II et al., 1995). In December 1996, an international symposium named "Comprehensive Land Use Simulation: Driving Issue Research" was held at Cranfield University in the United Kingdom, at which the participants summarized the LUCC research progress under the auspices of the IGBP and IHDP. Participants also developed a broad approach to LUCC research on the driving forces of LUCC, soil erosion and land degradation throughout Europe in recent history, and also identified research gaps, fostered international cooperation in LUCC research, and developed a cohesive approach to future activities. LUCC was again identified as a focus issue at a conference on the human factors in global change research held in Laxenburg, Austria in June 1997.

Many international organizations and countries have responded to the IGBP and IHDP and carried out research on LUCC and related areas, and have accumulated much experience (Krause, 2002; Ierodiaconou et al., 2005). For example, the International Institute for Applied Systems Analysis (IIASA) initiated the "Europe and North Asia Land Use and Land Cover Change Models" project; the United Nations Environment Program drew up the "Land Use and Land Cover Change" project; the US Global Change Research Committee classified land cover change and climate change, and the depletion of the ozone layer as the main fields of global change research and focused on land cover change research in North America; the Global Environment Research Center, Japanese National Academy of Sciences proposed the "Land Use for Global Environmental Conservation" project (LU/GEC); the Chinese Academy of Sciences constructed a relatively sophisticated national resource and environmental spatial database of China in the project "Remote Sensing Macro Survey and Dynamic Analysis of National Resources and Environment" and systematically analyzed the natural environmental factors that influence the land use degree and spatial distribution of land use and land cover in China and the rules that lead to changes.

1.2.2.2 Research Schools

The international organizations and countries that have carried out research on land use change have achieved a series of outputs and founded different schools of thought, including the North American, Japanese and European schools.

Researchers of the North American school have qualitatively analyzed large-scale land use change at a global scale and its interrelationship with global environmental change. The viewpoint of this school of thought is reflected in the relevant LUCC research plans of the IGBP and IHDP, and its representatives include Turner II et al. (1995). Since 1990, Turner II et al. have published several books, including "The Earth as Transformed by Human Action" (Turner II et al., 1990), and "Changes in Land Use and Land Cover: A Global Perspective" (Meyer and Turner, 1994) and also compiled the 24th IGBP report on LUCC research (Sato, 2004) and the subsequent 35th IGBP report. Additionally, many relevant papers have been published by the North American school, which reflect the research focus and methods of this school and to some extent also represent the mainstream of international LUCC research. The main components of the research from this school include: (i) driving forces of land use change; (ii) influence of land use change on land cover; (iii) spatiotemporal heterogeneity of land use change; and (iv) regional and global land use change models and prediction. Their main research methods include: (i) analyzing land use change and constructing models using comparative case study methods; and (ii) deducing comprehensive regional and global models to predict future land use change. However, due to the broad focus of this school, their research achievements often lack depth, and the models are generally conceptual, which are impractical.

The Japanese school of thought mainly uses quantitative and economic models to quantitatively analyze regional land use change. The representatives of this school include Kuninori at the Japanese National Institute for Environmental Studies (Kuninori, 1999), Kagatsume at Kyoto University, and Kitamura at Tokyo University of Agriculture (Kitamura et al., 1997). The research done by the Japanese school is mainly reflected in the LU/GEC project which started in 1995 and has been carried out in stages, focusing on the sustainability of land use in Asia-Pacific region. The main research objective in the first stage (1995–1997) was to predict the land use and land cover in this region in 2025 and 2050 and furnish protections for the primary productivity of the land. The researchers used methods such as RS, GIS monitoring and spatial modeling analysis to study the spatial distribution of LUCC, and the temporal dynamics and driving factors, and also strengthened research on corresponding measures and techniques. Following the first stage of research, they designed and developed a basic model concerning land use change. The researchers from this school selected the related explanatory variables with canonical correlation analysis method to determine the natural and socioeconomic factors that lead to land use change. They later simulated the driving forces resulting in additional land demand in different periods and also simulated the policy environment with simulation methods such as Kane's Simulation (Kane et al., 1991). Most recently, they have built relationship models among the gravity model (Paulo and Tomaz, 2010), the potential model and the River Analysis System method (USACE, 2001), and obtained estimation results of the land use ratio function with a multiple logistic analysis method (Huang et al., 2007).

Research on land use change within the European school of thought is represented by the IIASA plan and the LUCC plan, and starts from a welfare analysis, then builds relevant models and simulates future scenarios and the consequent changes in the natural environment and resources based on the study of land resource and food policy. The main representative of this school is Günter Fisher from the IIASA. Fisher et al. (2000) believed that welfare analysis and the study of welfare policy can provide an effective simulation of the social and economic driving forces that lead to land use change. They presume that highly nonlinear processes can be simulated simply by regulating welfare and the weights of other policy variables in the planning process, and the sensitivity and stability of the change trajectory determined by this method can be compared with those of the regression dynamic balance model or other methods, to create a new policy-related method by combining the two methods. Researchers of the European school consider LUCC as an integral system and identify the underlying socioeconomic driving forces by simulating past and present land use changes, and then simulating future land use scenarios and predicting trends in land use change until 2050 and assessing the consequent resource and environmental effects.

1.2.2.3 Research Directions under Exploration

The introduction above indicates that research on the driving forces has dominated land use change research. The existing research can acquaint people with the main types of driving forces and reflects the close relationship between the driving forces and land use change at a global scale over a long historical period. However, the research described above is generally limited to descriptions of the long-term land use change trends in a global sense or at the global scale, without strong connections to the land use change process or a deep and systematic analysis of various human driving forces which lead to these changes. The description of large-scale general trends often overlooks the actual land use change situations at small and medium scales. For example, the decrease in global forests and increase in global cultivated land are both very significant trends for the past 40 years, but in Western Europe the forest cover increased and cultivated land decreased during the same period. Furthermore, there is still a poor understanding as to how land use change is influenced by the configurations of socioeconomic factors such as economic development level, institutional land management systems, country policies, population pressure, international business, and how changes in the global carbon cycle or climate change changes the land features. There is also a need for deeper understanding of how human activities influence land cover features (Zhao et al., 2002; Kaufmann et al., 2007). All these problems make it difficult to accurately predict future land use and land cover changes, regardless of how complex the constructed mathematical model is.

(1) Improving comprehensive multidisciplinary studies

The interactions between land use change mechanism and changing natural and social factors is not fully understood. Natural scientists often analyze data according to geographical networks determined from the latitude and longitude, while social science data are seldom collected by latitude and longitude, and consequently there have been few successful examples of cooperative interdisciplinary research so far (Turner II et al., 1995). Many existing global agriculture and vegetation models only consider LUCC related to crop plants and seldom connect economic production with biophysical processes (Fisher et al., 2002). Other models mainly consider the one-way influence of socioeconomic conditions on natural conditions and seldom take into account the feedback effects of natural conditions on the socioeconomic situation (Verburg, 2006). Comprehensive LUCC models should be able to measure the main socioeconomic and natural driving forces behind LUCC and simulate the main feedback relationships (Veldkamp and Fresco, 1996; Veldkamp and Verburg, 2004; Aspinall, 2004; Parker et al., 2008). Future research should emphasize the mutual participation of social scientists, natural scientists and specialist GIS personnel, and comprehensive multidisciplinary studies should be carried out with the support of modern information technology (Deng, 2008).

(2) Improving mechanism and function models

Long-term (50–100 years) land use change and relevant biophysical parameters such as vegetation features and the accumulation and degradation of resources cannot be predicted well at proper spatial resolutions because definite spatial relationships between the variables have not been set up during the LUCC modeling process. A key development direction for LUCC research should start with the implications and research components of LUCC, and construct land use change models. To do this, a deeper understanding of land use change, spatial patterns and processes of land use change, and the spatiotemporal relevance of land use change research is required. From this information, future change trends and environmental effects can be predicted (Deng et al., 2009).

(3) Discussing the complexity of driving mechanisms

The land use system is a complex system involving many natural and socioeconomic factors, and research on land use should fully consider the sensitivity of LUCC to variables such as the policy, technological advances, population increase, economic development, market change, and the influence of cultural factors including human ideology and beliefs. In research on the driving forces and the complex relationship between those forces and LUCC, researchers should consider the following conditions: (i) for a given driving force, its function may vary with the land use change types involved in the research—the driving factors that promote LUCC in a particular land use type may inhibit LUCC in another land use type; (ii) the same kind of LUCC may result from different driving forces in different regions—there is not just one explanation for LUCC. For example, the reduction in forested areas due to expansion of cultivated land may be driven by the population growth in one case, while in another situation, population growth may be explained by the social, political and economic conditions, with the expansion of cultivated land affecting the population growth; and (iii) the relationship between different driving forces and LUCC may vary at different spatial and temporal scales; For example, a relationship between driving forces and LUCC at a global scale may be different at a regional scale. All the situations described above indicate that researchers must consider the types, spatial features and scales of driving forces when building LUCC models.

(4) Case studies conducted at different scales

The long-term goal of LUCC modeling research is to construct a series of models with good theoretical foundation and flexibility, which can combine many different methods. Since the trends at global and regional scales often mask small scale land use changes, it is necessary to get the support of grass-roots research for exploring the theoretical foundations for taking sustainable land use measures. Furthermore, to comprehensively integrate data at different scales and create a series of LUCC models, it is necessary to select typical case study areas, with representative land use change types and driving forces. Researchers should start with the study of spatial and temporal changes in land use and its driving mechanisms at a small scale and then expand the spatial dimension, and eventually couple the research results at different spatial scales to reveal the internal mechanism of land use change in the case study area and predict the future land use change.

1.2.3 Research Achievements of the LUCC Plan

The LUCC plan has resulted in a series of research achievements through theoretical exploration at global and regional scales and empirical studies.

1.2.3.1 Completion of Monitoring Techniques

Over the past few decades, the image data obtained from RS techniques such as NOAA/AVHRR and MODIS have provided regional and even global LUCC researchers with enough data (DeFries et al., 1995). Landsat TM/ETM has been one of the main data sources used in LUCC research at a regional scale, and RS image data with higher resolution such as SPOT, IKNOS and QuickBird has also been gradually introduced into LUCC research.

Based on the spectral features of RS images, the supervised classification of LUCC involves the reorganization and monitoring of land cover using various data image processing methods complemented with empirical knowledge for confirmation. There are two general types of LUCC monitoring methods.

One is the direct spectrum comparison method which mainly involves the interpolation method, the ratio method, the vegetation index method, principal component analysis and the change vector method. The disadvantage of the direct spectrum comparison method is that it does not provide land cover type information for the pixels before and after the changed and unchanged pixels simultaneously. The other method is the classification comparison method, which monitors LUCC mainly by comparing the classification results for the image data or the results of the original spectral histogram transformation. This method is widely used but is limited by many factors, for example, slight changes within a patch of one particular land cover type cannot be detected and it is difficult to guarantee the classification resolution. Research in this area mainly focuses on the exploration of new methods such as digital image processing of the spectral features of the image.

1.2.3.2 Understanding Driving Mechanisms and Environmental Effects

A consensus has been achieved on the driving mechanisms of land use change that must be included in a driving force analysis: biological, natural, climatic, economic, social, demographic and other driving forces. A general level of understanding has also been achieved. For example, regional land use change results from the combined effects of the driving factors of land use change which operate at a regional scale and also those functioning at a larger (e.g., global) scale. Understanding the driving mechanisms of LUCC has developed from simpler situations to more complex situations and eventually, universal conditions will be achieved.

Research on the environmental effects of LUCC is being expanded with the implementation of various IGBP research plans on both global and regional scales. For example, Kalnay and Cai (2003) compared the change trend of surface temperature on the continental United States by reanalysis of the global temperature in the past 50 years, and concluded that the average surface temperature increasing by about 0.27℃ per 100 years resulted from land use change. Matson et al. (1997) studied the impacts of agricultural land use intensity on ecosystems and determined that cultivated land expansion and enhancement of land use intensity are some of the most significant global changes in the 20th century which can change the biological interactions in an ecosystem and influence the scope and extent of land resource exploitation.

To conduct the research into LUCC that the IGBP demands, it is necessary to explore the overall impact of LUCC on ecosystems from the perspective of the ecosystem management. This includes impacts on ecological processes such as landscape pattern change, change in the biogeochemical cycle within the ecosystem, change in ecosystem productivity and loss of biodiversity. An effective way to achieve the outputs of LUCC research is to compare different case study areas during the same period. However, there has been relatively little research of this type, and this field is still being developed.

1.2.3.3 Development of Land Use Change Models and Analytical Methods

Modeling has been emphasized since the initiation of the LUCC research plan. There has been a general consensus that model construction is an important way to understand the dynamics and complexity of the land use system. The models widely and currently used in LUCC research fields can be divided into four categories: (i) empirical statistical models such as the multivariate regression model (Zang and Huang, 2006); (ii) random models such as the Markov chain model (Muller and Middleton, 1994; Kiira, 1995); (iii) optimization models such as models based on the economic theory (Lewis, 2010); and (iv) dynamic simulation models based on processes (Verburg et al., 2009).

It has become necessary to build and use more comprehensive models to further understand LUCC (Lambin, 2006). The 6th series of the LUCC reports specifically discussed the agent-based models of land use and land cover (ABM/LUCC) which consist of two parts, agent-based models (ABM) and the cellular automata model. The agent is the land manager making the land use plans, whose land use decision-making behavior is simulated by the agent-based models based on a series of input rules, while the cellular automata model reflects the impacts of the decision-making with simulated landscape change (Lambin et al., 2001; Aspinall, 2004).

There are still many aspects of relevant models of LUCC that require improvement. Given the complexity of the land use system, it is usually necessary to impose some restrictions on LUCC models so that they model only a single process, single field or limited area. Large scale LUCC often involves many factors, so it is necessary to construct land use system models to simplify and summarize the actual land use situation, but these simplifications inevitably lead to uncertainty in the simulation results. The cellular automata model of ABM/LUCC has the required spatial and scale characteristics, only time will verify whether the ABM can simulate the land use decision-making processes (including land use decision-making regulation based on feedback results).

Due to the complexity of the land use system, there are still many challenges in the construction of models that can actually reveal the driving mechanism of LUCC. Therefore, it is still necessary for the researchers to try to identify the driving mechanisms of LUCC and improve the basis of the existing models by in-depth study of case study areas. Additionally, further research could determine the way to divide the complex land use change processes into relatively simple sub-processes, and then model the sub-processes separately with the current models, and at last reintegrate the models, for instance, with the CLUE model and the ABM/LUCC model (Lu and Bai, 2006).

1.2.3.4 Accumulation of Information at Regional and Global Scales

The global scientific research plan develops continuously relying on the development of Earth detection technology, which has produced many data products. International researchers have carried out in-depth and detailed research on tropical rainforest degradation such as research on the degree of LUCC, its reasons and environmental effects in the Amazon Basin which is the largest tropical rainforest region on Earth and where 100–200 million ha of forest is cut each year (Walker et al., 2002; William et al., 2004). Much research has showed that such rapid and extensive deforestation will increase the CO_2 concentration in the atmosphere and change the local hydrological conditions and climate (Zhang et al., 2001). The forest disappears most quickly in the eastern and northern parts of the Amazon Basin, where 230 000 km^2 of forest disappeared in 1988, three times more than in the previous 10 years (Skole and Tucker, 1993). Two case studies carried out in one region of the Amazon Basin, Brazil showed that the amount of forest cleared each year increased from 4121 ha to 8634 ha over a 4-year period, and cultivated land increased 1.5 times its original area.

In addition to deforestation, the areas of forest degradation and sparse-woodland have also increased dramatically (Grainger, 1990). Furthermore, the speed of conversion from secondary forest into cultivated land has also tripled. All the data show that large-scale human reclamation activities have repeatedly disturbed forested land, converting primary and secondary forests into pastures (Skole and Tucker, 1993). It was once assumed that forest degradation mainly resulted from increasing population and population density; however, the results of statistical analyses show that there is no evident cause and effect relationship. The main reason why forests are destroyed to reclaim land is that local government policies and high inflation rates make agriculture and animal husbandry a safe and profitable business.

1.3 The Global Land Project

After the IGBP's core project "Global Environmental Change and Terrestrial Ecosystems" ended in November 2003 and the LUCC plan, cosponsored by the IGBP and IHDP, ended in October 2005, the IGBP and IHDP cosponsored the GLP, which emphasizes the interactions between humans and the biosphere and natural resources. This project highlights research on changes in the human-environment system from local to regional scales and expects to better understand land system change and consequent social, economic and political effects (GLP, 2005).

1.3.1 Background

Currently, the global environment faces severe challenges. Because the IGBP and IHDP cosponsor the GLP, they expect to improve the understanding of the human-environment system through detailed researches on the interactions between humans and natural resources. Implementation of the GLP will also enhance our understanding of the movement status of the land system at regional and global scales and promote the intersection, integration and development of fields related to global change.

The GLP focuses on changes in the human-environment system, emphasizes an understanding of land system dynamics, aims to reveal the mechanisms underlying the interaction among different land systems to predict future trends and explore the sustainability of the biosphere (GLP, 2005). Based on the previous achievements of IGBP and IHDP researches, the GLP will improve understanding of the land system at regional and global scales and promote the integration of science in the global change plan.

1.3.2 Formation and Development of the GLP

The IGBP and IHDP appointed a GLP workgroup in 2002 and held a series of meetings at the Natural Resource and Ecology Laboratory, Colorado State University in January 2002 and April 2003. In October 2002, the IGBP and IHDP held a meeting in Bilthoven, the Netherlands where the scientists discussed the direction of future development for the GLP.

The 2003 annual meeting of the IGBP provided the fundamental basis for the research framework for the GLP. The draft on the GLP was revisited and revised and the central issue and research topics were further clarified at the land science plan public meeting held in Morelia, Mexico in December 2003. In May 2004, the GLP advisory group appointed by the IGBP and IHDP revised the central issues of the plan further.

Research on the disturbance of human activities on the land system should not only consider the scale inference in the problem analysis, i.e., converting an understanding of the land system at local and regional scales to a global scale, but also consider the social and environmental factors and use this multi-disciplinary knowledge to improve the understanding of issues related to the land system. The LUCC plan advanced knowledge and experience related to land system dynamic change and its effects on the international academic community. Concurrently, the Global Change and Terrestrial Ecosystems (GCTE) plan also provided a foundation for improving the understanding of global environmental change and its potential impacts on natural and agricultural ecosystems. However, it is impossible to explore the long-term impacts of global change on human society only from the perspective of natural environmental research, and the level of understanding of the human-environment system requires improvement.

1.3.2.1 Research Focus

Changes in the human-environment system influence energy, water, and biological cycles at a global scale. Political and economic changes at a global scale (such as the implementation of international treaties and the formation of the free market) also have impacts on decisions about the exploitation and use of resources at local and regional scales. The GLP emphasizes the measurement, simulation and understanding of the human-environment system, focusing on the interrelationships among humans, biological organisms and natural resources including the terrestrial and water ecosystems at local and regional scales. The GLP approach of considering problems at the ecosystem level enables us to better understand changes in the human-environment system (including the impacts of biophysical changes on humans) and synergies with human activities and social structure (GLP, 2005). Therefore, the GLP provides the general framework for research on the fragility and sustainability of different regional human-environment systems.

1.3.2.2 Research Framework and Issues

The GLP emphasizes the coupled relationships among humans, ecosystems and natural resources in the terrestrial ecosystem, and advocates the use of case studies in typical regions to allow comparisons between global and regional scales (GLP, 2005).

The research goals of the GLP (2005) have determined its research framework. These goals are: (i) identify the agents, structures and nature of change in coupled socio-environmental systems on land, and quantify their effects on the coupled system; (ii) assess how the provision of ecosystem service is affected by the changes in (i) above; and (iii) identify the characteristic and dynamics of vulnerable and sustainable coupled socio-environmental land systems to interacting perturbations, including climate change.

Consequently, three themes have emerged from these objectives:

Theme 1: Land System Dynamics

Issue 1.1: How do globalization and population change affect regional and local land use decisions and practices?

Issue 1.2: How do changes in land management decisions and practices affect biogeochemistry, biodiversity, biophysical properties and disturbance regimes of terrestrial and freshwater ecosystems?

Issue 1.3: How do the atmospheric, biogeochemical and biophysical dimensions of global change affect ecosystem structure and function?

Theme 2: Consequences of Land System Change

Issue 2.1: What are the critical feedbacks in the coupled Earth system from ecosystem changes?

Issue 2.2: How do changes in ecosystem structure and functioning affect the delivery of ecosystem services?

Issue 2.3: How are ecosystem services linked to human well-being?

Issue 2.4: How do people respond at various scales and in different contexts to changes in ecosystem service provision?

Theme 3: Integrating Analysis and Modeling for Land Sustainability

Issue 3.1: What are the critical pathways of change in land systems?

Issue 3.2: How do the vulnerability and resilience of land systems to hazards and disturbances vary in response to changes in human-environment interactions?

Issue 3.3: Which institutions enhance decision making and governance for the sustainability of land systems?

The success of the GLP is that it has proposed strategic measures for understanding the human-environment system and improving land system management from the perspective of sustainable development to resolve the pressing issues of global environmental change.

1.3.2.3 Major Scientific Issues

The GLP research goal covers four main scientific issues.

(1) A more integrated approach from the current disciplinary fragmentation in the land system science community

The GLP has adopted a truly interdisciplinary approach for studying the human-land coupling system and addressing dynamic problems in the land system (GLP, 2005). This approach suggests that the GLP will move from research into the land system dynamics to the relatively complex and multi-scale study of the dynamics of natural, social and combined processes. The GLP integrates knowledge of natural science and social science, and identifies measures for improving the current land use status and guaranteeing the sustainability of the land use system by regulating human activities. This results from the coupling analysis of the relationship dynamics between society, the environment, and the development and use of resources.

The GLP emphasizes the interactions between biophysical and social processes and also considers the development and changes with time in the critical terrestrial environment (Theme 1), and ecosystem (Theme 2), which are influenced by the social and environmental fields. This approach forms a new type of scientific view, epistemology and methodology. It reveals the mechanism of the interactions between the social and environmental systems closely associated with the land system while promoting the development of interdisciplinary integration.

(2) True integration of scientific efforts to deal with the large-scale changes taking place in the land system

The LUCC case study indicates that there is a hierarchical structure of the factors leading to the land system change. The limited, graded, hierarchical factors will help to predict changing trends in the land use system. The GLP advocates the analysis of the multidimensional human-land system dynamics which avoids the problems that occur when land use processes are explained with threshold limit and nonlinear characteristics (GLP, 2005). The GLP proposes the use of RS and GIS techniques to carry out related thematic studies. These combined techniques allow several variables to be selected and the research can be carried out at multiple scales simultaneously.

(3) Methods for scaling across physical and scientific observational dimensions

The GLP aims to reveal the laws of dynamic spatiotemporal change in the land system at regional and global scales (GLP, 2005). The influence of global environmental change in the human-environment system in different regions varies greatly, with different reactions by the land system to biophysical changes (such as increased CO_2 concentrations in the atmosphere or increased soil erosion) and socioeconomic change (such as market globalization) in different regions. For example, environmental changes are greater in the Northern Hemisphere than in the Southern Hemisphere, in urban environments than in rural environments, and in developed countries than in developing countries. From these responses, the different reactions that further influence land use patterns can be identified by analyzing regional decisions about land use and the provision of ecosystem services. The complex changes in the human-environment system are not simply repeated, which indicates that an individual case study cannot predict the overall trend. An accurate definition model is required to establish regional comparisons, from which an overall conclusion representing the comprehensive features of worldwide land systems can be achieved (Theme 3). The outcomes of GCTE and LUCC and other research plans will provide an example for the GLP in constructing a global network

(4) Methods to incorporate historical aspects and timescales of social and environmental changes

The complex dynamics of the human-environment system require the construction of a large integrated model with multiple space-time scales (GLP, 2005). This model will integrate the "bottom to top" and "top to bottom" processes to carry out the multiple perspective comprehensive dynamic analysis of land system change and effectively deal with emergent and complex system phenomena.

The integrated multi-perspective comprehensive dynamic analysis model is expected to study relationships in the human-environment system (Deng et al., 2008a). However, the currently available empirical models and decision support systems are not mature enough. The GLP multi-perspective comprehensive dynamic simulation aims to construct a dynamic model for interactions in the social-environmental system and examine its accuracy with monitoring data.

1.3.2.4 Implementation of the GLP

The GLP advocates constructing multiple-source data models and carrying out multi-scenario simulation analyses (GLP, 2005). For example, integrating data at multiple space-time scales, and exploring the interaction of various factors including nature and society in the human-environment system from multiple perspectives based on different simulation scenarios.

(1) Development of a multi-scale modeling and scenario analysis strategy

The GLP emphasizes fields related to land systems, integration of models at different scales and results verification (GLP, 2005). Particularly, the GLP supports the development of a multi-scale model to integrate the various different models into multi-scale models. The GLP also encourages the use of scenario analysis using different models and methods at various scales to analyze natural and socioeconomic factors in the human-environment system. The GLP also promotes the development of a global dynamic vegetation model to develop for the global dynamic land model which includes the human-environment system.

(2) Establishment of regional and global scale databases

There is an urgent need for a range of global and regional scale databases to record changes in the global ecosystem structure and function. The GLP advocates establishing a dynamic land system spatiotemporal database and proposes global data sharing (GLP, 2005). The dynamic land system spatiotemporal database can identify extreme events, and the frequency and intensity of other disturbances and land use changes. The free and constantly updated land system database could provide data support for better assessing current land use situations and predicting future changes in land systems.

At present, global land cover data can be obtained from remote sensing satellites. However, it is difficult to obtain data for many other ecosystem elements such as biomass, carbon density, species distribution and soil composition, which hinders the progress of GLP research. The primary objective of the GLP in building the database is to construct a land use series maps at global and regional scales (GLP, 2005). Generally, most global cartographic products only describe land cover classification and limit land use to application levels such as cultivated land, pastures and cities. The database for the GLP analysis covers a range of required land use information, and reflects human activities and the extent and intensity of their impacts on the land system, including crop systems, irrigation, fertilization, crop production and livestock density.

(3) Establishment of a dynamic land analysis network and data coordination mechanism

The GLP requires the establishment of dynamic land analysis networks and a larger budget has been worked out for collecting, organizing and storing the necessary data sets and assessing the data quality to ensure the validity of the data (GLP, 2005). In addition, it is necessary to establish a standardized LUCC database based on relevant research from the UN Food and Agriculture Organization.

The GLP carries out dynamic land analysis based on the GCTE and LUCC programs (GLP, 2005). First, the two research plans have developed a detailed inventory of important variables in land system research; second, they have established evaluation criteria for some important variables. The standardization of these variables requires close collaboration and cooperation with related research programs, including Biological Diversity (DIVERSITAS), Millennium Ecosystem Assessment, Analysis, Integration and Modeling of the Earth System, Past Global Changes, and the Earth System Science Co-operation Program as well as the IGBP and IHDP.

(4) Promotion of data sharing

Data integration, especially the integration of data at multiple spatial scales, is one challenge to GLP data sharing. Socioeconomic, RS and ecosystem characteristics data are not matched in spatial and temporal resolutions, particularly in specific case studies, so the data integration and sharing will become more difficult.

The GLP should use existing file systems, including the Global Terrestrial Observing System and the global observation plans of LUCC to ensure data security (GLP, 2005). It should also be noted that international data exchange policies play an important role in promoting land use change research.

(5) Exchanging outputs and dissemination of knowledge from the land science plan

The GLP emphasizes the importance of reporting and publicizing the outputs from the key areas to attract the broad participation of physical and social scientists. The GLP will take full advantage of existing research networks, including GCTE, LUCC, Terrestrial ecosystem Response to Atmospheric and Climate Change, and Biosphere-Atmosphere Stable Isotope Network to establish a new research network (GLP, 2005). The GLP also includes the broad participation of Millennium Ecosystem Assessment scientists and coordinates research work into all aspects, and formulates new research topics on this basis.

1.4 Summary

Land use change is a research hot spot and includes core issues in current land science and global change research fields. Land use change is not only closely related to human production and life, but also has an important impact on terrestrial and marine ecosystems, and has increasingly attracted the attention of experts in relevant fields. Land use change has become a research topic closely linked with global environmental change and sustainable development and is closely related to regional land use planning and land resource management.

Land use change research based on the functional-structural theory and the theory of land prices makes use of the approaches and methods of system science and many new techniques to undertake comprehensive and in-depth research on land. The structure of the land system determines its internal regularity, which indicates that changes in the land system can be identified through land use conversion research. The non-linear interaction between the components of the land system determines its complexity, which illustrates the importance of using driving mechanism research as a focus for building system models.

Research on the land use system was addressed by the LUCC plan. This plan has made great advances in land cover change mechanism studies, understanding land use change mechanisms and constructing regional and global models. These outputs include developing a relatively complete monitoring technology, combining information on driving mechanisms and environmental effects, developing analysis methods for land use change models, and accumulating data and information on global and regional research.

More recently, the GLP which has been already implemented under the auspices of IGBP and IHDP global research, which has not only promoted the formation of a global network of new land science issues, but also the integration of natural and social sciences. The GLP enables experts in different fields to jointly participate in research and decision-making related to land system science and establishes the foundation for our research on land use conversion and driving mechanisms.

References

Abbasi M K and Rasool G. 2005. Effects of different land-use types on soil quality in the hilly area of Rawalakot Azad Jammu and Kashmir. Acta Agriculturae Scandinavica Section B—Soil and Plant Science, 55(3): 221–228.

Acevedo M A and Restrepo C. 2008. Land-cover and land-use change and its contribution to the large-scale organization of Puerto Rico's bird assemblages. Diversity and Distributions, 14(1): 114–122.

Aguiar A P D, Câmara G, Escada M I S. 2007. Spatial statistical analysis of land-use determinants in the Brazilian Amazonia: Exploring intra-regional heterogeneity. Ecological Modelling, 209(2–4): 169–188.

Ahlcrona E. 1988. The Impact of Climate and Man of Land Transformation in Central Sudan. Lund University Press, 140pp.

Annie O, Manuel M, Francoise B. 2000. Modelling consequences on butterfly mobility of rural landscape dynamics. Quantitative Approaches to Landscape Ecology: 107–114.

Aspinall R. 2004. Modelling land use change with generalized linear models—A multi-model analysis of change between 1860 and 2000 in Gallatin Valley, Montana. Journal of Environmental Management, 72: 91–103.

Burgi M and Turner M G. 2002. Factors and processes shaping land cover and land cover changes along the Wisconsin River. Ecosystems, 5: 184–201.

Cai Y L. 2000. Problems of farmland conservation in the rapid growth of China's economy. Resources Science, 22: 24–28.

Chen C C, Xie G D, Zhen L, Leng Y F. 2008. Long-term dynamics of cultivated land resources and their driving forces of Guyuan City in upper reaches of Jinghe River. Chinese Geographical Science, 18(1): 33–40.

de Koning G H J, Veldkamp A, Fresco L O. 1998. Land use in Ecuador: A statistical analysis at different aggregation levels. Agriculture Ecosystems and Environment, 70(2–3): 231–247.

de Koning G H J, Veldkamp A, Fresco L O. 1999. Exploring changes in Ecuadorian land use for food production and their effects on natural resources. Journal of Environmental Management, 57(4): 221–237.

De La Rosa D. 2005. Soil quality evaluation and monitoring based on land evaluation. Land Degradation and Development, 16(6): 551–559.

DeFries R S, Asner G P, Houghton R A. 2004. Trade-offs in land-use decisions: Towards a framework for assessing multiple ecosystem responses to land-use changed. Ecosystems and Land Use Change, 153: 1–9

DeFries R S, Bounoua L, Collatz G J. 2002. Human modification of the landscape and surface climate in the next fifty years. Global Change Biology, 8(5): 438–458.

DeFries R, Hansen M, Townsheld J. 1995. Global discrimination of land cover types from metrics derived from AVHRR pathfinder data. Remote Sensing of Environ, 54(3): 209–222.

Deng X Z. 2003. A study on the land use changes and their driving forces in the farming-pasturing interlocked areas of China. Institute of Geographic Sciences and Natural Resources Research. Beijing, Chinese Academy of Sciences. PHD: 210.

Deng X Z. 2008. Analysis of Land Use Conversions. Beijing: China Land Press.

Deng X Z, Huang J K, Rozelle S, Uchida E. 2006. Cultivated land conversion and potential agricultural productivity in China. Land Use Policy, 23(4): 372–384.

Deng X Z, Su H B, Zhan J Y. 2008a. Integration of multiple data sources to simulate the Dynamics of Land Systems. Sensors, 8(2): 620–634.

Deng X Z, Huang J K, Rozelle S, Uchida E. 2008b. Growth, population and industrialization, and urban land expansion of China. Journal of Urban Economics, 63: 96–115.

Deng X Z, Liu J Y, Zhuang D F. 2002. Modeling the relationship of land use change and some geophysical indicators: A case study in the ecotone between agriculture and pasturing in Northern China. Journal of Geographical Sciences, 12(4): 397–404.

Deng X Z, Lin Y Z, Huang H Q. 2009. Simulation of land system dynamics: A review. Chinese Journal of Ecology, 28(10): 2123–2129.

Fisher D S, Steiner J L, Endale D M, Stuedemann J A, Schomberg H H, Franzluebbers A J, Wilkinson S R. 2000. The relationship of land use practices to surface water quality in the Upper Oconee Watershed of Georgia. Forest Ecology and Management, 128(1–2): 39–48.

Fischer G, van Velthuizen H, Prieler S. 2001. Assessment of potential productivity of tree species in China, Mongolia and the former Soviet Union: Methodology and results. Interim Report IR-01-015. Laxenburg, Austria, International Institute for Applied Systems Analysis.

Fisher G., van Velthuizen H, Shah M, Nachtergaele F O. 2002. Global agroecological assessment for agriculture in the 21st century: Methodology and results, RR-02-02, FAO and IIASA, Laxenburg, Austria.

Frolking S, Xiao X M, Zhuang Y H, Salas W, Li C S. 1999. Agricultural land-use in China: A comparison of area estimates from ground-based census and satellite-borne remote sensing. Global Ecology and Biogeography, 8(5): 407–416.

Gao Z Q and Deng X Z. 2002. Analysis on spatial features of LUCC based on remote sensing and GIS in China. Chinese Geographical Science, 12(2): 107–113.

GLP. 2005. Science Plan and Implementation Strategy. IGBP Report No. 53/IHDP Report No. 19. Stockholm, IGBP.

Grainger A. 1990. Modelling deforestation in the humid tropics. Palo M, Mery G, editor, Deforestation or Development in the Third World? Helsinki: Finnish Forest Research Institute, 51–67.

Haberl H, Batterbury S, Moran E. 2001. Using and shaping the land: A long-term perspective. Land Use Policy, 18(1): 1–8.

Haberl H, Erb K H, Krausmann F, Adensam H, Schulz N B. 2003. Land-use change and socio-economic metabolism in Austria—Part Ⅱ: Land-use scenarios for 2020. Land Use Policy, 20(1): 21–39.

Haberl H, Wackernagel M, Wrbka T. 2004. Land use and sustainability indicators. An introduction. Land Use Policy, 21(3): 193–198.

Heilig G K. 1997. Anthropogenic factors in land-use change in China. Population and Development Review, 23(1): 139–168.

Heilig G K. 1999. China Food: Can China Feed Itself? International Institute for Applied Systems Analysis (IIASA), Laxenburg, Austria.

Hietel E, Waldhardt R, Otte A. 2004. Analysing land-cover changes in relation to environmental variables in Hesse. Landscape Ecology, 19: 473–489.

Huang Q H, Cai Y L, Peng J. 2007. Modeling the spatial pattern of farmland using GIS and multiple logistic regression: A case study of Maotiao River Basin, Guizhou Province, China. Environ Model Assess, 12: 55–61.

Huffman E, Eilers R G, Padbury G, Wall G, MacDonald K B. 2000. Canadian agri-environmental indicators related to land quality: Integrating census and biophysical data to estimate soil cover, wind erosion and soil salinity. Agriculture Ecosystems and Environment, 81(2): 113–123.

Ierodiaconou D, Laurenson L, Leblanc M, Stagnitti F, Duff G, Salzman S, Versace V. 2005. The consequences of land use change on nutrient exports: A regional scale assessment in south-west Victoria, Australia. Journal of Environmental Management, 74(4): 305–316.

Irwin E G and Geoghegan J. 2001. Theory, data, methods: Developing spatially explicit economic models of land use change. Agriculture Ecosystems and Environment, 85(1–3): 7–23.

Islam K R and Weil R R. 2000. Land use effects on soil quality in a tropical forest ecosystem of Bangladesh. Agriculture Ecosystems and Environment, 79(1): 9–16.

Kane S, Reily J, Tobey J. 1991. Climate change: Economic implications for world agriculture. Agricultural Economic Report No.647, U.S. Department of Agriculture, Economic Research Service, U.S. Government Printing Office, Washington, DC.

Kaufmann R K, Seto K C, Schneider A, Liu Z T, Zhou L M, Wang W L. 2007. Climate response to rapid urban growth: Evidence of a human-induced precipitation deficit. Journal of Climate, 20(10): 2299–2306.

Kerr S, Liu S, Pfaff A S P, Hughes R F. 2003. Carbon dynamics and land-use choices: Building a regional-scale multidisciplinary model. Journal of Environmental Management, 69(1): 25–37.

Kiira A. 1995. Simulation vegetation dynamics and land use in a mire landscape using a Markov model. Landscape and Urban Plannig, 31: 129–142.

Kitamura T, Kagatsume M, Hoshino S, Morita H. 1997. A theoretical consideration on the land-use change model for the Japan case study area. IIASA Interim Report IR-97-064, Laxenburg.

Krause P. 2002. Quantifying the impact of land use changes on the water balance of large catchments using the J2000 model. Physics and Chemistry of the Earth, 27(9–10): 663–673.

Krausmann F, Haberl H, Schulz N B, Erb K-H, Darge E, Gaube V. 2003. Land-use change and socio-economic metabolism in Austria—Part I: Driving forces of land-use change: 1950—1995. Land Use Policy, 20(1): 1–20.

Kalnay E and Cai M. 2003. Impact of urbanization and land-use change on climate. Nature (London), 423: 528–531.

Kuninori O. 1999. Land use for global environmental conservation (LU/GEC)—Final report of the LU/GEC first phase (1995—1997). National Institute for Environmental Studies, Environmental Agency of Japan.

Lambin E F, Geist H J, Lepers E. 2003. Dynamics of land-use and land-cover change in tropical regions. Annual Review of Environment and Resources, 28: 205–241.

Lambin H G. 2006. Land-Use and Land-Cover Change. Berlin: Springer Berlin Heidelberg.

Lambin E F, Rounsevell M D A, Geist H J. 2000. Are agricultural land-use models able to predict changes in land-use intensity? Agriculture Ecosystems and Environment, 82(1–3): 321–331.

Lambin E F, Turner B L, Geist H J, Agbola S B, Angelsen A, Bruce J W, Coomes O T, Dirzo R, Fischer G, Folke C, George P S, Homewood K, Imbernon J, Leemans R, Li X, Moran E F, Mortimore M, Ramakrishnan P S, Richards J F, Skanes H, Steffen W, Stone G D, Svedin U, Veldkamp T A, Vogel C, Xu J. 2001. The causes of land-use and land-cover change: Moving beyond the myths. Global Environmental Change, 11(4): 261–269.

Lewis D J. 2010. An economic framework for forecasting land-use and ecosystem change. Resource and Energy Economics, 32: 98–116.

Li X and Yeh A G O. 2004. Analyzing spatial restructuring of Land use patterns in a fast growing region using remote sensing and GIS. Landscape and Urban Planning, 69(4): 335–354.

Lin G C S and Ho S P S. 2003. China's land resources and land-use change: Insights from the 1996 land survey. Land Use Policy, 20(2): 87–107.

Liu J Y, Deng X Z, Liu M L, Zhang S W. 2002a. Study on the spatial patterns of land-use change and analyses of driving forces in Northeastern China during 1990—2000. Chinese Geographical Science, 12(4): 299–308.

Liu J Y, Liu M L, Deng X Z, Zhuang D F, Zhang Z X, Luo D. 2002b. The land use and land cover change database and its relative studies in China. Journal of Geographical Sciences, 12(3): 275–282.

Liu J Y, Liu M L, Tian H Q, Zhuang D F, Zhang Z X, Zhang W, Tang X M, Deng X Z. 2005. Spatial and temporal patterns of China's cropland during 1990—2000: An analysis based on Landsat TM data. Remote Sensing of Environment,

98(4): 442–456.

Liu J Y, Liu M L, Zhuang D F, Zhang Z X, Deng X Z. 2003. Study on spatial pattern of land-use change in China during 1995—2000. Science in China Series D—Earth Sciences, 46(4): 373–384.

Lu S G and Bai S Q. 2006. Study on the correlation of magnetic properties and heavy metals content in urban soils of Hangzhou City, China. Journal of Applied Geophysics, 60(1): 1–12.

Matson P A, Parton W J, Power A G, Swift M J. 1997. Agriculture intensification and ecosystem properties. Science, 277: 504–509.

McIntyre S and Lavorel S. 2007. A conceptual model of land use effects on the structure and function of herbaceous vegetation. Agriculture Ecosystems and Environment, 119(1–2): 11–21.

Meyer W B and Turner B L II. 1994. Changes in Land Use and Land Cover: A Global Perspective. New York: Cambridge University Press.

Miller S N, Kepner W G, Mehaffey M H, Hernandez M, Miller R C, Goodrich D C, Devonald K K, Heggem D T, Miller W P. 2002. Integrating landscape assessment and hydrologic modeling for land cover change analysis. Journal of the American Water Resources Association, 38(4): 915–929.

Ministry of Agriculture in China (MLRC). 2003. China Land Yearbook. Beijing: China Land Press.

Muller M R and Middleton J. 1994. A Markov model of land-use change dynamics in the Niagara region, Ontario, Canada. Landscape Ecology, 9(2): 151–157.

Nagendra H, Munroe D K, Southworth J. 2004. From pattern to process: Landscape fragmentation and the analysis of land use/land cover change. Agriculture Ecosystems and Environment, 101(2–3): 111–115.

Parker D C, Hessl A, Davis S C. 2008. Complexity, land-use modeling, and the human dimension: Fundamental challenges for mapping unknown outcome spaces. Geoforum, 39(2): 789–804.

Paulo S and Tomaz D. 2010. Spatial interaction model of land use: An application to Corvo Island from the 16th, 19th and 20th centuries. Computer, Environment and Urban Systems, 34: 91–103.

Pfaff A S P. 1999. What drives deforestation in the Brazilian Amazon? Evidence from satellite and socioeconomic data. Journal of Environmental Economics and Management, 37(1): 26–43.

Pfaff A S P and Sanchez-Azofeifa G A. 2004. Deforestation pressure and biological reserve planning: A conceptual approach and an illustrative application for Costa Rica. Resource and Energy Economics, 26(2): 237–254.

Rahman S, Rahman H, Keramat M. 2007. Study on the seasonal changes of land cover and their impact on surface albedo in the northwestern part of Bangladesh using remote sensing. International Journal of Remote Sensing, 28(5): 1001–1022.

Reenberg A. 1994. Land-use dynamics in the Sahelian zone in eastern Niger–monitoring change in cultivation strategies in drought prone areas. Journal of Arid Environments, 27(2): 179–192.

Reenberg A, Nielsen T L, Rasmussen K. 1998. Field expansion and reallocation in the Sahel—Land use pattern dynamics in a fluctuating biophysical and socio-economic environment. Global Environmental Change, 8(4): 309–327.

Reyers B, O'Farrell P J, Cowling R M, Egoh B N, Le Maitre D C, Vlok J H J. 2009. Ecosystem service, land-cover change, and stakeholders: Finding a sustainable foothold for a semiarid biodiversity hotspot. Ecology and Society, 14(1): 38.

Reynolds W D, Drury C F, Yang X M, Fox C A, Tan C S, Zhang T Q. 2007. Land management effects on the near-surface physical quality of a clay loam soil. Soil and Tillage Research, 96(1–2): 316–330.

Rozelle S and Rosegrant M W. 1997. China's past, present, and future food economy: Can China continue to meet the challenges? Food Policy, 22(3): 191–200.

Rudel T K, Coomes O T, Moran E, Achard F, Angelsen A, Xu J, Lambin E. 2005. Forest transitions: Towards a global understanding of land use change. Global Environmental Change Part A, 15(1): 23–31.

Sato Y. 2004. Comparative model evaluation in land use and land cover changes (LUCC) research. Land and Water Management: Decision Tools and Practices, 1–2: 1327–1334.

Seto K C and Kaufmann R K. 2003. Modeling the drivers of urban land use change in the Pearl River Delta, China: Integrating remote sensing with socioeconomic data. Land Economics, 79(1): 106–121.

Seto K C, Kaufmann R K, Woodcock C E. 2000. Landsat reveals China's farmland reserves, but they're vanishing fast. Nature, 406: 121.

Skole D and Tucker C. 1993. Tropical deforestation and habitat fragmentation in the Amazon: Satellite data from 1978 to 1988. Science in China (Series D), 260: 1905—1909.

Stehfest E, Heistermann M, Priess J A, Ojima D S, Alcamo J. 2007. Simulation of global crop production with the ecosystem model DayCent. Ecological Modelling, 209(2–4): 203–219.

Tang J and Wang X G. 2009. Analysis of the land use structure changes based on Lorenz curves. Environmental Monitoring and Assessment, 151(1–4): 175–180.

Tanrivermis H. 2003. Agricultural land use change and sustainable use of land resources in the mediterranean region of Turkey. Journal of Arid Environments, 54: 553–564.

Turner B L II. 2010. Sustainability and forest transitions in the southern Yucatan: The land architecture approach. Land Use Policy, 27(2): 170–179.

Turner B L II, Clark W C, Kates R W, Richard J F, Mathews J T, Meyer W B. 1990. The Earth as Transformed by Human Action: Global and Regional Changes in the Biosphere over the Past 300 Years. Cambridge: Cambridge University Press with Clark University.

Turner B L II, Lambin E F, Reenberg A. 2007. The emergence of land change science for global environmental change and sustainability. Proceedings of the National Academy of Sciences of the United States of America, 104(52): 20666–20671.

Turner B L II, Meyer W B, Skole D L. 1994. Global land-use land-cover change: Towards an integrated study. Ambio, 23(1): 91–95.

Turner B L II, Skole D, Sanderson S. 1995. Land-use and land-cover change. Science/Research Plan. IGBP Report; 35/HDP Report 7.

Turner M G, Collins S L, Lugo A E, Magnuson J J, Rupp T S, Swanson F J. 2003. Disturbance dynamics and ecological response: The contribution of long-term ecological research. Bioscience, 53(1): 46–56.

U.S. Army Crops of Engineers (USACE). 2001. HEC-RAS river analysis system:

Hydraulics reference manual version 3.0, Retrieved from *http://www.hec.usace.army.mil*, Public distribution unlimited.

Valbuena D, Verburg P H, Bregt A K, Ligtenberg A. 2010. An agent-based approach to model land-use change at a regional scale. Landscape Ecology, 25(2): 185–199.

Veldkamp A and Fresco L O. 1996. CLUE-CR: An integrated multi-scale model to simulate land use change scenarios in Costa Rica. Ecological Modelling, 91(1–3): 231–248.

Veldkamp A and Verburg P H. 2004a. Modelling land use change and environmental impact. Journal of Environmental Management, 72(1–2): 1–3.

Verburg P H. 2006. Simulating feedbacks in land use and land cover change models. Landscape Ecology, 21(8): 1171–1183.

Verburg P H, Chen Y Q, Veldkamp T A. 2000. Spatial explorations of land use change and grain production in China. Agriculture Ecosystems and Environment, 82(1–3): 333–354.

Verburg P H and Overmars K P. 2009. Combining top-down and bottom-up dynamics in land use modeling: Exploring the future of abandoned farmlands in Europe with the Dyna-CLUE model. Landscape Ecology, 24(9): 1167–1181.

Verburg P H, Schulp C J E, Witte N, Veldkamp A. 2006. Downscaling of land use change scenarios to assess the dynamics of European landscapes. Agriculture Ecosystems and Environment, 114(1): 39–56.

Verburg P H, van Berkel D B, van Doorn A M, van Eupen M, van den Heiligenberg H A R M. 2010. Trajectories of land use change in Europe: A model-based exploration of rural futures. Landscape Ecology, 25(2): 217–232.

Verburg P H, van de Steeg J, Veldkamp A, Willemen L. 2009. From land cover change to land function dynamics: A major challenge to improve land characterization. Journal of Environmental Management, 90(3): 1327–1335.

Verburg P H, van Eck J R R, de Nijs T C M, Dijst M J, Schot P. 2004. Determinants of land-use change patterns in the Netherlands. Environment and Planning B—Planning and Design, 31(1): 125–150.

Verburg P H, Veldkamp A, Fresco L O. 1999. Simulation of changes in the spatial pattern of land use in China. Applied Geography, 19(3): 211–233.

Vernadsky V L. 1926. The Biosphere. New York: Nevramont.

Vitousek P M, Mooney H A, Lucbchenco J, Melillo J M. 1997. Human domination of earth's ecosystem. Science, 277(25): 494–450.

Wang Y Q, Tobey J, Bonynge G, Nugrandad J, Makota V, Ngusaru A, Traber M. 2005. Involving geospatial information in the analysis of land-cover change along the Tanzania coast. Coastal Management, 33: 87–99.

Walker R, Wood C, Skole D, Chomentowski W. 2002. The impact of land titling on tropical forest resources. In: Remote Sensing and GIS Applications for Linking People, Place, and Policy, 131–153. Walsh S, Crews-Myer K. eds. Netherlands: Kluwer Academic Publishers.

William F L, Ana K M A, Philip M F, Heraldo L V, Leandro V F. 2004. Deforestation in Amazonia. Science, 304(5674): 1109–1111.

Yang H and Li X B. 2000. Cultivated land and food supply in China. Land Use Policy, 17: 73–88.

Zang S Y and Huang X. 2006. An aggregated multivariate regression land-use model and its application to land-use change processes in the Daqing region (northeast China). Ecological Modelling, 193: 503–516.

Zhang H, Henderson-Sellers A, McGuffie K. 2001. The compounding effects of tropical deforestation and greenhouse warming on climate. Climatic Change, 49(3): 309–338.

Zhang X Q, Ge Q S, Zheng J Y. 2003. Analysis of driving forces on the change of historical farmland use in Shandong Province during the Qing Dynasty (1644 – 1911). Chinese Geographical Science, 13(3): 207–215.

Zhao Y J, Zhang H N, Maimaitiati, Sun Y Q. 2002. Impact of oasis establishment on underground environment in salinized sandy lands. Science in China Series D — Earth Sciences, 45: 132–136.

Zhao Z Y, Wang R H, Sun H B, Zhang H Z. 2006. Assessment of water-recharging based on ecological features of riparian forest in the lower reaches of Tarim River. Chinese Science Bulletin, 51: 37–42.

Zhu Y B, Ge Q S, He L S, Lou D. 2005. A case study on land use change analysis using RS and GIS in the West Jilin Province in China. IGARSS 2005: IEEE International Geoscience and Remote Sensing Symposium, 1–8: 2287–2290.

Chapter 2 Modeling Framework

The dynamics of land system change, as both an important direct cause and response of global change, has always been one of the core themes of global change research (Deng, 2008a; Turner II, 2009; Verburg et al., 2009). With the development of research on land use change and the implementation of the global land science plan, people have increasingly realized that there is a close relationship between the dynamics of land system change and succession in the natural environment, terrestrial ecosystem processes and human activities. It is important to explore the interactions and relationships between various factors in the land system to identify the causes and effects of the dynamics of land system change from a system perspective (GLP, 2005). Inappropriate land use influences the foundation of human survival and development, and the dynamics of land system change has ecological and environmental impacts on the human socioeconomic system, which is also one of the main factors that influence and restrict regional sustainable development (Turner II et al., 1995; Seto et al., 2002; Veldkamp and Verburg, 2004).

Research on the dynamics and consequences of land system change, as an interdisciplinary research field, involves a wide range of subjects (GLP, 2005). It is necessary to simultaneously consider both spatial and temporal scales in the assessment of land system change and its effects, for example, during the multi-scale simulation of the dynamics of land system change from the regional to the pixel scale (Verburg et al., 1999a; Verburg and Overmars, 2009; Kaufmann and Seto, 2001). The study of the structural change in land systems needs to recognize the effects of various factors that influence that structural change, and develop different scenarios for the structural changes which reflect the changes in spatial units at different scales to analyze the consequences (Cai, 2001). This chapter introduces the modeling concepts and simulation procedures from mechanism analyses to effect assessments and illuminates the critical processes and links.

2.1 Modeling Strategy at Regional and Pixel Scales

Many studies have identified that occurrences, spatial distributions, coupling patterns and processes in geographic studies all depend on scale, i.e., they all have temporal, spatial or spatiotemporal characteristics (Simon et al., 1991; Schulze, 2000; Irwin and Geoghegan, 2001). Therefore, it is necessary to explore and study these concepts at continuous scale series to understand their underlying principles. However, much research can only be carried out at dispersed or individual scales for a specific period due to limitations in the levels of scientific knowledge, ability, time and energy. Thus, the selection of the scale, and the ability to downscale or upscale, are indispensable parts of the research process, and changing patterns and technical processes of modeling at regional and pixel scales become increasingly important (Levine and Painter, 2003; Deng et al., 2005).

Scale is a term that has been used extremely frequently in recent geographical research (Verburg et al., 1999b). However, there are some discrepancies and different opinions of the definition of scale, scale types, delimitation of scale domains, scaling mode and techniques. These differences can be seen in the following.

(i) Improper selection of the scale results in an unclear representation of the object of the study. Many details are neglected and the research becomes a "partial" estimation if the study scale is too large, while the research is focused on local issues and does not describe the overall situation when the research scale is too small.

(ii) Arbitrary scale conversion. Some researchers have asserted that they converted the scale of the research results, when in fact they only deduced the results subjectively. Some research results are used at different scales, or even across several scales, without changing the parameters accordingly (Kremen et al., 2000). The scale of some research results cannot be converted, but some researchers have ignored this restriction and converted the scale of the research results arbitrarily.

(iii) Improper use of scale conversion techniques. Some researchers do not understand that different strategies should be used in the scale conversion of conceptual, mechanism and statistical models; instead, they depend heavily on regression techniques.

(iv) Conscious or unconscious ignorance of the scale of the research results. In this case the results are reported without explaining the scale at which the results have been generated or are effective.

(v) The scopes of the spatial and temporal scales used in various disciplines are different, and ambiguity is often created in the presentation and understanding of research results. This occurs particularly in conditions where there is a large amount of interdisciplinary study, which increases the difficulty of integrating disciplines (Veldkamp and Fresco, 1996; de Koning et al., 1999).

The scale conversion used in research mainly involves the conversion from regional to pixel scales and the conversion from pixel to regional scales. The problems described above can be effectively avoided or reduced by demarcating the boundary between models at the regional scale and models at the pixel scale, clarifying modeling procedures from pixel to regional scales, and verifying and forcing the conversion from pixel to regional scales.

2.1.1 Modeling Procedures for Conversion from Pixel to Regional Scales

Conversion from regional to pixel scales is a process of reducing observations and simulation results from a macroscale to a precise scale. For example, the General Circulation Model (GCM) is used to deduce the regional precipitation and temperature (McGuffie and Henderson-Sellers, 1997). The conversion from the regional scale to the pixel scale aims to convert information with coarse spatial and temporal resolutions into heterogeneous information at a precise scale. The conversion aims to use the macro observational data or model simulation results in local regions to solve practical local problems such as how grain production, water resources and agricultural production react to changing of factors at the macroscale (e.g., global warming and the increase in CO_2 concentration).

2.1.1.1 Data from Investigations within Administrative Boundaries

Land system change leads to changes in the land output from changing land use types (Groot et al., 2007). Land system change is a complex process involving the natural and economic productions of land with the intervention of human activities, mainly comprising conversion among cultivated land, forestry, grassland, water areas, built-up areas and unused land. Land system change is mainly the result of three factors. First, the type and quantity of demand for land outputs (or services) vary at different stages of socioeconomic development, which leads to land system change, known as an endogenous or active change. Second, there is a change in land properties for natural or human reasons, such as changing societal goals and forcing changes in land use types. This is known as an exogenous or passive change. Third, the land system may change due to technical progress, known as a technical change.

The factors that influence land system change can be divided into natural controlling factors and socioeconomic driving factors (Liu et al., 2005; Deng et al., 2008). The natural controlling factors can be further divided into stable factors and inter-annually changing factors based on their characteristics. The stable factors include physical aspects such as elevation, slope, aspect, topography, soil and vegetation, while the inter-annually changing factors are relatively active, and include changes in temperature and precipitation. In short time periods, the influence of natural controlling factors on land system change at the regional scale is limited, while socioeconomic driving factors play an important role in land system change (Deng, 2008b; Shao et al., 2006). Since the factors influencing land system change are generally investigated within administrative boundaries at the regional scale, it is necessary to convert the information obtained from these investigations at the regional scale into the pixel scale with modeling procedures to carry out the model simulations.

2.1.1.2 Multi-source Data

Land system change involves a wide range of subjects and consists of very complex components; its core component is the structural change in land use. The principle that the structural change in land use determines the functional change in land systems is one of the theories widely used in land system research (de Koning et al., 1998), and is an effective way to identify land system change by analyzing the land system structure. Researchers generally identify the homogeneity of land types, relative differences in land types, conversion among land types and principles of territorial differentiation by analyzing the structural change in land use (e.g., landscape type comparisons, temporal succession and structural change in spatial composition). It is important to describe the process of land system change with the support of multi-source data, such as remote sensing data, field survey data, fixed-position observation data and national statistical data to better simulate the processes and consequences of land system change.

Multi-source data have different temporal and spatial scales, for example, remote sensing images are generally at the pixel scale, while fixed-position observation data are based on observation stations or sample plots with a given separation distance (often about 1/12 hectare) and national statistical data are based on a regional scale. To improve the simulation of the processes and consequences of land system change, it is important to use a modeling procedure to convert regional scale data to the pixel scale to better integrate and compare multi-source data. Land systems have evident spatial heterogeneity, and the patterns, processes, driving forces and effects of land system change all have distinctive multi-scale features. Only with multi-scale integration can the essence of land system change be reflected.

2.1.1.3 Dependence on the Analysis of Multi-source Data

Research on the simulation of structural changes in land systems, driving mechanism analysis and effects assessments based on multi-source data are helpful to explore the natural characteristics of the land and directions for land use and conversion. This research has provided an important scientific basis for the exploitation and use of land based on actual conditions and improving land productivity. All such research depends on the comprehensive analysis of multi-source data.

There are many perspectives on the identification of driving forces of land system change. Malthus (1820) identified that in the field of production systems, the structure of social production and demand depends on national traditions, education level, political systems and the income level of the general public. Kasperson et al. (1995) identified that human driving factors in the dynamics of land system change in a typical area include the population, technical level, degree of richness, political and economic structure, merit and attitude, while Ehrlich and Daily (1993) identified the main human driving factors as the population, degree of richness and technical development. The IHDP plan determined that the driving factors of land system change can be divided into direct factors and indirect factors. The indirect factors are population change, technical progress, economic development, political and economic policies, degree of richness and value orientation, which then act on the land system through the direct factors. The direct factors include the demand for the land products, investment in the land, degree of urbanization, degree of intensification of the land systems, land ownership, land system policies and the attitudes toward the protection of land resources (Kremen et al., 2000). Turner identified that the human driving forces should include population, income, technical development, political economic situation and culture (Turner II et al., 1990). Among the various driving factors, research was first conducted on population using quantitative methods, while the precise depiction of other factors lagged behind due to the difficulty in quantifying them. It is inarguable that population plays an important role in driving land system change (Turner et al., 1994), and population change is well correlated with land system change. Therefore, research on land system change should include at least the population, economic development and technical development when selecting the human driving factors (van Keulen et al., 1998; Plantinga et al., 2002). The identification and integration of these driving forces require comprehensive analysis of the multi-source data.

The spatial allocation of land use change is an issue often mentioned in geographic research. Errors in the spatial allocation of land use change can lead to the inappropriate allocation of resources and may influence the precision of model simulation results, meaning that any decisions based on the model results will lack efficiency and fairness. The spatial allocation of land use change depends on scale conversion to a large extent. Because the concept of scale is vague, conversion patterns are not unified, and the conversion results lack objective verification, affecting the understanding of the underlying principles. It is indispensable when exploring principles of the dynamics of land system change at the more precise pixel scale to spatially allocate area changes in land use types from the regional scale to the pixel scale.

Predictions of the land system structure, driving mechanism analysis, spatial allocation of land use change and effects assessment all depend to a large extent on the comprehensive analysis of multi-source data. The characteristics of these phenomena all have temporal, spatial or temporal-spatial scales, so only by investigating them at continuous scale series, can we understand their underlying principles. Therefore, it is necessary to explore the actual characteristics of land system change using the modeling procedure from the regional to the pixel scale.

2.1.1.4 Interaction among Variables at Different Scales

Natural factors in the land system such as the landform, climate, soil, hydrology and vegetation interact with each other and restrict the type, structure, level and regional differences in land use and limit land system change. The differences in land system change mainly result from changes in the driving factors, and therefore the selection of driving factor variables is crucial for understanding the principles of land system change. Driving factors influencing land system change include various factors such as land use change, socioeconomic change, and changes in human value outlooks. Representative variables for these different factors come from different scales, for example, socioeconomic data are usually at the county scale while natural geographic data are collected at the pixel scale, making it necessary to carry out uniform scale conversion on variables with different scales. The study area for general research often covers parts of several provinces and counties. Using the modeling procedure for converting from the regional to the pixel scale, we can link the correlation of variables at different scales and explore the principles of land system change.

2.1.2 Accuracy Verification and Deduction from the Pixel Scale to the Regional Scale

Conversion from the pixel to the regional scale is the process of scaling the results of observations, experiments and simulations to a larger scale, which is called the "coarse graining" of research results. For example, researchers employing the Forest Gap Model use the simulation results from dozens of sample plots with a given separation distance (about 1/12 hectares) to deduce the succession trend in the regional ecosystem under certain scenarios (Risch et al., 2005).

2.1.2.1 Extraction of Land System Change at the Pixel Scale

Research on the competitive processes of various land use types at the scale level will help to improve the understanding of the driving mechanism of regional land system change. Scholars in this field generally use the linear regression model or simple correlation analysis to analyze land system change and identify relationships between the driving factors at present (Veldkamp and Fresco, 1996; Serneels and Lambin, 2001; Stéphenne and Lambin, 2001; Aspinall, 2004; Zang and Huang, 2006; Munroe and Müller, 2007; Serra et al., 2008). However, there are many restrictions in the linear regression model, such as the lack of suitability when the dependent variable is a categorical variable rather than a continuous variable, as many social observation variables are categorical rather than continuous (Qiu et al., 2003; Goidts et al., 2009). The relationship between the dependent and independent variables in the linear probability model (LPM) is shown in Fig. 2.1. Although there is clearly a nonlinear relationship between the binary variables, the linear probability model cannot simulate this nonlinear relationship. Most of the stable natural influencing factors for land system change are categorical variables, such as soil type classifications like brown earth or chestnut soil, that impact regional land system change. However, the impacts from these categorical variables cannot be added into the LPM. Considering this, it is necessary to construct simulation models for land system change at the grid level, disaggregate the socioeconomic data, and construct a logistic regression model for land system change and its driving factors to explain the driving mechanism of regional land system change (Deng et al., 2008).

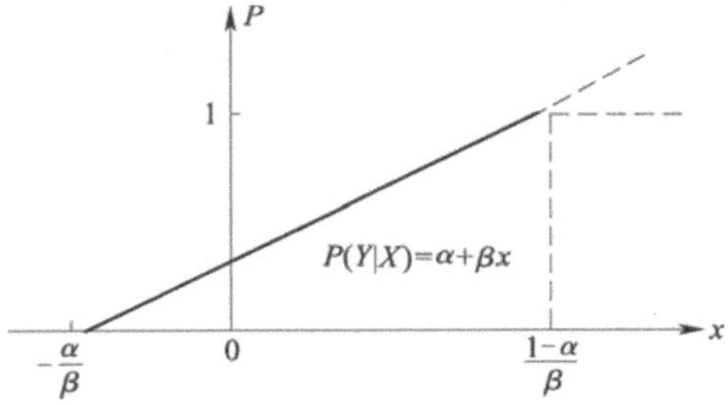

Fig. 2.1 Linear probability model.

Note: Y is the dependent variable, X is the independent variable and x is the observation of X.

Differences in land system change result from differences in the driving factors; the identification of different driving factors is directly related to the modeling process and the accuracy of the simulation results. The influencing mechanisms of natural and socioeconomic driving factors are different; researchers cannot directly construct models using the conventional ordinary least squares estimation method to explain the parameters in the models without any treatment of the two kinds of factors (Burgi, 2004). The stable natural influencing factors should not be isolated from the model construction, so it is necessary to convert them into binary dummy variables to include them in the model. Therefore, the use of binary data helps to extract land system change processes to a great degree. For example, in a case study of land use change in the northern agriculture-pasture transition zone of China from the mid-1980s to the late 1990s, Deng and Zhan (2004) identified that the expansion of cultivated land and decrease of grassland at the 5 km, 10 km, 15 km, 20 km, 25 km and 50 km grid scales, where "1" relates to the expansion of cultivated land or decrease in grassland at the pixel scale, and "0" indicates that there is no expansion of cultivated land or decrease of grassland. The binary values of the dependent variables are shown in Table 2.1.

The binary variables, "1" and "0", represent the changing situation related to the expansion of cultivated land or decrease of grassland, and this kind of binary variable is the dependent variable in the model. Different spatial scales are selected because the driving factors and land use change both correlate with the scale. The 5 km, 10 km, 15 km, 20 km, 25 km and 50 km grid scales were chosen to analyze and calculate the binary variables, recording the changes in cultivated land and grassland based on the data and hardware demands of the model. The results are saved as an ASCII file with spatial coordinate information, which can be used as the dependent variable in the model (Fig. 2.2).

Table 2.1 Remapping table representing the expansion of cultivated land and shrinkage of grassland

Grid scale		5 km	10 km	15 km	20 km	25 km	50 km
Cultivated land	Expansion	10 051	10 101	10 151	10 201	10 251	10 501
	Non-expansion	10 050	10 100	10 150	10 200	10 250	10 500
Grassland	Shrinkage	30 051	20 101	30 151	30 201	30 251	30 501
	Non-shrinkage	30 050	20 100	30 150	30 200	30 250	30 500

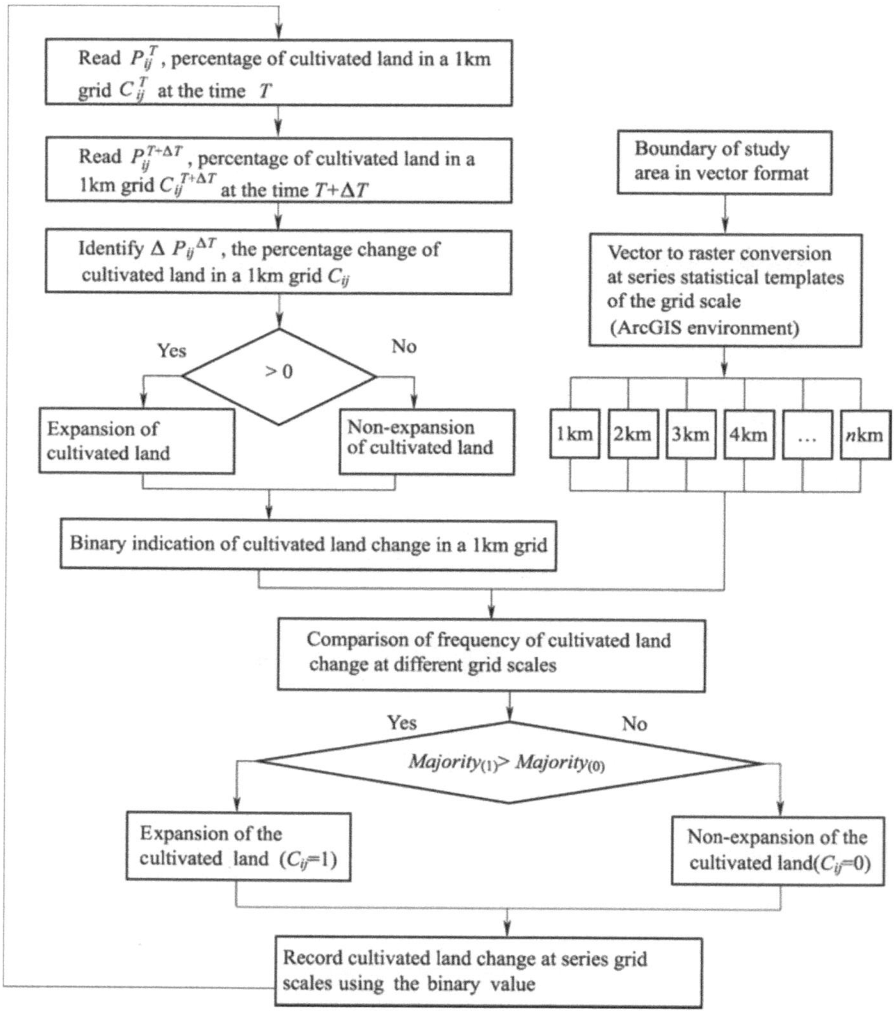

Fig. 2.2 Flow chart of identifying and presenting the expansion of cultivated land at pixel level using the binary values.

The stable factors such as landform are also typical binary variables. The landform has important impacts on regional land system change and controls its pattern and process. It is important to consider the effects of the landform to explain the driving mechanisms of land system change. To put the landform factors into the land system change model, researchers should first design a remapping table for the landform types according to the actual situation of the study area and the data demands of the model. A data conversion program can then be written depending on whether a certain landform type is present at certain scales, and the landform types can then be converted into binary variables with spatial information. If a particular landform type or soil type is present at a certain grid level, the basic unit is identified as "1", or "0" if not. The determination procedure is shown in Fig. 2.3.

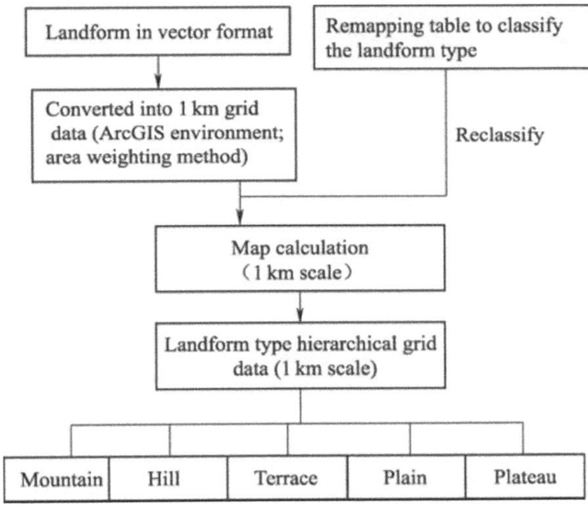

Fig. 2.3 Reclassification of landform types using category variables at the grid pixel scales.

With the landform type converted into a binary variable, researchers can then build models and analyze the influence of different landform types on land system change at different scales.

2.1.2.2 Area Percentage Model for Measuring Land Use Change

The area percentage data model can be used to simulate the process of land area change at the pixel scale, using area percentage data as the basis for representing land system change. The model uses grids of a certain size to represent the percentage of the area of one land use type in the grid. The area percentage data are a matrix consisting of a series of pixels of the same size, each of which records various land use area information extracted from remote sensing data (Deng, 2008b). It is a technique for extracting land use conversion information based on a remote sensing image and visual interpretation, and it unifies the classification system for land systems and forms a uniform interpretation criterion guaranteeing the accuracy of visual interpretation of the remote sensing data. The model design includes correction processing, interpretation and direct comparison of remote sensing images from two time periods. Fig. 2.4 shows how land system change information can be extracted by interpreting the conversion of land use (i.e., the direct interpretation of the dynamic blocks), sketching out the blocks of converted land use, and integrating the blocks of converted land use in the same way that the area percentage data are handled.

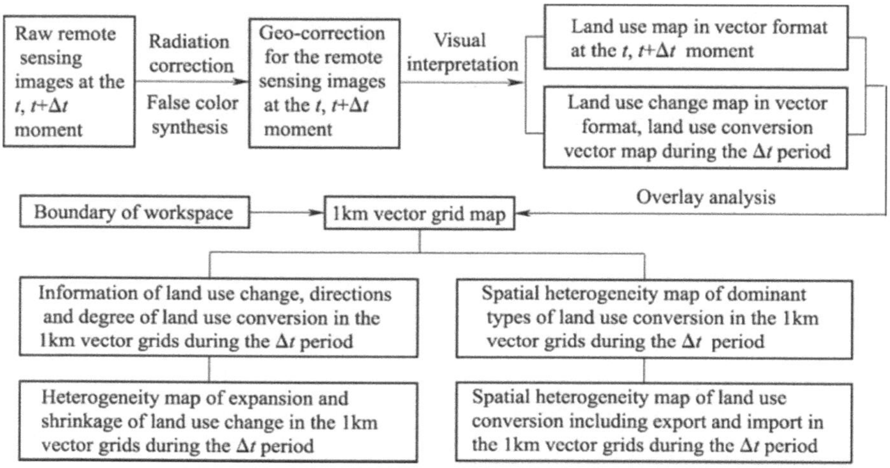

Fig. 2.4 Process of decoding the land use information and representing the spatial heterogeneity of land use changes at the 1×1 km scale.

There are seven main steps in the preparation of 1 km area percentage data for land use conversion: (i) open the corrected remote sensing digital images for the periods t and $t + \Delta t$ in the remote sensing interpretation software environment; (ii) sketch out the vector for the dynamic land use change block by comparing the remote images from t and $t + \Delta t$ using the remote digital images for the period t as a reference map, to form a dynamic map of land use change in the workspace; (iii) use the 'Generate' command in the Arc module to prepare a 1 km vector net map covering the entire workspace in the ArcGIS software environment, so that the property file contains the only unit code indicating each 1 km vector net; (iv) overlay the dynamic land use change map and the 1 km vector net map to obtain the area of land use type change and the areas converted between different land use types; (v) convert the area of land use type change and converted area in the 1 km vector net into an INFO file in which ArcGIS can read, and store the unit codes which record the 1 km vector net in the INFO file; (vi) link the INFO file recording the information of change and conversion of land use types during the period Δt with the unit code for the 1 km vector net to the 1 km vector net map in the ArcGIS software environment; and (vii) convert the 1 km vector net map into 1 km grid data with the area of land type changes and conversion areas for land use recorded in the property table under the Arc module. These data represent the structural change in land use and land use conversion for each 1 km grid by classification and layer. The area of land type change and conversion areas of land use are calculated from the percentage of the changed and converted areas in the total grid area in each1 km grid. The accuracy of the area percentage data generated by this method is consistent with the original data.

The actual decision-making needs for sustainability and multi-scale coordination of land management can only be met by summarizing the dynamic area based on the integration, verification and conversion from the pixel scale to the regional scale, reflecting the essence of land system change at multiple scales.

2.1.2.3 Differing Influences of Variables at Different Scales

Land system change has a multi-scale feature: variables at different scales and levels interact with each other and together influence the processes and outcomes of land system change (Deng, 2008a; Veldkamp and Fresco, 1996). Generally, the smallest scale involves issues related to specific techniques; the intermediate scale involves issues related to the approach and patterns, while the broad scale must also consider strategy and policy (Ding, 2003). The intensity and action of these issues and variables are different, and it is necessary to verify and include the variables at different scales in the modeling procedure converting from the pixel to the regional scale. Given the situation of multiple scales and variables influencing land system change, a methodology system for the comprehensive integration of the scales was discussed, and a comprehensive integration at the regional and pixel scales was conducted based on understanding the significance and connotation of the scales for land system change and determining the complex relationships at different scales (Veldkamp et al., 2001).

2.2 Shift from Mechanism Analysis to Effects Assessment

The research on the dynamics of land system change is one of the important research focuses in the current sustainable development strategy. The mechanism analysis and effect assessments of the dynamics of land system change are the key areas of land system research and the key processes in the simulation of the dynamics of the land system (Verburg et al., 2009; Veldkamp and Verburg, 2004). There have been many investigations into the simulation of the dynamics of the land system, and the principles, models and methods are being verified, complemented and improved (Veldkamp and Fresco, 1996).

The simulation methods, procedures and key processes involved in moving from the mechanism analysis to effects assessment of the dynamics of land system change are discussed below.

2.2.1 Mechanism Analysis of the Dynamics of Land System Change

The mechanism analysis of the dynamics of land system change is an important prerequisite for the effects assessment of the dynamics of land system change. The dynamics of land system change are a core component in global environment change study and it is controlled by natural factors and influenced by human factors such as society, economics and politics. The integrated effects of the dynamics of land system change influence the development of the global environment and in turn, human society, as the land system impacts basic factors for human survival and development such as climate, soil, vegetation, water resources and biodiversity, and also the structure and function of the Earth's biochemical sphere and the energy and materials cycle of the Earth system. The dynamics of land system change are closely related to the sustainability of interactions among global climate change, declining biodiversity, eco-environmental evolution, humans and the environment. Therefore, it is very important to study the driving mechanisms of the dynamics of land system change and analyze the consequences of land system change, as this influences the understanding of the regional eco-environment, the maintenance of ecological balance and the promotion of coordinated regional economic and environmental development.

The land system is a complex system involving various factors, and the study of the land system needs to consider the sensitivity of the dynamics of land system change to policies, technical progress, population growth, economic development, and market change, and also the influence of cultural factors such as human ideologies and beliefs (Deng, 2008b). The research on the driving forces of land system change and their complex relationship with the dynamics of land system change should consider a minimum of the following conditions: (i) for a given driving force, the function may vary when different land use types are involved, as the driving forces that promote one type of LUCC may restrict another; (ii) the same type of LUCC in different regions may be due to different causes, as there is no absolute explanation for a type of LUCC. For example, the expansion of cultivated land may be driven by population growth in one situation, but in another situation, the population growth may be related to certain social, political or economic conditions, in which the expansion of cultivated land affects the population growth; and (iii) the relationships between two driving forces and between the driving forces and LUCC may vary at temporal and spatial scales. For example, the relationships in the existing empirical model between some global driving forces and LUCC may be different at the regional scale. All the conditions described above confirm that it is important to consider the types, spatial features and scales of the driving forces when constructing a LUCC model.

2.2.1.1 Significance of Understanding the Driving Mechanisms

As global change becomes increasingly recognized, the study of the dynamics of land system change is not only of academic value but also of practical significance. The study of the dynamics of land system change is academically significant because of the following reasons.

Understanding the effects of human activities on global change

Scientifically, global environmental change originates from the interactions among the atmosphere, hydrosphere, lithosphere, biosphere and human activities. Therefore, the study of global change can be described as the mission of contemporary humans to maintain their own survival and sustainable development, rather than an action by the scientific community to meet the challenges posed by global environmental problems (Li et al., 2005; Shao et al., 2006). The study of global change has a history dating back more than 20 years from the 1980s, when people began to understand the complexity of global change at different temporal and spatial scales (Meador and Goldstein, 2003; Groot et al., 2007).

The difficulty in the study of global change is to distinguish the effects of natural factors and human activities and the interaction mechanisms between them. Only by having a clear understanding of the effects of both nature and humans themselves, can people carefully control the natural environment they depend upon for survival and lead it to develop in a direction beneficial to humans (Amsalu et al., 2007; Chen et al., 2008; Seto and Kaufmann, 2003). Human behavior toward global change is very complex, but considering the impacts on the dynamics of the Earth surface system, LUCC mechanisms are representative of global change. Land use and land cover are both a cause and effect of global change which directly reflects the leading factor in accelerating global change—human activities. LUCC has important impacts on the interactions between the biosphere and atmosphere and even the loss in biodiversity (Turner II et al., 1995). Therefore, it is important to simulate and assess the environment as a whole and understand the mechanisms of human activities in global change. This will reduce the uncertainty in predictions for understanding the driving mechanisms of the dynamics of land system change.

Promoting interdisciplinary research

The dynamics of land system change leads to land cover change, and is influenced by economic driving forces in human society. Thus, land system change can be considered as an intersection between natural and human processes. The implementation of research on the driving mechanisms of the dynamics of land system change must promote the further integration of natural and social sciences, and consequently promote the current global change research. Research on the driving mechanisms of the dynamics of land system change will also promote comprehensive research in related fields, such as geosciences, ecology, resource science and environmental science. The participation and collaboration between multiple disciplines can help to further reveal the mechanisms and effects of human activities on the global change.

2.2.1.2 Investigation Methods

The models for the driving mechanisms of the dynamics of land system change have been built and developed from long-term research on LUCC. International experts emphasize the large scale, interdisciplinary and comprehensive research on the driving mechanism models of the dynamics of land system change, and have built a series of models at different scales and on different themes (Turner II et al., 1995; Lambin et al., 2000; Pfaff et al., 2000; Veldkamp et al., 2001; Gao and Deng, 2002; Veldkamp and Verburg, 2004; Verburg, 2006). These models provide appropriate methods for thoroughly understanding the complexity of the dynamics of land system change. The function and goal of the driving mechanism models are to describe, explain and predict the dynamics of land system change and formulate appropriate countermeasures (Verburg et al., 2010).

There are many common driving mechanism models of the dynamics of land system change, most of which use core algorithms based on empirical statistical models and multiple statistical analysis methods to analyze the rate of contribution of each driving factor to the dynamics of land system change, thus exploring the true reasons for the dynamics of land system change. Modeling is an important way to analyze the relationships between the dynamics of land system change and various socioeconomic and natural driving forces. Models can effectively identify the key driving factors influencing the dynamics of land system change and determine their relationship with the dynamics of land system change. Empirical statistical models are good at identifying the main contradictions in complex systems and the important driving factors within systems. The conventional empirical statistical models include principal component analysis, grey relational analytical method, stepwise regression, canonical correlation analysis, partial correlation analysis, the spatial statistical model and the nonlinear regression model.

Principal component analysis

Principal component analysis involves a mathematical procedure that transforms a number of possibly correlated variables into a smaller number of uncorrelated variables called the principal components. These principal components are in descending order based on the variance. The first principal component accounts for as much of the variability in the data as possible, and each succeeding component accounts for as much of the remaining variability as possible. Principal component analysis of the dynamics of land system change uses several linear combinations of a group of driving variables for the dynamics of land system change to explain the variance and covariance structure of these driving variables to decrease the number of driving variables and explain the dynamics of land system change (Deng et al., 2010). Suppose there are N samples with a measured numerical value of P variables respectively; X_{ia} is the ith observation of the ath sample, i.e., vector X

$$X_a = \begin{bmatrix} X_{1a} \\ X_{2a} \\ \vdots \\ X_{pa} \end{bmatrix}, \alpha = 1, 2, \cdots, n \tag{2.1}$$

from which a data matrix is obtained:

$$X = \begin{bmatrix} X_{11} & X_{12} & \cdots & X_{1n} \\ X_{21} & X_{22} & \cdots & X_{2n} \\ \vdots & \vdots & & \vdots \\ X_{p1} & X_{p2} & \cdots & X_{pn} \end{bmatrix} \tag{2.2}$$

The estimate of the covariance matrix for the data matrix is

$$S = \frac{1}{n}(XX' - n\overline{XX'}) = [S_{ij}] \tag{2.3}$$

where

$$S_{ij} = \frac{1}{n}\sum_{a=1}^{n}(X_{ia} - \overline{X}_i)(X_{ja} - \overline{X}_j) \quad i, j = 1, 2, \cdots, p$$

And subsequently the correlation matrix is obtained

$$R = [r_{ij}] \quad r_{ij} = \frac{S_{ij}}{\sqrt{S_{ii}S_{jj}}}, \quad i, j = 1, 2, \cdots, p \tag{2.4}$$

Generally, the variables are normalized first, so that the average equals 0 and the variance equals 1, which means that the variance covariance matrix is consistent with the correlation matrix:

$$X'_{ia} = \frac{X_{ia} - \overline{X}_i}{\sqrt{S_{ii}}} \quad i = 1, 2, \cdots, p; a = 1, 2, \cdots, n \tag{2.5}$$

Now the relationship between the data matrix, X, and the correlation matrix, R, is

$$R = XX' \tag{2.6}$$

If $\lambda_1 \geqslant \lambda_2 \geqslant \cdots \geqslant \lambda_p$ is the eigenvalue of R, and $U = [U_1 U_2 \cdots U_p]$ is the eigenvalue matrix of R, then

$$XX' = U \begin{bmatrix} \lambda_1 & & & 0 \\ & \lambda_2 & & \\ & & \ddots & \\ 0 & & & \lambda_p \end{bmatrix} U' \tag{2.7}$$

Multiply it by U' to the left and then multiply it by U to the right, and obtain

$$U'XX'U = U'U \begin{bmatrix} \lambda_1 & & & 0 \\ & \lambda_2 & & \\ & & \ddots & \\ 0 & & & \lambda_p \end{bmatrix} U'U = \begin{bmatrix} \lambda_1 & & & 0 \\ & \lambda_2 & & \\ & & \ddots & \\ 0 & & & \lambda_p \end{bmatrix} \tag{2.8}$$

Let $F = U'X$, then

$$FF' = \begin{bmatrix} \lambda_1 & & & 0 \\ & \lambda_2 & & \\ & & \ddots & \\ 0 & & & \lambda_p \end{bmatrix} = A \tag{2.9}$$

where F is the corresponding principal component data matrix for this data matrix. We can generate $F_a = U'X_a$, $a = 1, 2, \cdots, n$, so that each F_a is the ath observation.

Then principal component analysis selects the components that can represent the overall changing situation from a number of components to make

$$\frac{\lambda_1 + \lambda_2 + \cdots + \lambda_M}{\lambda_1 + \lambda_2 + \cdots + \lambda_P} \geqslant 85\% \tag{2.10}$$

The extracted $F_1, F_2, \cdots, F_M$ are the principal components of the explanatory variables of the dynamics of land system change (Gao, 2005).

Research on the driving mechanisms of the dynamics of land system change using principal component analysis is mainly based on the natural and socioeconomic index systems, calculates a driving factor load matrix and uses the factor load and contribution rate to illustrate and analyze the reasons for the dynamics of land system change. Li et al. (2004) researched the driving mechanism of desertification of the Ejin Oasis using principal component analysis, and found that the contribution rates of the first and second principal components were 59.28% and 28.08%, respectively, and the factor load of socioeconomic driving factors in the first principal component was higher than that of the natural driving factors. This indicated that the driving factors of oasis desertification were multiple, comprehensive and dominated by human activities.

Grey relational analytical method

Grey relational analysis, a systematic factor analysis, mainly aims to distinguish the primary factors from the secondary factors in a system involving various factors (Deng, 1992). Grey relational analysis can measure the similarity of factors based on the degree of similarity or dissimilarity in their development tendencies, and can quantitatively analyze the dynamic development of the system and the developing trend based on the similarity of the curve shapes of each factor series. Research on the driving mechanisms of the dynamics of land system change often uses the change in land use types as the sequence and the driving factors as the sub-sequence in an overall correlation analysis. The general steps of grey relational analysis are as follows.

- ***Constructing the comparison data series***

  Obtain data that reflects the characteristics of each index by calculation or assessment, then normalize the index data to conveniently compare the indices.

- ***Determining the reference data series***

  The reference data series is the selection criterion for alternative schemes, and the factors in the reference data series are determined from the optimum values of the assessment indices in the alternative schemes. That is, the reference data series consists of the indices for the optimum schemes (Deng, 1992).

- ***Calculating the relational degree***

  When analyzing the reference data series and comparing the relational degree of the data series, it is necessary to analyze the relational degree between the indices and this can be represented by the relational coefficient calculated by:

$$\eta_i(\kappa) = \frac{\Delta_{Min} + \lambda\Delta_{Max}}{\Delta_i(\kappa) + \lambda\Delta_{Max}} \tag{2.11}$$

where λ is the resolution factor, which is generally between 0 and 1, and

$$\Delta_i(\kappa) = |X_i(\kappa) - X_0(\kappa)|\,; \Delta_{Min} = \underset{i}{\mathrm{Min}}\,\underset{\kappa}{\mathrm{Max}}\,|X_i(\kappa) - X_0(\kappa)|;$$
$$\Delta_{Max} = \underset{i}{\mathrm{Max}}\,\underset{\kappa}{\mathrm{Max}}\,|X_i(\kappa) - X_0(\kappa)|$$

Grey relational analysis has mainly been used to study environmental changes and water cycles at present. Zhang et al. (2003) analyzed the driving factors of land use change in the Shule River Basin using grey relational analysis method, by taking the changes in the cultivated land (x_1), population (x_2), livestock (x_3), high wind conditions (x_4) and precipitation (x_5) as the sub-series and the change in land use types including forestry, grassland and desertification land as the series, and analyzing the driving factors of land use change and the sequence of their influence.

Stepwise regression method

The stepwise regression method is one of the methods to formulate the optimum regression equation. Its basic principle is to introduce the independent variables individually; in other words, introduce an independent variable that significantly influences the dependent variable, check the variables already in the equation one by one each time and delete the variables that become insignificant from the equation. Repeat the process until no further variables can be deleted and no new variables can be introduced. In this way, the final equation does not omit any variables that have a significant influence on land use change or include any variables that have an insignificant influence on land use change. The principle of the stepwise regression method can effectively explain the relationship between the driving factors and the land use change.

Suppose the driving factors leading to regional land use change include n alternative variables, $x_1, x_2, \cdots, x_n$, which will be introduced individually in the stepwise regression. Let the sum of the squares of the partial regression of variables be:

$$V_j^{(1)} = (r_{jy}^{(0)})^2 / r_{jj}^{(0)} \quad j = 1, 2, \cdots, n \tag{2.12}$$

Select the first variable. If k_1 makes $V_{k_1}^{(1)} = \max\{V_j^{(1)}\}$, then x_{k_1} is added into the equation. Using the selection test, with the hypothesis of no correlation, calculate the statistics:

$$F_{in}(k_1) = \frac{(n-2)}{r_{yy}^{(0)} - V_{k_1}^{(1)}} \sim F(1, n-2) \tag{2.13}$$

If $F_{in}(k_1) > F_\alpha^*$, then x_{k_1} enters the regression equation. Next, select the second variable in the sequence, and repeat (Gao, 2005).

When a new variable is added to the regression equation, it is important to recheck the variables already in the regression equation individually to determine whether the variables are necessary or can be deleted. Repeat the process until no further variables can be introduced or deleted, and then write out the regression equation:

$$Y = \beta_0 + \beta_{k_1}^{(1)} x_{k_1} + \cdots + \beta_{k_l}^{(l)} x_{k_l} \tag{2.14}$$

This method is widely used in studying the quantitative relationships between the dynamics of land system change and the driving factors. Bai et al (2004) used the logistic stepwise regression to explore the degree of closeness in the relationships between the driving factors and six land use types (cultivated land, forestry, grassland, water, built-up area and unused land), and selected the main driving factors for each land use type in the study of the dynamics of land system change and its driving forces in the upper reaches of the Dadu River.

Canonical correlation analysis

Regression analyses explore the quantitative relationships between several variables and one fixed variable, resulting in a coefficient that reflects the relationship between two variables, but cannot reflect the inherent relationship between one set of variables and another (Lambin et al., 2001; Veldkamp et al., 2001). Research on the driving mechanisms of the dynamics of land system change simply aims to explain the relationship between the quantitative change in land use types and various driving factors. It is also necessary to identify the relationship between a set of independent variables and a set of dependent variables, and canonical correlation analysis does this. Canonical correlation analysis expands the relationship between indices to an inner link between two sets of random variables, and is therefore an effective method for analyzing the driving mechanisms of the dynamics of land system change.

Canonical correlation analysis converts the relationship between multiple variables $X_1, \cdots, X_p$ and $Y_1, \cdots, Y_p$ into the relationship between two new comprehensive variables. It searches $\alpha = (\alpha_1, \cdots, \alpha_p)'$ and $\beta = (\beta_1, \cdots, \beta_q)'$ to form a relationship between the new comprehensive variables as close as possible:

$$V = \alpha_1 X_1 + \alpha_2 X_2 + \cdots + \alpha_p X_p = \alpha' X \tag{2.15}$$

$$W = \beta_1 Y_1 + \beta_2 Y_2 + \cdots + \beta_q Y_q = \beta' Y \tag{2.16}$$

and determine a correlation coefficient:

$$\rho(\alpha' X, \beta' Y) = \frac{Cov(\alpha' X, \beta' Y)}{\sqrt{Var(\alpha' X)}\sqrt{Var(\beta' Y)}} \tag{2.17}$$

Meng et al. (2003) performed a statistical analysis of the dynamic of land system change and its influencing factors in the Zhangye Oasis using the canonical correlation analysis method. They used changes in the area of six land use types (increasing or decreasing) as the dependent variables and n driving factors as the independent variables. Thus extracting the canonical variables and corresponding canonical load factors to reveal the driving mechanisms of the dynamics of land system change in this region.

Partial correlation analysis

The partial correlation analysis method is used when measuring the influence of a certain driving factor among the many factors affecting the dynamics of land system change. The index of partial correlation analysis is the partial correlation coefficient, represented by the following expression:

$$r_{xy,z} = \frac{r_{xy} - r_{xz} r_{yz}}{\sqrt{(1 - r_{xz}^2)(1 - r_{yz}^2)}} \tag{2.18}$$

where r_{xy}, r_{xz} and r_{yz} are the correlation coefficients of the variables x and y, x and z, and y and z, respectively.

The partial correlation coefficient is the correlation coefficient between the dependent variable and one specific independent variable when all other variables are effectively controlled. The land use types and driving factors influence and restrict each other, and when the studied variable correlates with other driving factors, a simple correlation coefficient does not truly reflect the correlation between the two variables, but partial correlation analysis can solve this problem. For example, Zhou and Shi (2006) studied the influence of climate change and human activities on the organic carbon content in soil in China. The results identified that there was a strong positive correlation between temperature and precipitation and the organic carbon content, which is clearly different from the general opinion that increases in temperature will promote the soil respiration and therefore decrease the organic carbon content in soil. Because the positive correlation between the temperature and the organic carbon content identified may be entirely possible due to the influence of a third variable (precipitation), the result of partial correlation analysis agrees with actual observations.

Spatial statistical model

The spatial statistics which were developed in the 1970s provide an important direction for research into principles related to the distribution and accumulation of "points" in space and provide methods for measuring this accumulation intensity. Spatial statistics introduce the definition of "proximity" into statistical analysis and consequently a series of new models and methods have been deduced.

There are special and general definitions of proximity. The special definition of proximity relates to the geographical neighborhood, e.g., the provinces, cities or grids in the neighborhood. The general definition of proximity abstractly refers to the proximity of other properties, for example, similarities in the population, GDP, and total amount of water resources in different counties can all reflect a definition of proximity from different perspectives.

The individual in spatial statistical analysis is represented by points. If there are N individuals that are represented by $1, 2, \cdots, N$, their proximity can be described with the matrix:

$$W = (\omega_{ij})_{N \times N} \tag{2.19}$$

where ω_{ij} is the factor of W which reflects the proximity of the ith and jth points.

The definition of proximity in spatial statistics overturns some hypotheses in traditional models. For example, each observation value in conventional linear regression models can be represented as the sum of the predicted value and error:

$$y_i = \hat{y}_i + \varepsilon_i = a_0 + a_1 x_{i1} + a_2 x_{i2} + \cdots + a_n x_{in} + \varepsilon_i \tag{2.20}$$

where the error ε_i is independently distributed. While in spatial statistics which introduced proximity, ε_i is no longer considered to be independent and can be written as

$$\begin{bmatrix} \varepsilon_1 \\ \varepsilon_2 \\ \vdots \\ \varepsilon_N \end{bmatrix} = \rho W \begin{bmatrix} \varepsilon_1 \\ \varepsilon_2 \\ \vdots \\ \varepsilon_N \end{bmatrix} + \begin{bmatrix} u_1 \\ u_2 \\ \vdots \\ u_N \end{bmatrix} \tag{2.21}$$

where u_i is the random influence error which is independent of individuals; W indicates the influence of proximity and ρ reflects the degree of correlation resulting from the proximity, with a value between -1 and 1.

Nonlinear regression model

Most researchers use the nonlinear regression model based on a microscale (grid pixel) when studying the microscale, discontinuous dynamics of land system change and its driving factors.

Suppose $p_i^k = P(y_i^k = 1|X_i, \hat{y}_i^k)$ is the probability that the kth land use type is present in the ith grid. The nonlinear spatial statistical model supposes that the conditional probability can be represented in the form of a logistic function:

$$\begin{aligned} p_i^k &= \frac{1}{1+\exp[-(a_0^k + a_1^k x_{i1} + a_2^k x_{i2} + \cdots + a_l^k x_{il} + \cdots + a_L^k x_{iL} + r\hat{y}_i^k)]} \\ &= \frac{1}{1+\exp[-(a_0^k + a^k X_i + r\hat{y}_i^k)]} \end{aligned} \tag{2.22}$$

where p_i^k, the probability that the kth land use type is present in grid i, is $p_i^k = P(y_i^k = 1|X_i, \hat{y}_i^k)$; a_l^k are the coefficients corresponding to the natural and socioeconomic factors, and the coefficient matrix $a^k = (a_1^k, a_2^k x_{i2}, \cdots, a_l^k x_{il}, \cdots, a_L^k)$ consists of these coefficients; and r is the coefficient of the spatial autocorrelation factors.

The odds of the event that the kth land use type is present in grid ith can be calculated from p_i^k:

$$\begin{aligned} \frac{p_i^k}{1-p_i^k} &= \exp(a_0^k + a_1^k x_{i1} + a_2^k x_{i2} + \cdots + a_l^k x_{il} + \cdots + a_L^k x_{iL} + r\hat{y}_i^k) \\ &= \exp(a_0^k + a^k X_i + r\hat{y}_i^k) \end{aligned} \tag{2.23}$$

which is usually called the likelihood ratio or the odds. Calculating the logarithm of the odds, we can obtain a model which has many properties of linear regression:

$$\begin{aligned} \text{logit}(y) &= \ln(p_i^k/(1-p_i^k)) \\ &= a_0^k + a_1^k x_{i1} + a_2^k x_{i2} + \cdots + a_l^k x_{il} + \cdots + a_L^k x_{iL} + r\hat{y}_i^k \\ &= a_0^k + a^k X_i + r\hat{y}_i^k \end{aligned} \tag{2.24}$$

2.2.2 Effects Assessment

The effects assessment for the land system change is a key approach of the research outputs from the driving mechanism analysis of land system change and an important foundation for land use decision making. The land system change has been intensified by various natural phenomena and rapid socioeconomic development in recent years, and ecological processes have also changed. There are many effects from the land system change, such as atmospheric effects, hydrological effects, effects on soil, ecological effects, and environmental effect (Turner II et al., 1994). Research on the effects of the land system change is of direct significance for eco-environmental protection and restoration.

2.2.2.1 Effect Classification

Atmospheric effects

The land system change is an important influencing factor on the amount of CO_2, CH_4, N_2O, CO and photochemical smog in the atmosphere. Photochemical smog has an increasing influence on the environment, which not only impacts air quality, but also changes the radiation received by the land surface by dispersing and absorbing the solar radiation, thus causing negative impacts on the living environment for humans.

The land system change influences the climate because changes in the land surface pattern lead to changes in the physical properties of the underlying surface layer. For example, changes in the reflectance of the land surface, roughness, vegetation leaf area and the proportion of vegetation cover can lead to changes in the temperature, humidity, wind speed and precipitation, and consequently cause local and regional climate change. The spatiotemporal change in the land surface properties can also lead to differences in the spatiotemporal distribution of atmospheric energy which can influence climate change. A typical example of this type of change is the urban heat island effect caused by the influence of the expansion of urban built-up areas on the local climate (Xiao et al., 2005).

Gao et al. (2007) explored the influence of the land system change in China in recent years on the regional climate. Their results indicate that land system change led to a decrease in the annual average precipitation in the northwest of China, an increase in the annual average temperature in the central regions, and a decrease in the annual average temperature in the coastal regions. The same land system change in different geographical environments can lead to regional differences in climate change.

Hydrological effects

Research indicates that changes in the quantitative and spatial structure of forests, grasslands, wetlands, irrigated lands and built-up areas all influence evaporation, precipitation and runoff (Deng, 2003). Deforestation influences the land surface reflectance, canopy closure and surface roughness, all of which are related to the water and energy balance. The expansion of irrigated land increases the evaporation area which consequently increases the amount of water in the lower atmosphere, increasing humidity and decreasing the reflectance and daily average temperature, and contributes to forming rain. The decrease in woods and vegetation during the urbanization process reduces evaporation and canopy closure and increases the amount of sediment in rivers, while the construction of sealed land surfaces such as industrial and residential land, and roads reduces surface infiltration and groundwater level, and increases surface runoff and correspondingly the risk of flooding.

The land system change influences the water resource through impacts on water quantity, water quality and the spatial distribution of water resources. The influence of vegetation cover change on the hydrology in a catchment basin may vary due to differences in the basin area, climate and vegetation type, but similar effects such as river sediment increase, reduction in the water conservation capacity in the basin, flood risks, degradation of water quality and harm to aquatic organisms often resulting from vegetation decrease caused by inappropriate land use within a basin (Wan and Yang, 2005). The demand for water resources increases rapidly with the increased scope and intensity of land development and use, which has led to water shortages in many regions in China. The shortage of water resources severely affects the daily life of residents and threatens industrial and agricultural production, and also leads to a series of ecological and environmental problems such as the drying-up of rivers and seawater intrusion into groundwater.

Effects on soil

The land system change influences the quantity and quality of energy exchange between the soil system and the environment. It also affects the water allocation process on the soil surface and material allocation process on the land surface, and changes the rate of ecological metabolic processes within the soil system (Yu et al., 2004). Current research has mainly focused on the following areas: (i) the influence of the dynamics of land system change on soil nutrient transfer; and (ii) changes in land use patterns, and the quantity, quality and spatial structure of land and the consequent influence on the occurrence and intensity of soil erosion.

Urbanization has a significant influence on the quantity and quality of the soil resource, such as the complete disappearance of some ecological functions of soil caused by sealing the soil surface, deterioration of soil physical properties, human influences on morphological characteristics and evolutionary process in soil, declining the overall microbial diversity, soil pollution and soil nutrient enrichment. Land use change during the urbanization process has a series of eco-environmental effects on the soil such as increasing nutrient loss in surface runoff, decreased heat buffering capacity and an increased risk of pollution transfer.

Inappropriate land use (such as deforestation, mine exploitation, reclamation on steep slopes and excessive grazing) leads to significant changes in the physicochemical properties of soil which leads to soil loss and degradation (such as soil erosion, salinization, water logging, acidification, malnutrition and drought). However, the appropriate allocation of limited land resources can effectively control soil erosion and lead to sustainable regional development.

Ecological effects

The dynamics of land system change has an important influence on both ecosystem structure and function. The influence on the ecosystem structure is mainly represented by ecological invasion and biodiversity loss. Different ecosystems and communities absorb and fix nutrients such as carbon and nitrogen at different speeds, which has an important influence on the distribution of nutrients in the soil, atmosphere and water. Thus the dynamics of land system change have a significant impact on the structure and function of the ecosystem at different scales. At the biotic community level, the dynamics of land system change lead to landscape fragmentation, changes in surface water and vapor channels and species introduction and invasion. This results in significant changes in the composition of the biotic community over a large area and may cause fatal interferences and damage to the development and succession process of the natural biotic community. At the ecosystem level, the change in land use patterns has a great influence on the structure and function of the ecosystem. Current research on this topic has mainly focused on material cycles and energy flow with respect to ecosystem functions. At the landscape level, the dynamics of land system change can cause changes in the landscape type, structure and function (Yu et al., 2004).

2.2.2.2 Assessment Methods

The remote sensing retrieval method is a method of directly monitoring the dynamics of land system change, which has a wide coverage but low accuracy. Field surveys are an important method for detecting the dynamics of land system change, but their accuracy depends on the size of the survey unit and number of sampling points. Additionally, a series of biogeochemical cycle simulation models have been constructed for analyzing the soil organic and soil carbon content, such as the CENTURY model (Kelly et al., 1997; Cerri et al., 2007) and the CEVSA model (Yan et al., 2007; Tang et al., 2010).

Remote sensing retrieval method

The ecological effects of the dynamics of land system change are a key focus for current research (Chen et al., 2005; de Almeida et al., 2005). It is important for formulating appropriate land use policies to study the dynamics of land system change and analyze its causes and consequent ecological and resource problems (de Koning, et al., 1999; Conway and Lathrop, 2005). Remote sensing can be used to detect eco-environmental change, but it has a low spatial resolution and results are at the macroscale. Furthermore, relatively few eco-environmental indices can be retrieved from remote sensing data, which can only detect the distribution and change in the eco-environment over a large area.

The remote sensing retrieval method is, however, widely used, and a typical use is in determining the net primary productivity (NPP), which is an important ecological index representing the sustainable development of the ecosystem (DeFries et al., 2004; Langpap et al., 2008). The NPP is the net production of organic compounds through the process of photosynthesis, and reflects the ability of the plant community to produce organic compounds under natural environmental conditions. It is an important ecological index for understanding the land surface carbon cycle, estimating the supporting capacity of the Earth, and evaluating sustainable development in the terrestrial ecosystem (Giltrap and Hewitt, 2004). The NPP is influenced by the biotic characteristics of plants, soil characteristics, precipitation and temperature (Deng et al., 2002).

Model research focusing on agricultural productivity has seen a trend of rapid development with the implementation of the International Biological Program (IBP, 1964–1974), the IGBP under UNESCO and the improvements in computer and remote sensing technology since the 1950s. There have been countless models for estimating NPP, which can be categorized into three general types: statistical models, parameter models and process models (Table 2.2).

Field surveys

Field surveys, especially with fixed-position observations, are widely used in the effects analysis of the dynamics of land system change. It is particularly important for observations of land surface characteristics such as soil properties, ground water resources, wind erosion conditions and soil and water loss, which cannot be retrieved from remote sensing images. There is also some research that combines remote sensing retrieval with field surveys to improve the accuracy of the field survey (Huffman et al., 2000; Wan et al., 2004). The use of field surveys can provide researchers engaged in the dynamics of land system change with plentiful detailed data.

Macroscopic simulation models of biogeochemical cycles

Research on macroscopic simulations of biogeochemical cycles is of great significance for solving global climate change and global eco-environmental problems resulting from the dynamics of land system change (Yue et al., 2005a; Yue et al., 2008). Macroscopic simulation models of biogeochemical cycles are the most important means and most effective tools for studying the ecological and environmental effects of the dynamics of land system change. The Estimation System of Land Productivity (ESLP) model can simulate and estimate the land productivity by different combinations of natural characteristics and socioeconomic factors at the grid land unit (Deng et al., 2010).

The CENTURY model is a typical model for simulating biogeochemical

Table 2.2 List of models to estimate NPP

Model	Name	Developer	Expression and interpretation
Parameter models	Chikugo Model	Uchijima and Seino (1985)	$NPP = 0.29 \exp\left[-0.216(RDI)^2\right] \cdot R_n$ where the unit of the NPP is $tDW/\ (ha \cdot year)$ (where DW is the dry weight). RDI is the radiation dryness index (=Rn/Lr), where L is the latent heat of vaporization; r is the annual precipitation and R_n is the net radiation received by the land surface. This model is established assuming a sufficient supply of soil water, so the estimated NPP is actually the potential or maximum NPP, which varies somewhat from the actual situation.
	Beijing model	Zhu (1993)	$NPP = \begin{cases} 6.93[-0.224(RDI)^{1.82}] \cdot R_n, & when RDI \leqslant 2.1 \\ 8.26[-0.498(RDI)] \cdot R_n, & when RDI > 2.1 \end{cases}$ where the letters relate to the same parameters described above. Sufficient forest data are used in the determination process for determining parameters, so the practicality of this model is somewhat limited.
	Compreh-ensive model	Zhou and Zhang (1995)	$NPP = RDI \cdot \dfrac{r \cdot R_n(r^2 + R_n^2 + r \cdot R_n)}{(r + R_n)(r^2 + R_n^2)} \cdot \exp(-\sqrt{9.87 + 6.25RDI})$ where the parameters have the same symbols as above. This model is based on a deduction process similar to that of the Chikugo Model. This model is constructed based on the eco-physiological characteristics of plants and the actual evapotranspiration model which links the energy balance equation, water balance equation, and natural vegetation data including 23 groups of forest, grassland and desert and corresponding climate data. It is applicable to dry and semi-dry areas.
Statistical models	Miami model	Lieth and Box (1977)	$NPP_t = 3\ 000/(1 + e^{1\ 315 - 0.119\ 6t})$ $\quad NPP_r = 3\ 000/(1 - e^{-0.000\ 664r})$ where NPP_t is the dry matter yield of plants calculated from the annual average temperature; NPP_r is the dry matter yield of plants calculated from the annual average precipitation; t is the annual average temperature and r is the annual average precipitation. The Miami model only considers temperature and precipitation, but NPP is also influenced by other environmental factors such atmospheric and soil factors, so the model result is somewhat different from the actual NPP.

Continued

Model	Name	Developer	Expression and interpretation
Statistical models	Montreal model	Thonthwaite and Mather (1957)	$NPP_E = 3\ 000/(1 - e^{0.000\ 969\ 5(E-20)})$ $E = \frac{1.05R}{\sqrt{1+(1+1.05R/L)^2}}$ $L = 3\ 000 + 25t + 0.05t^3$ where *NPP* is the plant climate productivity; E is the actual evapotranspiration; L is the local annual average evapotranspiration; t is the annual average temperature and R is the annual average precipitation. This model considers multiple factors, and the difference between the estimated result and the actual value is slight, making it better than the Miami model.
Process models	BACROS model MAGIC model FORENA model FORET model	de Wit (1978) Cosby et al. (1985) Solomon (1986) Shugart and West (1977)	All these methods have a significant role in promoting research on evaluating the *NPP* of plants, simulating crop growth, studying the interaction between terrestrial processes and climate, and predicting the eco-environment change. It is difficult to obtain the required input parameters at a regional scale, so the mechanism models have always been limited to studies in small areas, their use at the regional level is severely restricted, and their advantages have not been fully realized.

cycles such as the long-term dynamics of C, N, P and S in the soil system, and has been widely used in dynamic simulation research on the productivity and biomass of ecosystems such as cultivated land, forests and savannas (Yue et al., 2005b; Wang and Yang, 2007). The CENTURY model can simulate plant production, the dynamics of organic matter in soil, and nutrient cycles with input parameters such as precipitation, temperature, soil texture and land management practices. The agricultural ecosystem model within the CENTURY model integrates climate, soil and cultivation activities, and was once used to simulate the ecological process for an agricultural land use model. Furthermore, the CENTURY model incorporates related variables of land use into the model system, so it can effectively link social processes and ecological processes. The analysis methods included in the CENTURY model are the trend test statistical method and the multiple linear regression method.

– ***Trend test statistical method***

Among the methods used to detect and predict climate change, the following method is believed to be the most suitable for testing trends in time series

$$Y_t = a + bt + E_t \tag{2.25}$$

where Y_t is the forest *NPP* for the temperature and precipitation during t year; and E_t is the deviation from the trend line, which is generally supposed to be a stable random process with an average of 0.

– ***Multiple linear regression method***

The analysis of the interactions between annual fluctuations in forest productivity and climate factors generally uses the multiple linear regression method. The multiple linear regression method uses the equalized forest NPP to analyze its relationship with the annual average temperature and annual precipitation, using the basic expression:

$$CI_t = aTI_t + bPI_t + c \tag{2.26}$$

Based on the value of the coefficients in the regression equation, a, b and c, the importance of the influence of the parameters on the forest carbon density can be tentatively estimated. In addition, since the standard errors of the coefficients are different, the regression coefficients do not make sense unless they are larger than their corresponding standard errors. Therefore, the coefficients of each factor are divided by the corresponding standard errors to guarantee the validity of the model by:

$$E = ST_t b_i / e_i \tag{2.27}$$

where E is the influencing factor; ST_t is the influence of temperature or precipitation. When the temperature is positively correlated with the forest carbon content, $ST_t = 1$, otherwise $ST_t = -1$. The influence of precipitation is similar to that of temperature; b_i is the regression coefficient for the factor i in the equation; e_i is the standard error of the regression coefficient i. It can be seen that only when $|E| > 1$, does the regression of the corresponding parameter b on CI_t make sense, and the larger the E is, the greater the contribution of the corresponding parameter of b_i to CI_t will be. Therefore, the influence of various parameters on the forest carbon content can be estimated based on the value of E (Zhao and Zhou, 2005; Verburg et al., 2008).

2.2.3 Multiple Scales in the Dynamics of Land System Change

Research into the dynamics of land system change is a multi-scale and logically consecutive process from the mechanism analysis to scenario simulations and effects assessment. The systematic and spatiotemporally heterogeneous characteristics of the dynamics of land system change require not only a macro analysis of the factors influencing the dynamics of land system change in a given administrative region at the macro level, but also the measurement of the change in indices at the precise level. In addition, it is also important to reflect the structural change in land use under the influence of the various factors onto a grid at a given spatiotemporal accuracy. Finally, it is necessary to integrate all the natural and social factors into one model system to study their joint effects on the dynamics of regional land use change and explore the modes of action and mechanisms of various factors. Therefore, research on the dynamics of land system change must develop in both macroscopic and microscopic directions. Currently, most driving mechanism analyses and scenario simulations of the dynamics of land system change are carried out at a regional scale, while the effects assessment has been generally accurate to various pixel scales.

2.2.3.1 Multiple Scales in the Driving Mechanism Analysis

Simulations of the dynamics of land system change must first determine the driving relationships between the distribution of land use types and the influencing factors. The characteristics of the land system such as mechanisms, feedback, complexity and integrity determine that the distribution of regional land use types is the result of the interactions and influences of multiple factors. We can extract the main influencing factors for land system change at different accuracy levels and depict the interactions between them by constructing restriction of land use distribution models at different scales.

The driving mechanism analysis of the dynamics of land system change at the regional scale can quantitatively represent the spatial dependency between the structural change in the land system and the driving factors at large scales. The simulation of the dynamics of land system change needs to consider the homogeneity and convergence of the region in the land system, and thus it is usually necessary to integrate the driving mechanism model into the driving mechanism analysis framework. We constructed an explanatory linear model for land use patterns to reveal the driving mechanisms of the regional distribution·of land use types.

The driving mechanism analysis of the dynamics of land system change at the pixel scale can more precisely depict the driving effects of various factors on the distribution of land use types. A grid is the simplest and most direct spatial expression vector for land use types and is the basic unit of the driving mechanism analysis of land system succession. To describe and depict the complex nonlinear relationships in the land system, we have introduced discrete variables relating to nature and socioeconomic conditions into the driving mechanism model. We have also improved the variable system for factors influencing the distribution of land use types, and removed the restriction that the variables must be continual by constructing a nonlinear model for the restriction of land use distribution at the pixel scale, which is suitable for the simulation of the dynamics of land system change at a microscopic scale.

2.2.3.2 Multiple Scales in the Scenario Simulation

The scenario simulation in the land system change predicts the various possible types of land use change based on reasonable hypotheses of driving factors in the structural change in the land system such as the regional economy, industry, policy and technologies. The scenario simulation of the dynamics of land system change is first carried out at a regional scale. Different scenarios are developed by setting the input parameters and changing their combination using methods such as system dynamics (Deng et al., 2008). Since there is much uncertainty around the direction of the structural change in regional land use, several different development directions may all occur in the future, so the approaches to different results are not unique (Frolking et al., 1999; Pontius et al., 2007).

The scenario design for the structural change in regional land use aims to describe the possible future and identify methods by which this may occur. For example, we can design scenarios for the structural change in regional land use to include baseline conditions, economic priority conditions, environmental protection conditions, and others.

A baseline scenario mainly reflects the actual conditions in the study area and identifies future development trends based on those actual conditions, particularly the actual conditions of local land use.

An economic priority scenario considers possible developments in the economy, industry, policies and technology and predicts the structural change in regional land use based on the actual local conditions. Under an economic priority scenario, the leading industry in the region is supported and policies lead to the development of the local economic structure. A local produce and labor market system is established and improved, the level of agricultural mechanization increases, the technology use in farming increases, and the development of distinctive agriculture and tourism is encouraged.

In addition, an environmental protection scenario can be developed by regulating the structural change in regional land use. Under an environmental protection scenario, crops are grown in an environmentally responsible manner, population growth is strictly controlled, the scale of livestock herds is controlled, breeds are developed in house and the input of chemicals and agricultural pollution is also reduced.

Having estimated the characteristics of the structural change in land use under different scenarios at the regional scale, the spatial allocation of the structural change in land use needs to be more precisely determined at the pixel scale to satisfy the land use structure under different scenarios and achieve a balance between supply and demand. Therefore, it is necessary to balance supply and demand at the regional scale along with supply and demand at the pixel scale.

2.2.3.3 Multiple Scales in the Effects Assessment

The effects assessment of the land system change is also experiencing a development from the pixel scale to the regional and global scales. The effects assessment for the land system change focusing on different scales is a scientific frontier and a hot research topic in physical geography. "Scale-Change-Process-Effect" is the basic philosophy of land system research. The land system change and succession processes vary depending on scales and the results of the effects assessment may vary greatly. It is very important to reveal the response processes of the land system change when constructing effects assessment models of the land system change aimed at different scales.

There are many effects of the land system change, covering various aspects such as the atmosphere, hydrology, soil and ecology. There are also multiple indices for the effects assessment of the land system change such as NPP, the landscape diversity index, greenhouse gas content and degree of soil erosion. We have represented the effects of the land system change at regional and pixel scales to make it convenient for different regions to make appropriate regulations depending on the effects specific to their region.

Land productivity is an important index in the effect assessment of the land system change (Deng, 2008b). The land system change and pattern succession lead to a change in the land suitability and land quality and directly influence land productivity. The estimation of land productivity initially involves a scenario analysis of the structural change in the land system at the pixel scale based on light, temperature, water, soil, input level and management mode conditions, integrated with GIS techniques. This generates the change in land productivity at a given temporal scale and obtains the spatial differentiation characteristics for that scenario based on the natural, social and economic properties of the land resource. Finally, results of the effect assessment of the land system change at the pixel level are integrated by regions to obtain the effect assessment at the regional scale.

2.2.4 Key Processes from the Mechanism Analysis to the Effects Assessment

The key processes in the mechanism analysis, scenario analysis and effects assessment of the land system change constitute the complete procedure from the mechanism analysis to the effects assessment (Deng, 2008b). The cumulative change in the land system influences the change in chemical components in the atmosphere by affecting the change in the NPP and biogeochemical cycles, which leads to further global or regional climate change and consequently causes a series of ecological effects (Irwin and Geoghegan, 2001). Therefore, it has become a key international focus in land use and land cover research to analyze the driving mechanisms of land system change, reveal the principles underlying spatial change in the land system and the evaluate the effects of the land system change.

Although there have been great advances made in research on the simulation of the land system change (Deng and Zheng, 2004; Verburg et al., 2004), there is currently no complete set of methodologies to systematically analyze the mechanisms of and effects of land system change. The separation of mechanisms from effects has directly led to inconsistencies in the spatial resolution of parameters and contradictions between variable selection principles, and also caused the separation of research on the land system change, simulation models for land use patterns and the effects analysis models of land system change. Furthermore, these separations make it difficult to directly apply the simulation results of the land system and land use pattern to the effect analysis of land system change and verify the effect analysis process of land system change (Verburg et al., 1999; Wang et al., 2005; Deng et al., 2008). In addition, most models and methods used for simulations generally involve only one of several land use types, lack an overall view of the pattern succession of the regional land system, depend too heavily on quantitative analysis and seldom fully embody the principles of land system change (Turner II et al., 1995; Veldkamp and Fresco, 1996; Deng, 2003).

The simulation of the dynamics and effects of land system change requires the construction of a three-tier model which uses the regional land system as a research object to explore the driving mechanisms of the regional land system change, simulate the pattern succession of regional land use and analyze the land productivity change resulting from land system change. The parameters within the three tiers are interdependently supportive.

The key processes from the driving mechanism analysis to the effect assessment include the following procedures. First, the statistical relationships between the distributions of land use types and driving factors at the regional and pixel scales are analyzed, and the effects of natural environmental conditions and socioeconomic factors on the spatiotemporal pattern of regional land use are measured. From this, the key factors influencing the distribution of different land use types can be extracted. Second, a reasonable judgment should be made for the changing trend of the key factors that influence land use patterns based on the historical characteristics of regional land use and the current state of the structural change in regional land use. Third, choose a reasonable scenario and allocate the demand for different land use types to different industries based on the supply and demand of the land for different industries at different temporal cross sections during the forecast period under this scenario. Fourth, determine the spatial allocation of different land use types at a 1×1 km grid from the analysis of the balance between supply and demand for different land use types at the pixel scale. Land use pattern succession maps and spatial distribution maps of cultivated land can then be generated. Finally, the spatial distribution of land productivity at the pixel scale and the changing rules of land productivity over large temporal scale can be estimated based on climate variables, effective soil factors, the spatial distribution of cultivated land and the input and management level (Fig. 2.5).

2.2.4.1 Mechanism Analysis

The land use structure is the result of joint effects of various factors. The changing trend of regional land use structure can therefore be predicted by quantitatively representing the spatial dependencies between the structural changes in the land system and driving factors and constructing spatial-econometric models.

Selection of driving factors

The structural change in land use is influenced by natural, social and economic factors simultaneously. The natural environment is a key factor in the change in land cover and the distribution of land use types, and determines the basic tendency of land use change at the macroscopic scale. Human factors such as social and economic factors and technology have a decisive influence on the differentiation trend of land use types and restrict the direction and intensity of land use change at the regional scale.

Geophysical factors

The land is a natural complex formed by interactions among natural factors such as the terrain, climate, soil, hydrology and vegetation. The various natural factors determine the pattern, structure, level and regional heterogeneity of land use, and natural driving factors for different sources and properties may have different effects on driving the dynamics of land system change. The natural exogenous factors which influence the dynamics of land system change include elevation, slope, aspect, landform and soil. In addition to the controlling factors, climate change is also an indispensable background factor to land use conversion, while natural disasters such as droughts, floods, wind and snow resulting from climate factors can restrict the dynamics of land system change.

The influence of human activities on the dynamics of land system change is more significant than that of natural factors in the short-term. At the

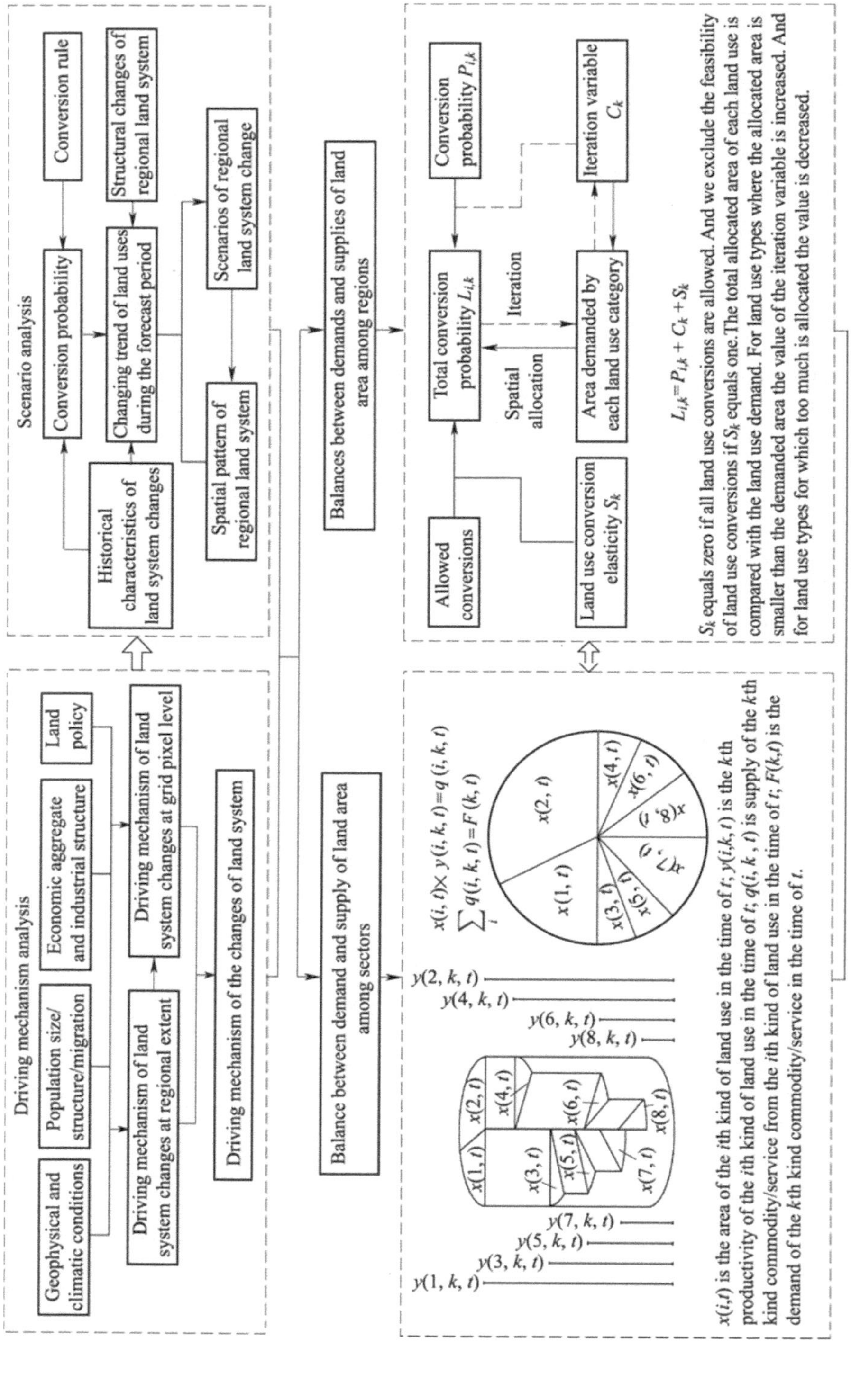

Driving mechanism analysis
Geophysical and climatic conditions
Population size/structure/migration
Economic aggregate and industrial structure
Land policy
Driving mechanism of land system changes at regional extent
Driving mechanism of land system changes at grid pixel level
Driving mechanism of the changes of land system
Scenario analysis
Conversion rule
Conversion probability
Historical characteristics of land system changes
Changing trend of land uses during the forecast period
Structural changes of regional land system
Scenarios of regional land system change
Spatial pattern of regional land system
Balance between demand and supply of land area among sectors
Balances between demands and supplies of land area among regions
Allowed conversions
Conversion probability $P_{i,k}$
Total conversion probability $L_{i,k}$
Spatial allocation
Iteration
Land use conversion elasticity S_k
Area demanded by each land use category
Iteration variable C_k
$L_{i,k}=P_{i,k}+C_k+S_k$
S_k equals zero if all land use conversions are allowed. And we exclude the feasibility of land use conversions if S_k equals one. The total allocated area of each land use is compared with the land use demand. For land use types where the allocated area is smaller than the demanded area the value of the iteration variable is increased. And for land use types for which too much is allocated the value is decreased.
$x(i,t)\times y(i,k,t)=q(i,k,t)$
$\sum_i q(i,k,t)=F(k,t)$
y(1, k, t)
y(2, k, t)
y(3, k, t)
y(4, k, t)
y(5, k, t)
y(6, k, t)
y(7, k, t)
y(8, k, t)
x(1, t)
x(2, t)
x(3, t)
x(4, t)
x(5, t)
x(6, t)
x(7, t)
x(8, t)
$x(i,t)$ is the area of the ith kind of land use in the time of t; $y(i,k,t)$ is the kth productivity of the ith kind of land use in the time of t; $q(i,k,t)$ is supply of the kth kind commodity/service from the ith kind of land use in the time of t; $F(k,t)$ is the demand of the kth kind commodity/service in the time of t.

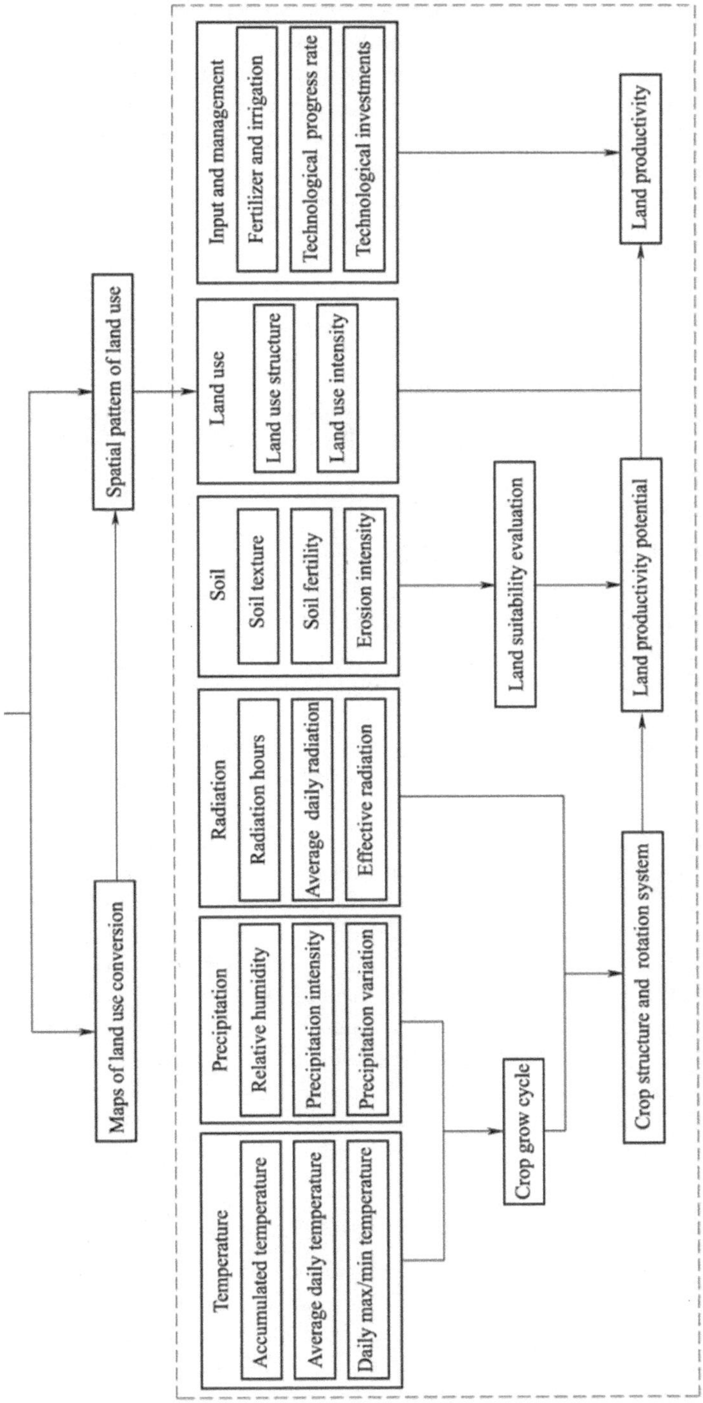

Fig. 2.5 Framework of exploring the driving mechanism, simulating the spatial pattern and evaluating the consequence of land system changes from a multi-scale domain.

macroscopic scale, decisions on land use, changes in the socioeconomic conditions at the country level and changes in human values are all important influencing factors for land use change. The IHDP Science Plan divided the socioeconomic factors into direct and indirect factors. The indirect factors include population change, technical progress, economic growth, politics and economic policies. The direct factors include the demand for land products, investment in the land, degree of urbanization, intensity of land use, property rights and land use policies.

Location conditions

At the spatial scale, the location of the study area directly influences local socioeconomic development and consequently indirectly determines the direction and intensity of land use change. The location condition is often neglected in the driving mechanism analysis of land system change. Common location condition data include the distance from the study area or grid point to the provincial city, the locations of other large cities, major traffic highways, railways and water areas and traffic densities.

Estimation of the driving mechanisms

The current method for measuring of the interactions between the structural change in land use and the influencing factors is generally constituted by developing a hypothesis to analyze the influence of a given factor independently. However, the structural change in land use as a consequence of the interaction between natural and human factors does not interact with the multiple social, economic, technological and natural environmental conditions in a simply linear manner in the complex regional human-land relationship system.

To precisely measure and analyze the driving mechanisms of the dynamics of land system change, researchers generally use empirical statistical methods such as the logistic regression method, principal component analysis method and gray correlation analysis method to construct driving mechanism models for the dynamics of land system change. This allows an estimation of the influence of various factors on the dynamics of land system change.

The basic principles of structural change in land use can be explored by analyzing the interactions between the land system structure and the driving factors and any changes (Hubacek and Sun, 2000; Deng, 2008a; Hubacek and Vazquez, 2002). Scenario predictions for the future land use structure can then be developed to prepare a foundation for the simulation of the dynamics of the land system.

Accuracy verification and interpretation

Verification of the accuracy of the driving mechanism model is an important part of confirming the applicability of the models. The accuracy verification methods for the different driving mechanism models are different. We will use the logistic regression model as an example to illustrate the main methods for verifying model accuracy. There are generally three methods that can be used to verify the accuracy of the logistic regression model.

The first method is the pseudo coefficient of determination, i.e., the pseudo R^2 index. The pseudo coefficient of determination can be considered to be the proportion of the variation of the dependent variable that can be explained by the model (Amemiya, 1985). When the independent variables are unrelated to the dependent variable, the pseudo R^2 index approaches zero, but when the simulation model accurately predicts the dependent variable, the pseudo R^2 index approaches one. It should be noted that the pseudo R^2 index is dimensionless, and is unrelated to the measurement units used in the model.

The second method is the correlation between the forecast probability and observation values (Hilbe, 2009). There are several types of indices that can be used to assess this kind of correlation. Typically, the larger the index value, the closer the correlation between the predicted probability and response of the observed variable.

The third method is the classification table (Hosmer, 2000). The classification table is a tabulation method that divides observations into the occurrence and nonoccurrence of events, which can be used to verify the accuracy of the logistic regression model.

The results of models can reveal the driving mechanism processes for the dynamics of land system change. The results of different driving mechanism models vary greatly. Here again, we will use the logistic regression model as an example. The logistic regression coefficients can be explained as the change in the dependent variable caused by the unit change in the corresponding independent variable. If the logistic regression coefficient is positive and not zero, it means that given the condition that other independent variables are controlled, the log of the odds ratio will increase with the increasing value of the corresponding independent variable. When the coefficient is negative and not zero, it means the log of the odds ratio will decrease with the increasing value of the corresponding independent variable. If the coefficient is almost zero, it means the corresponding independent variable does not differ significantly from zero in the statistical sense.

2.2.4.2 Scenario Analysis

The scenario analysis for the land system change predicts the possible structural change in land use for the future based on various reasonable hypotheses of changes about driving factors such as the regional economy, industry, policies and technical development. Different scenarios are developed by controlling the value and combination of the input parameters based on the design framework of the simulation model for the structural change in land use.

The scenario analysis module for the structural change in land use is mainly based on two simulation models and uses reasonable scenario assumptions.

CGE-based analysis of the structural change in regional land uses

A Computable General Equilibrium (CGE)-based modeling framework is capable of simulating the structural change in regional land use by integrating various socioeconomic factors such as the regional industrial structure, trade environment, economic policies and institutional arrangement. This constructs a multi-sector open balance system to explore the principles of the dynamic structural change in regional land use. This model consists of five modules: regional macro quantitative analysis, thematic quantitative analysis, driving mechanism analysis of the distribution of land use, regional influence of agricultural policy and a scenario analysis of the influence of forestry policies (Fig. 2.6).

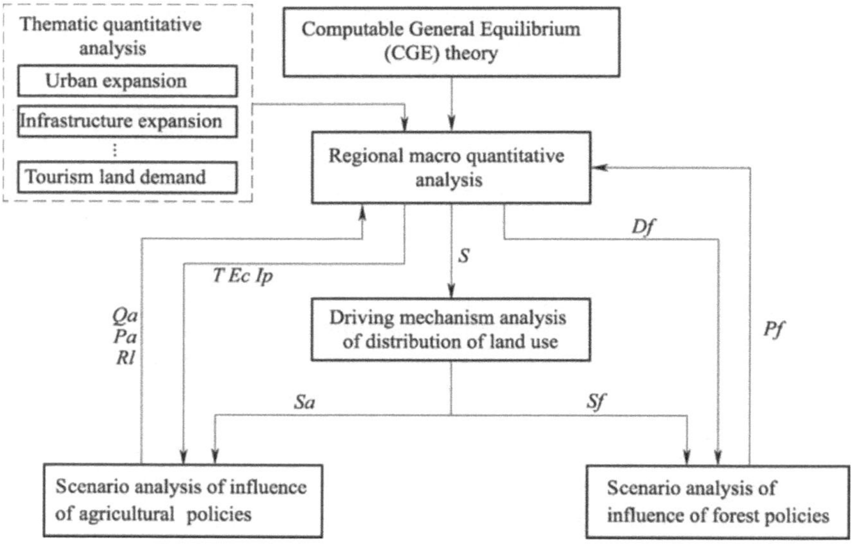

Fig. 2.6 Conceptual framework of simulating land use change at a regional scale based on a CGE modeling strategy.

Note: *S*, land use per sector of each province; *Sa*, agricultural land use area in each county; *Sf*, forest area; *Ip*, input price indices; *T*, technical progress indices; *Ec*, consumer expenditure; *Df*, wood demand; *Rl*, land rent; *Qa*, total agricultural output; *Pa*, price index of agricultural outputs; *Pf*, projected demands of woods.

System Dynamics-oriented analysis of the structural change in regional land use

The System Dynamics model of structural change in regional land use links the structural change in land use and socioeconomic development in a socioeconomic system and describes their interaction quantitatively, providing an effective tool for predicting the structural change in regional land use. It consists of many modules which are selected depending on the goal of the simulation and the analysis of the dynamics of land system change (Le et al., 2008; Calvo-Iglesias et al., 2009; Le et al., 2010). For example, it can be set to consist of the structure of land use module, the population module, the economic module, and the agricultural production module which can be subdivided into crop farming and animal husbandry modules (Fig. 2.7). There is positive and negative feedback between sub-modules and connections with other land use modules.

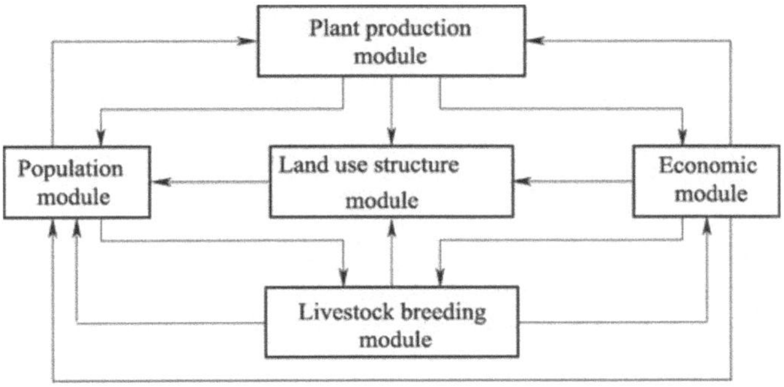

Fig. 2.7 Conceptual framework of simulating land use changes at a regional scale based on a system dynamics approach.

Scenario analysis

The scenario analysis is based on the two simulation models of the structural change in regional land use described above. A scenario analysis specifies the changing trend of variables based on the crucial variables for regional development, introduces emergencies and their influences and develops scenario hypotheses for land use structure based on given conditions (Fig. 2.8). The change in land use structure can be modeled under different scenarios, such as a baseline scenario, an economic development priority scenario and an environmental protection scenario (Deng et al., 2008). Baseline scenarios aim to reflect the future structural change in the land system based on historical trends. Economic priority scenarios consider possible significant changes in

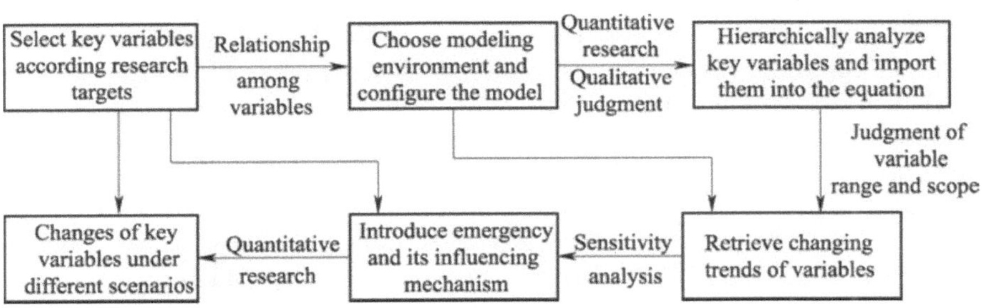

Fig. 2.8 Generic procedures of scenario analysis of the dynamics of land system.

the economy, industries, policies or technology in the future, and predict the result of their change regarding the structural change in the land system. Environmental protection scenarios hypothesize that people in the study area will undertake a series of environmental protection, ecological restoration and sustainable development strategies.

Scenario analyses are based on specific demands in the study area. There are many methods for constructing scenarios of the structural change in the land system, such as a simple trend extrapolation method or relatively complex economic models. The selection of methods for constructing scenarios depends on the actual needs of the research, with the main requirement that the scenario should adequately reflect the possible development tendency for structural change in the regional land system.

2.2.4.3 Effects Assessment

The assessment and analysis of the effects of the land system change are important to identify the comprehensive consequences of the dynamics of land system change. As land system change becomes increasingly intensive, its effects become multi-layered at multiple scales. Therefore, the methods and procedures for the effect analysis are varied and complex. Land productivity is one of the important indices of effects assessment of the dynamics of land system change, and this has been used as an example to illustrate the key procedures of the effect assessment of the dynamics of land system change.

The estimation of land productivity needs to cover land suitability assessment, the assessment of land productivity and advanced applications which use the land resource as basic input information. During the land productivity estimation process, we drew agricultural zoning maps and land suitability assessment maps and collected property data such as cropping area and yield per unit area. This information provides a fundamental decision making basis for estimating the effects of the dynamics of land system change and optimizing regional land allocation.

Land productivity is the comprehensive production capacity based on the light, temperature, water, soil and input and output conditions, which is closely associated with agricultural ecological zones. Therefore, the agricultural ecological zoning, which considers the soil, terrain and climate, should be assessed first. Climate factors influences the growing period of crops, while soil texture and terrain affect the crop growing types and crop rotation systems. The land productivity at each grid is estimated by integrating the agricultural ecological zoning, land use information and socioeconomic information and analyzing the restrictions of factors at different levels on the land productivity using a weighted analysis method.

Land productivity can be determined at multiple scales, from a precise 1km gird to a regional or even global scale. The estimation of land productivity considers the influence of multiple cropping on land productivity, so that the assessment of land quality, productivity and carrying capacity can be determined by computers. Furthermore, information related to the input and management levels should also be included in the operating parameters for the estimation process of land productivity. This forms an open and expandable system to assist decision-making which integrates the theory and methods of eco-economic planning and is applicable to sustainable agricultural management.

2.3 Summary

The pattern, succession processes, driving mechanisms and effects assessment of the dynamics of land system change all depend on scale. Therefore, the scale effect is an important factor that should be considered in the simulation process of the dynamics of land system change. The modeling process from the regional to the pixel scale is a process which allows observations and simulation results to be converted from large scales to precise scales. The modeling process generally uses observations at the administrative boundary level and makes a comprehensive analysis of land system structure, driving mechanism analysis, spatial allocation and effects assessment with multi-source data. The accuracy verification from the pixel scale to the regional scale is an important test of the feasibility and suitability of the scale conversion. The accuracy verification includes the extraction of land system change processes at the pixel scale, integration of the balance of land supply and demand at the regional scale, and analysis of the differences of intensity and modes of action of the model variables at different scales.

The mechanism analysis of the dynamics of land system change is an important premise of the effects assessment. The dynamics of land system change is one of the important components of global environmental change research, which is constrained by natural factors and influenced by human factors such as society, the economy and politics. The dynamics of the regional land system are a consequence of the joint effects of the driving factors acting at the regional and larger scales (such as the global scale). Currently, experts have established a number of driving mechanism models for the dynamics of land system change with core algorithms that are generally improved versions of empirical statistical algorithms. These models provide important tools for understanding the driving mechanisms of LUCC.

Changes in the human living environment due to the dynamics of land system change mean that the effects assessment of the dynamics of land system change is currently a hot research topic, which is developing with the implementation of various research plans launched by the IGBP. Experts in relevant fields have done a highly effective job to assess the effects at global and regional scales. Thus far, three types of methods have been used for the effects assessment of the dynamics of land system change: remote sensing retrieval, field surveys and macroscopic simulation models of biogeochemical cycles. All these methods provide important tools for the effects assessment of the dynamics of land system change.

The spatiotemporal variations in the dynamics of land system change require the land system research to involve macro analysis at the macroscopic level and at certain administrative units. The change in various indices should be measured at the precise grid level and reflect the structural change in land use under the influence of the different factors onto the grid at a given spatiotemporal accuracy. Thus, research on the dynamics of land system change will develop in both macroscopic and microscopic directions.

Although great advances have been made in research on the simulation of the dynamics of land system change, there is not yet a complete methodology system to systematically analyze the mechanisms and effects of land system change. The separation of the mechanism and effect processes has directly led to inconsistencies in the spatial resolution of parameters and contradictions between variable selection principles. This has caused further separation in the research on the dynamics of land system change between the simulation models for land use patterns and the effects analysis models for land system change.

The key processes of mechanism analysis, scenario analysis and effects assessment constitute a three-tier modeling approach, and together form a complete process to analyze the dynamics of land system change. Consequently, these combined procedures provide a complete methodology and analysis process for land system research.

References

Amsalu A, Stroosnijder L, de Graaff J. 2007. Long-term dynamics in land resource use and the driving forces in the Beressa watershed, highlands of Ethiopia. Journal of Environmental Management, 83(4): 448–459.

Amemiya T. 1985. Advanced Econometrics. Cambridge, MA: Harvard University Press.

Aspinall R. 2004. Modelling land use change with generalized linear models—A multi-model analysis of change between 1860 and 2000 in Gallatin Valley, Montana. Journal of Environmental Management, 72(1–2): 91–103.

Bai W Q, Yan J Z, Zhang Y L. 2004. Land use/land cover change and driving forces in the region of upper reaches of the Dadu River. Progress in Geography, 23(1): 71–78.

Burgi M and Turner M G. 2002. Factors and processes shaping land cover and land cover changes along the Wisconsin River. Ecosystems, 5(2): 184–201.

Cai Y L. 2001. A study on land-use/cover change: The need for a new integrated approach. Geographical Research, 20(6): 645–652.

Calvo-Iglesias M S, Fra-Paleo U, Díaz-Varela R A. 2009. Changes in farming system and population as drivers of land cover and landscape dynamics: The case of enclosed and semi-openfield systems in Northern Galicia (Spain). Landscape and Urban Planning, 90(3–4): 168–177.

Cerri C, Easter M, Paustian K, Killian K, Coleman K, Bernoux M, Falloon P,

Powlson D, Batjes N, Milne E. 2007. Simulating SOC changes in 11 land use change chronosequences from the Brazilian Amazon with RothC and CENTURY models. Agriculture Ecosystems and Environment, 122(1): 46–57.

Chen C C, Xie G D, Zhen L, Leng Y H. 2008. Long-term dynamics of cultivated land resources and their driving forces of Guyuan City in upper reaches of Jinghe River. Chinese Geographical Science, 18(1): 33–40.

Chen S S, Chen L F, Liu Q H, Li X. 2005. Remote sensing and GIS-based integrated analysis of coastal changes and their environmental impacts in Lingding Bay, Pearl River Estuary, South China. Ocean and Coastal Management, 48(1): 65–83.

Conway T M and Lathrop R G. 2005. Modeling the ecological consequences of land-use policies in an urbanizing region. Environmental Management, 35(3): 278–291.

Cosby B J, Wright R F, Hornberger G M, Galloway J N. 1985. Modeling the effects of acid deposition: Estimation of long-term water quality response in a small forested catchment. Water Resour Res, 20(11): 1591–1601.

de Almeida C, Monteiro M, Camara G, Soares Filho B S, Cerqueira G, Pennachin C L. 2005. GIS and remote sensing as tools for the simulation of urban land-use change. International Journal of Remote Sensing, 26(4): 759–774.

de Koning G H J, Veldkamp A, Fresco L O. 1998. Land use in Ecuador: A statistical analysis at different aggregation levels. Agriculture Ecosystems and Environment, 70(2–3): 231–247.

de Koning G H J, Veldkamp A, Fresco L O. 1999. Exploring changes in Ecuadorian land use for food production and their effects on natural resources. Journal of Environmental Management, 57(4): 221–237.

DeFries R S, Asner G P, Houghton R. 2004. Trade-offs in land-use decisions: Towards a framework for assessing multiple ecosystem responses to land-use changed. Ecosystems and Land Use Change, 153: 1–9.

Deng J. 1992. Introduction to the Gray Athematics-Gray Dim Collection. Wuhan: Huazhong University of Science and Technology Press.

Deng W H and Zheng G M. 2004. Landscape and habitat factors affecting cabot's tragopan Tragopan caboti occurrence in habitat fragments. Biological Conservation, 117(1): 25–32.

Deng X Z, Liu J Y, Zhuang D F, Zhan J Y. 2002. Modeling the relationship of land use change and some geophysical indicators: A case study in the ecotone between agriculture and pasturing in Northern China. Journal of Geographical Sciences, 12(4): 397–404.

Deng X Z. 2003. A study on the land use changes and their driving forces in the farming-pasturing interlocked areas of China. Institute of Geographical Sciences and Natural Resources Research. Beijing, Chinese Academy of Sciences, pp: 210.

Deng X Z, Zhan J Y, Chen R. 2005. The patterns and driving forces of urban sprawl in China. IGARSS 2005: IEEE International Geoscience and Remote Sensing Symposium, 1–8: 1511–1513.

Deng X Z, Su H B, Zhan J Y. 2008. Integration of multiple data sources to simulate the Dynamics of Land Systems. Sensors, 8(2): 620–634.

Deng X Z. 2008a. Analysis of Land Use Conversions. Beijing: China Land Press.

Deng X Z. 2008b. Simulation of Land System Dynamics. Beijing: China Land Press.

Deng X Z, Lin Y Z, Zhan J Y, He S J. 2010. Robust estimation for the determinant model of land use pattern based on the area percentage dataset of land uses. Progress in Geography, 29(2): 179–185.

de Wit C T. 1978. Simulation of assimilation, respiration and transpiration of crops. Simulation Monographs. Wageningen: Pudoc.

Ding C R. 2003. Land policy reform in China: Assessment and prospects. Land Use Policy, 20(2): 109–120.

Ehrlich P R and Daily G C. 1993. Population extinction and saving bio-diversity. Ambio, 22(2–3): 64–68.

Frolking S, Xiao X, Zhuang Y, Salas W, Li C. 1999. Agricultural land-use in China: A comparison of area estimates from ground-based census and satellite-borne remote sensing. Global Ecology and Biogeography, 8(5): 407–416.

Gao H X. 2005. Applied Multivariate Statistical Analysis. Beijing: Peking University Press.

Gao X J, Zhang D F, Chen Z X, Pal J S, Giorgi F. 2007. Land use effects on climate in China as simulated by a regional climate model. Science in China Series D—Earth Sciences, 50(4): 620–628.

Gao Z Q and Deng X Z. 2002. Analysis on spatial features of LUCC based on remote sensing and GIS in China. Chinese Geographical Science, 12(2): 107–113.

Giltrap D J and Hewitt A E. 2004. Spatial variability of soil quality indicators in New Zealand soils and land uses. New Zealand Journal of Agricultural Research, 47(2): 167–177.

GLP. 2005. Science Plan and Implementation Strategy. IGBP Report No. 53/IHDP Report No. 19. Stockholm, IGBP.

Goidts E, van Wesemael B, van Oost K. 2009. Driving forces of soil organic carbon evolution at the landscape and regional scale using data from a stratified soil monitoring. Global Change Biology, 15(12): 2981–3000.

Groot J C J, Rossing W A H, Jellema A, Stobbelaar D J, Renting H, van Ittersum M K. 2007. Exploring multi-scale trade-offs between nature conservation, agricultural profits and landscape quality: A methodology to support discussions on land-use perspectives. Agriculture Ecosystems and Environment, 120(1): 58–69.

Hilbe J M. 2009. Logistic Regression Models. Chapman and Hall/CRC Press.

Hosmer D W and Lemeshow S. 2000. Applied Logistic Regression. New York: Wiley.

Hubacek K and Sun L. 2000. Land use change at the national and regional level in China: A scenario analysis based on input-output modeling. Interim Report IR-00-053. Laxenburg, Austria.

Hubacek K and Vazquez J. 2002. Economics of land use. In: Knowledge Base for Sustainable Development. An Insight into the Encyclopedia of Life Support Systems, Volumes I, II, III. UNESCO Publishing-Eolss Publishers, Oxford, UK.

Huffman E, Eilers R G, Padbury G, Wall G, MacDonald K B. 2000. Canadian agri-environmental indicators related to land quality: Integrating census and biophysical data to estimate soil cover, wind erosion and soil salinity. Agriculture Ecosystems and Environment, 81(2): 113–123.

Irwin E G and Geoghegan J. 2001. Theory, data, methods: Developing spatially explicit economic models of land use change. Agriculture Ecosystems and Environment, 85(1–3): 7–23.

Kasperson J X, Kasperson R E, Turner B L II. 1995. Regions at Risk: Comparisons of Threatened Environments. Tokyo: United Nations University.

Kaufmann R K and Seto K C. 2001. Change detection, accuracy, and bias in a sequential analysis of Landsat imagery in the Pearl River Delta, China: Econometric techniques. Agriculture Ecosystems and Environment, 85(1–3): 95–105.

Kelly R H, Parton W J, Crocker G J, Graced P R, Klír J, Körschens M, Poulton P R, Richter D D. 1997. Simulating trends in soil organic carbon in long-term experiments using the CENTURY model. Geoderma, 81(1–2): 75–90.

Kremen C, Niles J O, Dalton M G, Daily G C, Ehrlich P R, Fay J P, Grewal D, Guillery R P. 2000. Economic incentives for rain forest conservation across scales. Science, 288(5472): 1828–1832.

Lambin E F, Rounsevell M D A, Geist H J. 2000. Are agricultural land-use models able to predict changes in land-use intensity? Agriculture Ecosystems and Environment, 82(1–3): 321–331.

Lambin E F, Turner B L, Geist H J, Agbola S B, Angelsen A, Bruce J W, Coomes O T, Dirzo R, Fischer G, Folke C, George P S, Homewood K, Imbernon J, Leemans R, Li X B, Moran E F, Mortimore M, Ramakrishnan P S, Richards J F, Skanes H, Steffen W, Stone G D, Svedin U, Veldkamp T A, Vogel C, Xu J. 2001. The causes of land-use and land-cover change: Moving beyond the myths. Global Environmental Change—Human and Policy Dimensions, 11(4): 261–269.

Langpap C, Hascic I, Wu J. 2008. Protecting watershed ecosystems through targeted local land use policies. American Journal of Agricultural Economics, 90(3): 684–700.

Le Q B, Park S J, Vlek P L G. 2010. Land Use Dynamic Simulator (LUDAS): A multi-agent system model for simulating spatio-temporal dynamics of coupled human-landscape system 2. Scenario-based application for impact assessment of land-use policies. Ecological Informatics, 5(3): 203–221.

Le Q B, Park S J, Vlek P L G, Cremers A B. 2008. Land-Use Dynamic Simulator (LUDAS): A multi-agent system model for simulating spatio-temporal dynamics of coupled human-landscape system 1. Structure and theoretical specification. Ecological Informatics, 3(2): 135–153.

Levine D I and Painter G. 2003. The schooling costs of teenage out-of-wedlock childbearing: Analysis with a within-school propensity-score-matching estimator. Review of Economics and Statistics, 85(4): 884–900.

Li L, Zhang P Y, Hou W. 2005. Land use/cover change and driving forces in southern Liaoning Province since 1950s. Chinese Geographical Science, 15(2): 131–136.

Li S, Li F, Sun W, Li B S. 2004. Modern desertification process in Ejina Oasis and its dynamic mechanism. Scientia Geographica Sinica, 24(1): 61–67.

Liu J Y, Zhan J Y, Deng X Z. 2005. Spatio-temporal patterns and driving forces of urban land expansion in China during the economic reform era. Ambio, 34(6): 450–455.

Lieth H and Box E. 1977. The gross primary production pattern of the land vege-

tation: A first attempt. Tropical Ecology, 18: 109–115.
Malthus T. 1820. Principles of Political Economy. Cambridge University Press.
McGuffie K and Henderson-Sellers A. 1997. A Climate Modelling Primer. New York: John Wiley and Sons.
Meng J J, Wu X Q, Li Z G. 2003. Landuse/landcover changes in Zhangye oasis of Hexi Corridor. Journal of Geographical Sciences, 13(1): 71–75.
Meador M R and Goldstein R M. 2003. Assessing water quality at large geographic scales: Relations among land use, water physicochemistry, riparian condition, and fish community structure. Environmental Management, 31(4): 504–517.
Munroe D K and Müller D. 2007. Issues in spatially explicit statistical land-use/cover change (LUCC) models: Examples from western Honduras and the Central Highlands of Vietnam. Land Use Policy, 24(3): 521–530.
Pfaff A, Kerr S, Hughes F, Liu S, Sanchez G, Schimel D, Tosi J, Watson V. 2000. The Kyoto protocol and payments for tropical forest: An interdisciplinary method for estimating carbon-offset supply and increasing the feasibility of a carbon market under the CDM. Ecological Economics, 35(2): 203–221.
Plantinga A J, Lubowski R N, Stavins R N. 2002. The effects of potential land development on agricultural land prices. Journal of Urban Economics, 52(3): 561–581.
Pontius R G Jr, Walker R, Yao-Kumah R, Arima E, Aldrich S, Caldas M, Vergara D. 2007. Accuracy assessment for a simulation model of Amazonian deforestation. Annals of the Association of American Geographers, 97(4): 677–695.
Qiu Y, Fu B J, Wang J, Chen L D. 2003. Spatiotemporal prediction of soil moisture content using multiple-linear regression in a small catchment of the Loess Plateau, China. Catena, 54(1–2): 173–195.
Risch A C, Heiri C, Bugmann H. 2005. Simulating structural forest patterns with a forest gap model: A model evaluation. Ecological Modelling, 181(2–3): 161–172.
Schulze R E. 2000. Modelling hydrological responses to land use and climate change: A southern African perspective. Ambio, 29(1): 12–22.
Serneels S and Lambin E F. 2001. Proximate causes of land-use change in Narok District, Kenya: A spatial statistical model. Agriculture Ecosystems and Environment, 85(1–3): 65–81.
Serra P, Pons X, Sauría D. 2008. Land-cover and land-use change in a Mediterranean landscape: A spatial analysis of driving forces integrating biophysical and human factors. Applied Geography, 28(3): 189–209.
Seto K C, Woodcock C E, Song C, Huang X, Lu J, Kaufmann R K. 2002. Monitoring land-use change in the Pearl River Delta using Landsat TM. International Journal of Remote Sensing, 23(10): 1985–2004.
Seto K C and Kaufmann R K. 2003. Modeling the drivers of urban land use change in the Pearl River Delta, China: Integrating remote sensing with socioeconomic data. Land Economics, 79(1): 106–121.
Shao J A, Wei C F, Xie D T. 2006. An insight on drivers of land use change at regional scale. Chinese Geographical Science, 16(2): 176–182.
Shugart H H and West D C. 1977. Development of an appalachian deciduous forest model and its application to assessment of the impact of the chestnut blight. Journal of Environmental Management, 5: 161–179.

Simon Z, Tedesco M J, Gianello C. 1991. Long-term land application of activated-sludge from a petrochemical waste-water treatment-plant. Water Science and Technology, 24(11): 19–31.

Solomon A M. 1986. Transient response of forests to CO_2-induced climate change: Simulation modeling experiments in eastern North America. Oecologia, 68: 567–579.

Stéphenne N and Lambin E F. 2001. A dynamic simulation model of land-use changes in Sudano-sahelian countries of Africa (SALU). Agriculture Ecosystems and Environment, 85(1–3): 145–161.

Tang H J, Qiu J J, Wang L G, Li H, Li C S, van Ranst E. 2010. Modeling soil organic carbon storage and its dynamics in croplands of China. Agricultural Sciences in China, 9(5): 704–712.

Thonthwaite C W and Mather J R. 1957. Instructions and tables for computing potential evapotranspiration and the water balance. Publication in Climatology, 10: 181–311.

Turner B L II. 2009. Land change science. International Encyclopedia of Human Geography. Rob K, Nigel T. Eds. Oxford, Elsevier.

Turner B L II, Meyer W B, Skole D L. 1994. Global land-use land-cover change: Towards an integrated study. Ambio, 23(1): 91–95.

Turner B L II, Skole D, Sanderson S. 1995. Land-use and land-cover change. Science/Research Plan. IGBP Report; 35/HDP Report 7.

Turner B L II, Clark W C, Kates R W, Richards J F, Mathews J T, Meyer W B. 1990. The Earth as Transformed by Human Action: Global and Regional Changes in the Biosphere over the Past 300 Years. Cambridge: Cambridge University Press with Clark University.

Uchijima Z and Seino H. 1985. Agroclimatic evaluation of net primary productivity of natural vegetation: (1) Chikugo model for evaluating primary productivity. Journal of Agricultural Meteorology, 40: 343–352.

van Keulen H, Kuyvenhoven A, Ruben R. 1998. Sustainable land use and food security in developing countries: DLV's approach to policy support. Agricultural Systems, 58(3): 285–307.

Veldkamp A and Fresco L O. 1996. CLUE-CR: An integrated multi-scale model to simulate land use change scenarios in Costa Rica. Ecological Modelling, 91(1–3): 231–248.

Veldkamp A, Verburg P H, Kok K, de Koning G H J, Priess J, Bergsma A R. 2001. The need for scale sensitive approaches in spatially explicit land use change modeling. Environmental Modeling and Assessment, 6(2): 111–121.

Veldkamp A and Verburg P H. 2004. Modelling land use change and environmental impact. Journal of Environmental Management, 72(1–2): 1–3.

Verburg P H, Veldkamp A, Fresco L O. 1999. Simulation of changes in the spatial pattern of land use in China. Applied Geography, 19(3): 211–233.

Verburg P H and Overmars K P. 2009. Combining top-down and bottom-up dynamics in land use modeling: Exploring the future of abandoned farmlands in Europe with the Dyna-CLUE model. Landscape Ecology, 24(9): 1167–1181.

Verburg P H, van de Steeg J, Veldkamp A, Willemen L. 2009. From land cover change to land function dynamics: A major challenge to improve land characterization. Journal of Environmental Management, 90(3): 1327–1335.

Verburg P H. 2006. Simulating feedbacks in land use and land cover change models. Landscape Ecology, 21(8): 1171–1183.

Verburg P H, de Koning G H J, Kok K, Veldkamp A, Bouma J. 1999a. A spatial explicit allocation procedure for modelling the pattern of land use change based upon actual land use. Ecological Modelling, 116(1): 45–61.

Verburg P H, Eickhout B, van Meijl H. 2008. A multi-scale, multi-model approach for analyzing the future dynamics of European land use. Annals of Regional Science, 42(1): 57–77.

Verburg P H, van Berkel D B, van Doorn A M, van Eupen M, van den Heiligenberg H A R M. 2010. Trajectories of land use change in Europe: A model-based exploration of rural futures. Landscape Ecology, 25(2): 217–232.

Verburg P H, Veldkamp A, Fresco L O. 1999b. Simulation of changes in the spatial pattern of land use in China. Applied Geography, 19(3): 211–233.

Verburg P H, Veldkamp A, Villemen L, Overmars K P, Castella J C. 2004. Landscape level analysis of the spatial and temporal complexity of land-use change. Ecosystems and Land Use Change, 153: 217–230.

Wan Z, Zhang Y, Zhang Q, Li Z L. 2004. Quality assessment and validation of the MODIS global land surface temperature. International Journal of Remote Sensing, 25(1): 261–274.

Wan R R and Yang G S. 2005. Discussion on some issues of hydrological effects of watershed land use and land cover change. Progress in Geography, 24(3): 25–33.

Wang C K and Yang J Y. 2007. Rhizospheric and heterotrophic components of soil respiration in six Chinese temperate forests. Global change Biology, 13(1): 123–131.

Wang Y Q, Tobey J, Bonynge G, Nugrandad J, Makota V, Ngusaru A, Traber M. 2005. Involving geospatial information in the analysis of land-cover change along the Tanzania coast. Coastal Management, 33(1): 87–99.

Xiao Z S, Zhang Z B, Wang Y S. 2005. Effects of seed size on dispersal distance in five rodent-dispersed fagaceous species. Acta Oecologica-International Journal of Ecology, 28(3): 221–229.

Yan H M, Cao M K, Liu J Y, Tao B. 2007. Potential and sustainability for carbon sequestration with improved soil management in agricultural soils of China. Agriculture Ecosystems and Environment, 121(4): 325–335.

Yu X X, Yang G S, Wang Y. 2004. Advances in researches on environmental effects of land use/cover change. Scientia Geographica Sinica, 24(5): 627–633.

Yue T X, Fan Z M, Ji Y L. 2005a. Changes of major terrestrial ecosystems in China since 1960. Global and Planetary Change, 48(4): 287–302.

Yue T X, Tian Y Z, Liu J Y, Fan Z M. 2008. Surface modeling of human carrying capacity of terrestrial ecosystems in China. Ecological Modelling, 214(2–4): 168–180.

Yue Y J, Wang J A, Zou X Y, Shi P J. 2005b. Land use optimization at ecological security level in desert regions: A case study of Horqin Sandy Land. In: Progress in Safty Science and Technology, Vol.V (Part B): 2111–2116. Beijing: Science Press.

Zang S Y and Huang X. 2006. An aggregated multivariate regression land-use model and its application to land-use change processes in the Daqing region (northeast China). Ecological Modelling, 193: 503–516.

Zhao M and Zhou G S. 2005. Estimation of biomass and net primary productivity of major planted forests in China based on forest inventory data. Forest Ecology and Management, 207(3): 295–313.

Zhang Y S, Wang L X, Zhang H Q, Li X Y. 2003. An analysis on land use changes and their driving factors in Shule River: An example from Anxi County. Progress in Geography, 22(3): 270–278.

Zhou T and Shi P J. 2006. Indirect impacts of land use change on soil organic carbon change in China. Advances in Earth Science, 21(2): 138–143.

Zhou G S and Zhang X S. 1995. A natural vegetation NPP model. Acta Phytoecologica Sinica, 19: 15–21.

Zhu Z H. 1993. A calculate natural vegetation NPP model. Chinese Science Bulletin, 38: 1422–1426.

Chapter 3 The CGELUC Model and Its Application

The structure of regional land use is influenced by socioeconomic factors, including industrial structure, trade environment, economic policies and institutional arrangements. These multi-dimensional factors should be taken into consideration by different departments as part of an open, balanced economic system. The model of Computable General Equilibrium of Land Use Change (CGELUC) uses the framework of the Computable General Equilibrium (CGE) to analyze the factors that influence regional land use types. The analysis is based on macroscopic quantitative analysis and reveals relationships among the land use structure of cultivated land, economic forest[①], meadow for grazing, and economic development. The CGELUC model constructs a mechanism-based model to analyze dynamic laws of evolving land use structure at regional scales. The CGE model is applicable to policy the analysis associated with economic activities (Armington; 1969; Dixon et al., 1984; Conrad, 2001; Gelan, 2002; Liu et al., 2003). Economic activities are the main driving force behind structural changes in land use and are also constrained by the structure of regional land use (Rozelle and Rosegrant, 1997; Krausmann et al., 2003; Veldkamp and Verburg, 2004; Conway and Lathrop, 2005). Therefore, a solid theoretical basis exists for using the CGE model to simulate structural changes in regional land use (Fu et al., 1999; Böhringer and Löschel, 2006; Deng et al., 2010a). The CGELUC model uses the CGE model to study structural changes in regional land use based to some extent on computable general equilibrium ideas.

3.1 The CGELUC Model

Generally, the CGELUC model is divided into two parts when simulating structural changes in regional land use, including a thematic quantitative

① Economic forest and meadow for grazing are closely related to industrial production and livestock production that directly indicate economic values. In the CGELUC model, the equilibrium among cultivated land, economic forest, meadow for grazing are simulated according to the CGE modeling approach. Apart from cultivated land, economic forest and meadow for grazing, the public welfare forest and grassland cover, together with water, built-up area and unused land, are predicted based on econometric models, which differ from CGE modeling.

analysis section and an equilibrium analysis section of regional land area supply and demand. The two parts are linked by feedbacks from a series of relevant parameters. The thematic quantitative analysis is used to analyze the unsolvable relationships between industrial development and area changes in developed regions of water, grassland, woodland and unused land. These are then put into the equilibrium analysis section, in which supply and demand of regional land areas are input as exogenous variables. The changing processes and driving mechanisms of these types of land use are difficult to describe with general formulas, while cultivated land, economic forest and grassland[1] are closely associated with economic development. Economic activity related to social demand is the main factor driving structural changes in three types of land use and is also constrained by the structure of regional land use. The equilibrium analysis section of regional land use structure mainly simulates the relationship between land use structure and economic activities (Deng et al., 2010a).

The thematic quantitative analysis is mainly used to simulate and predict total changes in developed regions of water, grassland, woodland and unused land. Changes in these land use areas are then exported under specific scenarios to the equilibrium analysis section of land area supply and demand, and the influence of exogenous factors (such as land policy and planning) on regional land use structure is then analyzed. The equilibrium analysis section of land area supply and demand calculates changes in cultivated land, economic forest and grassland areas, and these calculated parameters of regional land use structure can then serve to spatially allocate land use change at the simulated grid scale. Macroeconomic variables such as production volume, price index and land rent are used as land policy parameters, and the total economic output, employment rate and energy consumption are used as characteristic variables that indicate industrial development of land-consumption sectors (Haberl et al., 2001; Lambin et al., 2001). Analysis of the influence of land policies can be used to make corresponding baseline hypotheses and calculations according to the current amount of land use and land use characteristics. The analysis is based on results of government investments, technical progress of sectors consuming land, structural changes in product consumption. The impacts of macroeconomic policies on the economic variables are then included in the equilibrium analysis section of land area supply and demand (Lehtonen et al., 2005; Leip et al., 2008). This section estimates and quantifies product demand, economic development and land use efficiency. The regional quantitative analysis section further corrects the parameters based on feedback of the modules mentioned above. The process above cycles is deducted through a number of iterations and restricted by the total amount of land use area until it reaches a balance between supply and demand of areas with types of different land use types among regional sectors.

Land plays a key role in the CGELUC model. On one hand, land is involved in production activities and is traded in the factor market as a commodity. Alternatively, land uses change with changing human activities, such as farmland returning to forest or grassland, reclaiming wasteland and clearing forest for farmland expansion. The change in land property is generally called land use conversion (Deng et al., 2008).

The computer-based CGELUC model is constructed based on the CGE theory, the areas of five land use types and the connections between economic development and land use structure of developed areas of economic forest and grassland. It consists of production, demand, price, trade, income distribution and macroeconomic closure modules. On one hand, all input land, or land associated with various types of production activities, will receive an income from rent. On the other hand, the socioeconomic benefits of different land use types differ, and this external difference drives conversion among land use types that requires capital. Finally, agricultural, forest and livestock products produced directly on the land are land output products, while other products are non-land output products. The difference between the two is that the land with non-land output products is considered as an input factor, and the land with land output products is considered as a commodity. Here, the module equations associated with land use structure are highlighted, and other equations are similar to the equation of the CGE model. The following sections of this chapter will use factor inputs and land conversion in the process of commodity production as an example (the production structure of the CGELUC model is shown in Fig. 3.1) to introduce the relationship between variables in the thematic quantitative analysis section. An emphasis is placed on the quantitative expression of the relationship between the land and its socioeconomic variables.

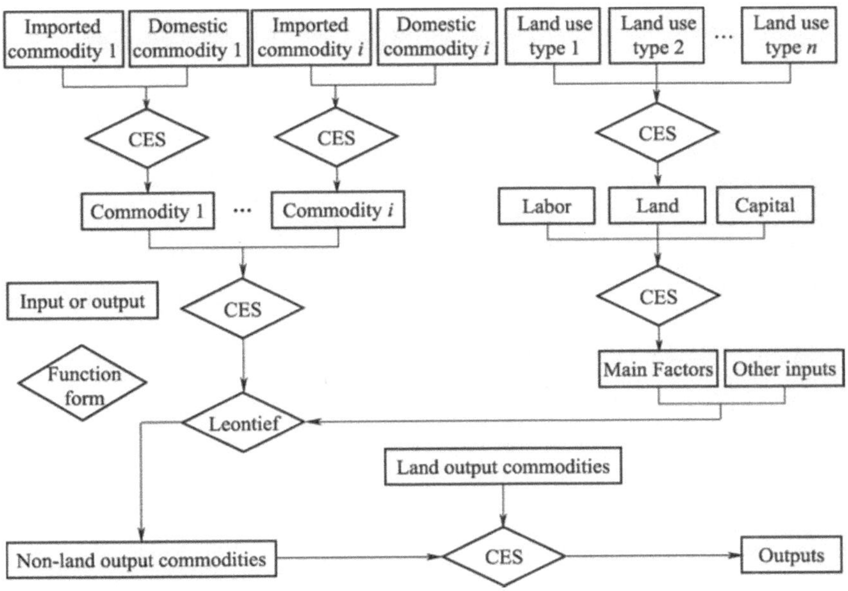

Fig. 3.1 Rationale of the CGELUC model.

3.1.1 Framework of the CGELUC Model

CGELUC models vary in complexity and size; their scope can be as large as the world or as small as a town. The model complexity is mainly described by studying the number and behavior of objects in the economic system. For example, a description of government expenditure based on a budget is far simpler than actual government consumption behavior. In addition, government consumption behavior is also constrained by the development of the whole economy, institutional reform and advancement of social welfare in the practical operation of the economy. The size of the model is based on the "small country hypothesis" on whether the economy involved is world-wide or in a town. The CGELUC model differs from empirical statistical models because it is a mechanistic model based on microeconomic theory and can effectively reflect mechanisms in structural changes in regional land use.

3.1.1.1 Model Features

One developing trend in the CGELUC model is to make the model more delicate and complex, including finer divisions of the model's sectors, wider classifications of consumers and non-recursive dynamics of the model. The other trend is to make the model more suited for analysis of economic and structural changes in regional land use by combining more practical characteristics of the economy. These include accounting for imperfect competition, technological progress and institutional factors endogenously in the model. The CGELUC model retains three main features of the traditional CGE model:

- The number of commodities and factors and the relative prices are decided by the endogenous model;
- The model can calculate the numerical solution of the prices of commodities and factor prices when they are entirely removed;
- Despite having multiple sections, the model's description of the whole system is still highly general (Wong and Alavalapati, 2003). Because of needs for simulating and analyzing land system dynamics, this book describes the CGELUC model as a multi-economic, multi-numeric market model that simulates optimized behavior based on relevant information.

The CGELUC model has significant benefits and unique characteristics for simulating land use conversion. First, it is an econometric model that systematically combines the mechanism-based CGE model with traditional empirical statistics. Its statistical mechanism emphasizes the area demand for regional land use types that cannot be revealed at the commodity level. Derivation of the theoretical mechanism model directly links with structural changes in cultivated land, economic forest and grassland related to commodity output. The CGELUC model integrates the behavior of microscopic subjects into the model system framework, which produces model explanations for results that have a reasonable theoretical basis. Second, the CGELUC model shows effects of market mechanisms. It introduces a price adjustment mechanism, replaces a linear function in the traditional model with a non-linear function and describes the response of the land use structure to disturbances, such as external policy and trade. Finally, an interaction and volatility transmission mechanism exists within the CGELUC model, i.e., if any part of the model suffers an external disturbance, the influence will be transmitted to land use linked with decision-making and behavior of the subjects of the whole economic system and lead to regional land use conversion. This process reflects the "general equilibrium" feature of the CGELUC model where a slight move in one part may affect the entire system.

3.1.1.2 Model Composition

The primary objective of the regional equilibrium development analysis module of the CGELUC model is to characterize the behavior of pursuing maximum profit or the effects of subjects within respective budgets that lead to structural changes in regional land use and to determine how this behavior leads to such changes. The macroeconometric model can be used to determine input parameters for simulation and analysis to maintain a balance in the total amount of regional land. The most basic CGE model includes three sets of equations that represent supply, demand and the balance between supply and demand (Gelan, 2002). We can view them from the basic framework of the CGELUC model (Fig. 3.2).

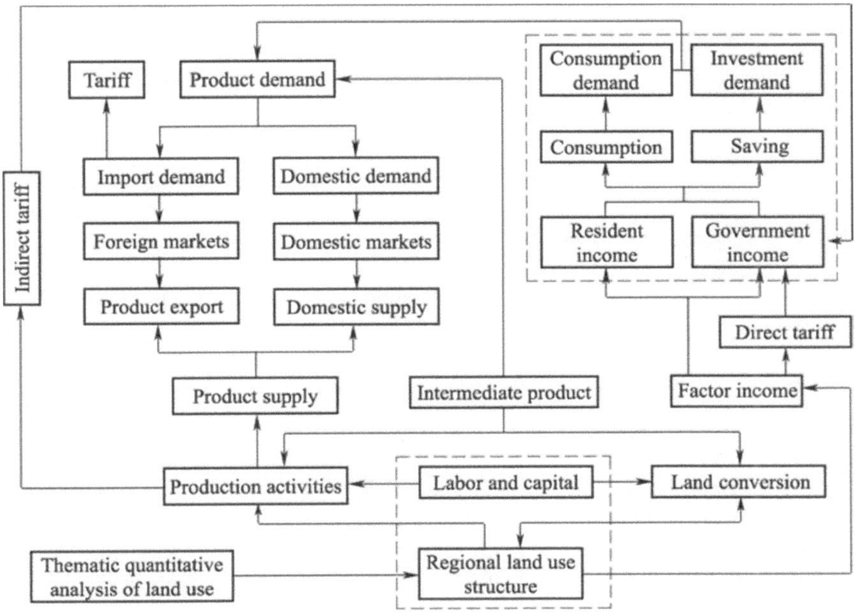

Fig. 3.2 Elements included in the CGELUC model.

It is generally necessary to add more economic subjects or to divide the model more precisely in accordance with different research needs in the simulated regional land use structure. In this book, the CGELUC model is divided into thematic quantitative analysis, production behavior, land use conversion, consumption behavior, government action, foreign trade, market equilibrium and macroscopic closure.

Thematic quantitative analysis

The CGELUC model describes the relationships among land desertification, changes in water area and expansion of developed area and the factors that influence quantitative analysis. The dynamics of land system change, desertification and changes in water area, grassland excluding pasture grassland and forest excluding economic forest are mainly influenced by natural processes (Hietel et al., 2004). The developed areas are significantly influenced by population, economic aggregation and technical progress, generally change directionally and are highly suitable for simulation and estimation with econometric methods.

Production behavior

The CGELUC model characterizes production behavior with a quantitative description of the supply of products related to regional land use conversion and includes two types of equations: descriptive production equations and producer optimization equations. The common forms of descriptive production equations include the Cobb-Douglas function, constant elasticity of substitution (CES) function and two-tier or multi-tier nested CES function. The quantitative relationships among the production factor inputs, intermediate inputs and outputs can be described with these equations. Different production functions are generally chosen according to different research purposes for practical applications. The aim of the producer optimization equation or profit maximization equation is to define producer behavior, determine producer demand for various factors by making marginal returns of factors equal to their corresponding marginal productivity and describe how producers pursue minimum costs or maximum profits under constraint of the production function.

Land use conversion

In the CGELUC model, land use conversion requires investments of capital, labor, land and intermediate inputs, which are considered to be production behavior. Two types of equations characterize land use conversion: descriptive production equations and producer optimization equations. The descriptive production equations include the Cobb-Douglas function, the CES function and the two-tier or multi-tier nested CES function, which are used to describe the quantitative relationships among production factor inputs, intermediate inputs and outputs (Rozlle and Rosegrant, 1997; Hanasaki et al., 2008). Different land use conversion functions are generally chosen based on different research purposes and study areas. The land use conversion optimization equation aims to determine demands of producers for various factors by making marginal returns of various factors equal to their corresponding marginal conversion rates.

Consumption behavior

The CGELUC model characterizes consumption behavior mainly with descriptive equations and demands for relevant products of regional land use conversion, which includes the descriptive production equation and the consumer optimization equation. The descriptive production equation is mainly used to describe the constraints on consumers' budgets, i.e., the income and disposable income of consumers. The consumers' utility optimization equation is mainly used to describe the behavior of consumer's utility maximization, which includes the Cobb-Douglas function, the CES function and the Stone-Geary utility function. This type of equation aims to describe the behavior of consumers' pursuits of individual utility maximization under the constraint of a consumption budget.

Government behavior

Policy behavior such as government revenue, interest rates and subsidies is added to the model equation system only as exogenous variables in the CGELUC model. When the government changes its policy, i.e., when these control variables change, the changes influence the entire economic system. Government behavior in the CGELUC model is not limited to formulating relevant policies; more importantly, the government also acts as a consumer in the CGELUC model.

Foreign trade

The CGELUC model involves foreign trade as an important component to more accurately describe the system. The CGELUC model uses the small country assumption, i.e., imports and exports in the study area will not affect the stability of the world price. This assumption helps to describe the issues conveniently, but the complexity of the equation caused by involvement of foreign trade still cannot be avoided. For example, the model not only requires exports to be distinguished from commodities from a production aspect, but also requires imported commodities to be distinguished from domestic commodities from a consumption aspect. A common approach is to assume that domestic commodities and imported commodities are not completely replaceable and to describe the behavior of imports with CES equations and the behavior of exports with the constant elasticity of transformation equation.

Market equilibrium

Equilibrium is the core of the CGELUC model and mainly includes market equilibrium and the balance between income and expenditures.

– Product market equilibrium

Product market equilibrium requires that the total supply of products equals the total demand for products, i.e., equilibrium is achieved between production and consumption.

– Capital market equilibrium

Capital market equilibrium means that total investment equals total savings. If investments and savings are unbalanced, then corrections will be made through selling bonds, introducing foreign capital or changing the government's fiscal reserves.

– Factor market equilibrium

Factor market equilibrium mainly refers to equilibrium between supply and demand of labor and land market equilibrium. The factors flow between different departments due to differences in marginal benefits to achieve producer and consumer optimization.

– Residents' income and expenditure equilibrium

Residents' income and expenditure equilibrium means that residents spend all income, such as payments for labor and net foreign remittance, after paying individual income tax on consumption and savings.

– Government budget equilibrium

The government budget equilibrium is a generalized equilibrium. If government expenditures do not equal income, then a fiscal deficit will be added to government revenue as a variable so that the disequilibrium of the government budget can be expressed with a set of equations.

– International income and expenditure equilibrium

If a trade surplus or deficit exists, the net inflow of foreign capital is taken as the variable, i.e., international income and expenses should also maintain equilibrium.

Macroscopic closure

The different variables under various equilibrium conditions in the CGELUC model, e.g., changes in inventory, unemployment, surplus and deficit, provide an important way to study the actual state of disequilibrium. However, it is unrealistic to assume that the market, income and expenditures of various departments can simultaneously balance; only a conditional equilibrium can be achieved. Generally, four programs can be used to solve the problems above in the macroscopic closure theory of the CGELUC model, and different solutions are the main differences between different CGE schools of thought:

– Keynes formula: Forfeit the requirement that labor and commodity markets achieve equilibrium simultaneously. Take the employment rate as an endogenous variable, i.e., surplus labor is adequate in the whole system and can meet the demand for labor in the production sectors at any time. This reflects Keynes' assumption of deficient demand and surplus supply (Johanson, 1960).

– Kim Hansen formula: Consider government expenditures to be an endogenous variable and the total investment level to be an exogenous variable, maintaining maximum producer profits (Scarf and Hansen, 1973).

– Koldorian formula: Forfeit optimal conditions of production factors and consider the investment level and the government expenditure level as exogenous variables (Adelman and Robinson, 1978).

– Neoclassical formula: Consider the government expenditure level as an exogenous variable and the investment level as an endogenous variable to maintain the optimal conditions for producer profits. The total investment level will then be automatically adjusted to the savings level (Dervis, 1975).

The macroscopic closure theory of the CGELUC model makes trade-offs among the labor market, government budget and investment-saving equilibriums and optimal conditions for production.

3.1.2 Modules of the CGELUC Model

The CGELUC model can be divided into eight modules, i.e., the quantitative analysis module, production module, land use conversion module, product demand module, price module, income distribution module, saving-investment module, foreign trade module and equilibrium closure module.

3.1.2.1 Quantitative Analysis Module

The areas of developed regions, unused land, water, grassland with indirect economic value such as ungrazed or commonwealth grassland and forest with indirect economic value such as ecological commonwealth forest are simulated with the macroscopic econometric model.

Spatially lagged model

The spatially lagged model mainly explores whether the influence of variables is spatially diffuse (Irwin and Geoghegan, 2001; Verburg and Veldkamp, 2001). It is expressed as:

$$Y = \rho WY + X\beta + \varepsilon \tag{3.1}$$

where Y is a dependent variable, which is the area of the land use types mentioned above; X is an explanatory variable to represent the factors that cause changes in the area of the land use types mentioned above; ρ is the spatial correlation coefficient; W is the spatial weight matrix; WY is a spatially lagged dependent variable; ε is the random error term.

Spatial error model

The spatial error model is used to measure the degree of spatial influence of the dependent variable. Its mathematical expression is:

$$\begin{aligned} Y &= X\beta + \varepsilon \\ \varepsilon &= \lambda W\varepsilon + \mu \end{aligned} \tag{3.2}$$

where Y is the dependent variable, which is the area of land use types mentioned above; X is an explanatory variable representing the factors that cause changes in the area of land use types mentioned above; ε is a random error term; λ is spatial error coefficient of the cross-section dependent vector; W is the spatial weight matrix and μ is the vector of random error with normal distribution.

3.1.2.2 Product Production Module

Production of final products

$$Z_c(t) = \min_{d,l} \left\{ \frac{X_{d,c}(t)}{ax_{d,c}(t)}, \frac{LK_{l,c}(t)}{al_{l,c}(t)}, \frac{Y_c(t)}{ay_c(t)} \right\} \tag{3.3}$$

where $Z_c(t)$ represents the amount of final products produced in the tth year; $X_{d,c}(t)$ is the amount of the intermediate product d consumed in the production process of the final product c; $ax_{d,c}(t)$ stands for the consumption coefficient of the intermediate product d in the production process of the final product c; $LK_{l,c}(t)$ represents the amount of the lth type of land consumed in the production process of the product c; $al_{l,c}(t)$ is the consumption coefficient of the l types of land in the production process of the final product c; $Y_c(t)$ signifies the amount of intermediate products consumed in the production process of the final product c; $ay_c(t)$ represents the consumption coefficient of the intermediate products in the production process of the final product c.

When production is optimized, there must be:

$$\begin{cases} Y_c(t) = ay_c(t) Z_c(t) \\ X_{d,c}(t) = ax_{d,c}(t) Z_c(t) \\ LK_{l,c}(t) = al_{l,c}(t) Z_c(t) \end{cases} \tag{3.4}$$

Intermediate product production

$$Y_c(t) = b_c(t) \prod_f Fc_{f,c}(t)^{\beta_{f,c}(t)} \tag{3.5}$$

where $b_c(t)$ represents the production scale coefficient of the intermediate product c; $Fc_{f,c}(t)$ is the number of the input factor f in the production process of the intermediate product c; $\beta_{f,c}(t)$ is the share of factor f in the production process of the intermediate product c.

Integrated products for home sale

$$Q_c(t) = \gamma_c(t) \left(\delta m_c(t) M_c(t)^{\eta_c(t)} + \delta d_c(t) DK_c(t)^{\eta_c(t)} \right)^{1/\eta_c(t)} \tag{3.6}$$

where $Q_c(t)$ is the number of integrated products sold at home in the tth year; $\delta m_c(t)$ stands for the proportion of imported products in the integrated products sold at home; $M_c(t)$ is the number of imports; $\delta d_c(t)$ stands for the proportion of locally produced products in the integrated products sold at home; $DK_c(t)$ is the number of products that are locally produced and sold; $\gamma_c(t)$ represents the scale parameters of the Armington function; $\eta_c(t)$ is the elasticity of substitution between the local product c and the imported product c.

Number of products locally produced and sold

$$DK_c(t) = \left(\frac{\gamma_c(t)^{\eta_c(t)}\,\delta d_c(t)\,Pq_c(t)}{Pd_c(t)}\right)^{1/(1-\eta_c(t))} Q_c(t) \tag{3.7}$$

where $Pq_c(t)$ represents the price of the integrated product c sold at home; $Pd_c(t)$ is the domestic selling price of the domestic product c.

Total quantity of domestic products

$$Z_c(t) = \theta_c(t)\left(\xi e_c(t)\,EK_c(t)^{\Phi_c(t)} + \xi d_c(t)\,DK_c(t)^{\Phi_c(t)}\right)^{1/\Phi_c(t)} \tag{3.8}$$

where $\theta_c(t)$ represents the scale parameters of the transfer function; $\xi e_c(t)$ is the share parameter of the export c in the conversion function; $\xi d_c(t)$ is the share parameter of the product c produced and sold at home in the conversion function; $EK_c(t)$ stands for the quantity of the export c; $\Phi_c(t)$ is the elasticity of substitution between the product c produced and sold at home and the export c.

Quantity of products locally produced and sold

$$DK_c(t) = \left(\frac{\theta_c(t)^{\Phi_c(t)}\,\xi d_c(t)\,(1+\tau_c(t))\,Ps_c(t)}{Pd_c(t)}\right)^{1/(1-\Phi_c(t))} Z_c(t) \tag{3.9}$$

where $\tau_c(t)$ is the indirect tax rate of the product c; $Ps_c(t)$ represents the domestic price of supply of the domestic product c.

3.1.2.3 Land Use Conversion Module

Land use conversion

$$Dl_{zl}(t) = \min\left\{\frac{Xl_{c,zl}(t)}{axl_{c,zl}(t)},\ \sum_l Fl_{l,zl}(t),\ \frac{Yl_{zl}(t)}{ayl_{zl}(t)}\right\} \tag{3.10}$$

where $Dl_{zl}(t)$ is the amount of the zlth newly-increased land in the tth year; $Xl_{c,zl}(t)$ stands for the amount of intermediate input c consumed in the zlth land use conversion process; $axl_{c,zl}(t)$ is the consumption coefficient of the intermediate input c in the zlth land use conversion process; $Fl_{l,zl}(t)$ is the area of the lth land input into the zlth land use conversion process; $Yl_{zl}(t)$ represents the quantity of intermediate products consumed in the zlth land use conversion process; $ayl_{zl}(t)$ stands for the consumption coefficients of the intermediate products in the zlth land use conversion process.

When efficiency of the conversion reaches a peak, there must be:

$$\begin{cases} Yl_{zl}(t) &= ayl_{zl}(t)\, Dl_{zl}(t) \\ Xl_{c,zl}(t) &= axl_{c,zl}(t)\, Dl_{zl}(t) \\ Fl_{l,zl}(t) &= \omega_{l,zl}(t)\, Dl_{zl}(t) \end{cases} \tag{3.11}$$

Production of intermediate products input into land use conversion

$$Yl_{zl}(t) = bl_{zl}(t) \prod_{f} Fll_{f,zl}(t)^{\beta l_{f,zl}(t)} \tag{3.12}$$

where $bl_{zl}(t)$ is the scale parameter of the production function of the intermediate product input into the zlth land use conversion; $Fll_{f,zl}(t)$ stands for the amount of factor f input into the production of intermediate products of the zlth land use conversion; $\beta l_{f,zl}(t)$ stands for the share of factor f in the production of intermediate products of the zlth land use conversion.

*Amount of various land use types in the (t+1)*th *year*

$$FFl_l(t+1) = FFl_l(t) + Dl_{zl}(t) - \sum_{zk} Fl_{l,zk}(t) \tag{3.13}$$

where $FFl_l(t)$ is the amount of the lth land use type in the tth year.

3.1.2.4 Product Demand Module

Intermediate input

$$Xc_c(t) = \sum_{d} X_{c,d}(t) + \sum_{zl} Xl_{c,zl}(t) \tag{3.14}$$

where $Xc_c(t)$ is the total demand of the intermediate input for the product c.

Government procurement

$$Xg_c(t) = \frac{\mu_c(t)}{Pq_c(t)} \left(Td(t) + \sum_{d} T_d(t) + \sum_{d} Tm_d(t) + \sum_{zl} Tl_{zl}(t) - Sg(t) \right) \tag{3.15}$$

where $Xg_c(t)$ is the quantity of product c purchased by the government; $\mu_c(t)$ is the proportion of expenditures on product c in the total government expenditure; $Td(t)$ is the direct tax; $T_d(t)$ is the indirect tax from the production of product d; $Tm_d(t)$ is the tariff on the exported product d; $Tl_{zl}(t)$ is the indirect tax of the zlth land use conversion; $Sg(t)$ is government savings.

Investment demand

$$Xv_c(t) = \frac{\lambda_c(t)}{Pq_c(t)} \left(S(t) + Sg(t) + \varepsilon(t)\, Sf(t) \right) \tag{3.16}$$

Demand of household consumption

$$Xp_c(t) = \frac{\alpha_c(t)}{Pq_c(t)}\left(\sum_f r_f(t)\,FF_f(t) + \sum_l rl_l(t)\,FFl_l(t) - S(t) - Td(t)\right) \tag{3.17}$$

where $Xp_c(t)$ is the quantity of product c demanded by household consumption; $\alpha_c(t)$ is the proportion of expenses of product c in the total household expenditure; $r_f(t)$ is the price of the factor f; $FFl_l(t)$ is the total amount of the factor f; $rl_l(t)$ is the price of the lth land; $FFl_l(t)$ is the amount of the lth land; $S(t)$ represents household savings.

$$Xpl_{zl}(t) = \frac{\alpha l_{zl}(t)}{rll_{zl}(t)}\left(\sum_f r_f(t)\,FF_f(t) + \sum_l rl_l(t)\,FFl_l(t) - S(t) - Td(t)\right) \tag{3.18}$$

where $Xpl_{zl}(t)$ is the quantity of the zlth newly-increased land demanded when the family purchases it; $\alpha l_{zl}(t)$ is the proportion of expenditures on the zlth newly increased land in total household expenditures; $rll_{zl}(t)$ is the price of the zlth newly increased land.

Factor demand

$$F_f(t) = \sum_c Fc_{f,c}(t) + \sum_{zl} Fll_{f,zl}(t) \tag{3.19}$$

where $F_f(t)$ is the total demand for the factor f in the tth year; $Fc_{f,c}(t)$ is the demand for the factor f in the production process of product c; $Fll_{f,zl}(t)$ is the demand for the factor f in the zlth land use conversion.

$$\begin{cases} Fc_{f,c}(t) = Y_c(t)\,(\beta_{f,c}(t)\,Py_c(t)/r_f(t)) \\ Fll_{f,zl}(t) = Yl_{zl}(t)\,(\beta l_{f,zl}(t)\,Pyl_{zl}(t)/r_f(t)) \end{cases} \tag{3.20}$$

Land demand

$$LF_l(t) = \sum_{zl} Fl_{l,zl}(t) + \sum_c L_{l,c}(t) \tag{3.21}$$

where $LF_l(t)$ is the total demand for land in the tth year.

3.1.2.5 Price Module

Price of land supply

$$rll_{zl}(t) = ayl_{zl}(t)\,Pyl_{zl}(t) + \sum_c axl_{c,zl}(t)\,Pq_c(t) + \sum_l \frac{Fl_{l,zl}(t)}{Dl_{zl}(t)} rl_l(t) \tag{3.22}$$

where $Pyl_{zl}(t)$ is the price of the intermediate product of the zlth land use conversion.

Price equation of product supply

$$Ps_c(t) = ay_c(t)\,Py_c(t) + \sum_d ax_{d,c}(t)\,Pq_d(t) + \sum_l al_{l,c}(t)\,rl_l(t) \quad (3.23)$$

where $Py_c(t)$ is the price of the intermediate product in the production process of product c.

Export price

$$Pe_c(t) = \varepsilon(t)\,Pwe_c(t) \quad (3.24)$$

where $Pe_c(t)$ is the domestic price of product c, which is produced at home for export (signified in national currency); $\varepsilon(t)$ is the exchange rate; $Pwe_c(t)$ is the foreign price of product c, which is produced at home for export (signified in foreign currency).

Import price

$$Pm_c(t) = \varepsilon(t)\,Pwm_c(t) \quad (3.25)$$

where $Pm_c(t)$ is the domestic price of import c (signified in national currency); $Pwm_c(t)$ is the foreign price of import c (signified in foreign currency).

3.1.2.6 Tax Module

Indirect tax

$$\begin{cases} T_c(t) = \tau_c(t)\,Ps_c(t)\,Z_c(t) \\ Tl_{zl}(t) = \tau l_{zl}(t)\,rll_{zl}(t)\,Dl_{zl}(t) \end{cases} \quad (3.26)$$

where $\tau l_{zl}(t)$ is the indirect tax rate of the zlth land use conversion.

Direct tax

$$Td(t) = \tau d(t)\left(\sum_f r_f(t)\,FF_f(t) + \sum_l rl_l(t)\,FFl_l(t)\right) \quad (3.27)$$

where $\tau d(t)$ is the direct tax rate.

Tariff

$$Tm_c(t) = \tau m_c(t)\,Pm_c(t)\,M_c(t) \quad (3.28)$$

where $\tau m_c(t)$ is the tariff on the product c.

3.1.2.7 Savings-investment Module

Household savings

$$S(t) = ss(t)\left(\sum_{f} r_f(t) FF_f(t) + \sum_{c}\sum_{l} rl_l(t) LK_{l,c}(t) + \sum_{zl}\sum_{k} rl_k(t) Fl_{k,zl}(t)\right) \tag{3.29}$$

where $ss(t)$ is the household savings rate.

Government savings

$$Sg(t) = ssg(t)\left(\sum_{c} T_c(t) + \sum_{zl} Tl_{zl}(t) + \sum_{c} Tm_c(t) + Td(t)\right) \tag{3.30}$$

where $ssg(t)$ is the government savings rate.

3.1.2.8 Foreign Trade Module

Quantity of imports

$$M_c(t) = \left(\frac{\gamma_c(t)^{\eta_c(t)}\,\delta m_c(t)\,Pq_c(t)}{(1+\tau m_c(t))\,Pd_c(t)}\right)^{1/(1-\eta_c(t))} Q_c(t) \tag{3.31}$$

Quantity of exports

$$EK_c(t) = \left(\frac{\theta_c(t)^{\Phi_c(t)}\,\xi e_c(t)\,(1+\tau_c(t))\,Ps_c(t)}{Pe_c(t)}\right)^{1/(1-\Phi_c(t))} Z_c(t) \tag{3.32}$$

where $EK_c(t)$ is the quantity of the exported product c.

3.1.2.9 Equilibrium Closure Module

Product market equilibrium

$$Q_c(t) = Xp_c(t) + Xg_c(t) + Xv_c(t) + Xc_c(t) \tag{3.33}$$

$$Pq_c(t) = Pd_c(t) \tag{3.34}$$

$$Pq_c(t) = (1+\tau_c(t))\,Ps_c(t) \tag{3.35}$$

Factor market equilibrium

$$FF_f(t) = F_f(t) \tag{3.36}$$

$$FFl_l(t) = LF_l(t) \tag{3.37}$$

Foreign trade equilibrium

$$\sum_{c} Pwe_c(t)\, EK_c(t) + Sf(t) = \sum_{c} Pwm_c(t)\, M_c(t) \tag{3.38}$$

where $Sf(t)$ is the total amount of foreign savings.

3.1.2.10 Objective Function

$$\max UU(t) = \prod_{c} Xp_c(t)^{\alpha_c(t)} \tag{3.39}$$

As can be seen from the main descriptive equations of the various modules, the CGELUC model involves various socioeconomic levels related to land system structure and not only has openness and convergence at the macroscopic level but also has a solid microscopic theoretical foundation that can better simulate structural changes in regional land use.

3.2 The CGELUC Model Database

The CGELUC model can simulate regional land use structure and its changes because it can simulate and predict changes in total demand of different sectors for developed areas, water area, grassland, forest and unused land based on the thematic quantitative analysis module. It then exports the changes in area of different land use types under different scenarios and inputs these area changes into the area framework of various regional land use types to conduct equilibrium analysis of the area of different land use types.

3.2.1 Database of Thematic Quantitative Analysis

Simulation of developed areas, forest other than economic forest, grassland except pasture, water area and unused land in the thematic quantitative analysis module includes natural environmental conditions, climate change, human population, economic output, industrial structure and other factors (Table 3.1).

In the spatial quantitative model of the thematic quantitative analysis module, Moran's I statistic is used to check for spatial autocorrelation (Deng et al., 2006). Moran's I is defined as follows:

$$Moran'I = \frac{\sum_{i=1}^{n}\sum_{j=1}^{n} w_{ij}\left(Y_i - \bar{Y}\right)\left(Y_j - \bar{Y}\right)}{S^2 \sum_{i=1}^{n}\sum_{j=1}^{n} w_{ij}} \tag{3.40}$$

Table 3.1 Variables to explore the driving mechanisms of land system change in a case study of the North China Plain

Variable	Specific explanation
Geophysical condition	
Landform	0: Hill 1: Plain 2: Terrace 3: Plateau
Soil pH	The higher the value, the lower the soil acidity.
Soil depth	Top soil depth
Average elevation	Average elevation of each 1 km grid
Slope	Slope extracted based on digital elevation model
Climatic variables	
Temperature	Annual average temperature
⩾ 0℃ accumulated temperature	Accumulated temperature of days with an average daily temperature above 0℃
⩾ 10℃ accumulated temperature	Accumulated temperature of days with an average daily temperature above 10℃
Sunshine percentage	Percent of sunshine
Total amount, structure and migration of population	
Population density	Disaggregated population density based on the population distribution model
Proportion of non-agricultural population	Proportion of non-agricultural population in the total population in one certain administrative region
Proportion of migrate population	Proportion of the migrate population in the total population in one certain administrative region
Urbanization level	Proportion of non-agricultural population in the total population in one certain administrative district
Agricultural research investment	Proportion of investment in agricultural research
Economic output, industrial structure	
GDP	Total amount of GDP per unit of land area
Share of the secondary industry GDP in the total GDP	Share of the secondary industry GDP in the total GDP in one certroid administrative region
Share of the tertiary industry GDP in the total GDP	Share of the tertiary industry GDP in the total GDP in one certain administrative region
Trade environment	
Tariff rate	Rate of duty to tax the taxpayers set by the tariff rules
Proximity variables	
Distance to the provincial capital	Distance between the center of one administrative region and the provincial capital
Distance to the nearest highway	Distance between the center of one administrative region and the nearest highway
Distance to the nearest provincial highways	Distance between the center of one administrative region and the nearest provincial highway
Policies, shifts of institution	
Subsidies for returning cultivated land	Amount of subsidies for returning cultivated land per hectare
Percentage of cultivated land with slope above 15°	Percentage of cultivated land with slope above 15°

where
$$\begin{cases} S^2 = \dfrac{1}{n}\sum\limits_{i=1}^{n}\left(Y_i - \bar{Y}\right)^2 \\ \bar{Y} = \dfrac{1}{n}\sum\limits_{i=1}^{n} Y_i \end{cases} \tag{3.41}$$

where Y_i is the change in developed areas, ecological forest, ecological commonwealth grassland, water area and unused land; n is the total grid number; and w_{ij} is the spatial weight, assigned as follows:

$$w_{ij} = \begin{cases} 1 & \text{When the distance between } i \text{ and } j \text{ is within certain scope} \\ 0 & \text{When the distance between } i \text{ and } j \text{ exceeds certain scope} \end{cases} \tag{3.42}$$

Positive values of Moran's I indicate the existence of positive spatial autocorrelation among changes in developed areas, ecological forest, ecological commonwealth grassland, water area and unused land and the other factors i.e., natural environmental conditions, climate change, total population and structural change, economic aggregate and structural change. Negative values of Moran's I indicate that there is negative spatial autocorrelation between the aforementioned factors. A zero value indicates random spatial patterns of the factors (Deng et al., 2008).

Spatial autocorrelation is checked by constructing Z statistics (Deng et al., 2010b):

$$Z = \frac{Moran'I - E\left(Moran'I\right)}{\sqrt{VAR\left(Moran'I\right)}} \tag{3.43}$$

where
$$\begin{cases} E\left(Moran'I\right) = -\dfrac{1}{n-1} \\ VAR\left(Moran'I\right) = \dfrac{n^2 w_1 + n w_2 + 3w_0^2}{w_0^2\left(n^2-1\right)} - E_0^2\left(Moran'I\right) \end{cases} \tag{3.44}$$

where
$$\begin{cases} w_0 = \sum\limits_{i=1}^{n}\sum\limits_{j=1}^{n} w_{ij} \\ w_1 = \dfrac{1}{2}\sum\limits_{i=1}^{n}\sum\limits_{j=1}^{n}\left(w_{ij} + w_{ji}\right)^2 \\ w_2 = \sum\limits_{i=1}^{n}\left(\sum\limits_{j=1}^{n} w_{ij} + \sum\limits_{j=1}^{n} w_{ji}\right)^2 \end{cases} \tag{3.45}$$

3.2.2 The SAM

The Social Accounting Matrix (SAM) dataset serves as a basis for running the CGELUC model, the construction of which facilitates parameter estimation of the model. The structural change in regional land use is analyzed by expanding the traditional SAM dataset and adding factors and commodities of several land use types balanced among sectors and regions in the CGELUC model. The SAM dataset complements and expands the input-output (IO) tables because it indicates interdependence of production activities, income distribution factors and income distribution of different sectors. It also determines expenditure patterns of different sectors (Table 3.2).

The economic meaning of each land factor in the SAM table is briefly explained below. Macroscopic SAM in the CGELUC model generally describes the economic cycle of production, distribution and consumption in the economic system starting from commodities.

Commodity account #1 in Table 3.2 is mainly used to record various commodities, including the destination of various imported commodities and services. Income of the commodity account mainly comes from the supply of commodities and services to the six economic entities: intermediate inputs for other commodity accounts ($t_{1,1}$), input consumption for the land use conversion process ($t_{1,2}$), consumer goods sold to residents and the government ($t_{1,6}$ and $t_{1,7}$), investment goods for the investment account ($t_{1,8}$) and exported consumer goods ($t_{1,12}$). Expenditures of this type of account are primarily used to purchase other types of commodities as intermediate inputs ($t_{1,1}$), to pay for charges of various production factors (labor, capital and land) ($t_{3,1}$, $t_{4,1}$, $t_{5,1}$) and to pay indirect taxes ($t_{11,1}$) and tariffs ($t_{12,1}$).

Conversion account #2 is mainly used to record the relationship between income and expenditures in different land use conversion processes. Income of this type of account mainly comes from commodities and intermediate inputs in the land use conversion process ($t_{2,1}$ and $t_{2,2}$) in addition to the investment demand of consumption of residents, government and capital for land use conversion ($t_{2,6}$, $t_{2,7}$ and $t_{2,8}$). Expenditures of this type of account mainly include expenses for intermediate inputs of commodities ($t_{1,2}$) and various production factors (labor, capital and land) ($t_{3,2}$, $t_{4,2}$ and $t_{5,2}$). In addition, indirect taxes ($t_{9,2}$) generating from the process of land use conversion are also included in the expenditures.

Labor account #3, capital account #4 and land account #5 are also referred to as factor accounts. The three types of accounts are mainly used to record the origin of income and destination of expenditures of the various initial factors in the production process. Labor, capital and land conversion acquire factor income ($t_{3,1}$, $t_{4,1}$, $t_{5,1}$ and $t_{3,2}$, $t_{4,2}$, $t_{5,2}$) by supplying their own resource endowment to commodity and conversion accounts. Subsequently, this income will be distributed to residents in the form of labor income ($t_{6,3}$, $t_{6,4}$ and $t_{6,5}$) and form the main source of residents' income. Part of the factor income goes into direct tax accounts in the form of direct taxes ($t_{10,3}$, $t_{10,4}$ and $t_{10,5}$).

Income for residents' account #6 includes the distribution of profits of enterprises ($t_{6,4}$), residents' proceeds from land transfer ($t_{6,5}$) and various government transfer payments (such as subsidies) ($t_{6,7}$), besides residents' labor remuneration ($t_{6,3}$).

Table 3.2 Macro SAM table with land factors

		Commodities	Conversion	Labor	Capital	Land	Resident	Government
		#1	#2	#3	#4	#5	#6	#7
Commodities	#1	$t_{1,1}$	$t_{1,2}$				$t_{1,6}$	$t_{1,7}$
Conversion	#2	$t_{2,1}$	$t_{2,2}$				$t_{2,6}$	$t_{2,7}$
Labor	#3	$t_{3,1}$	$t_{3,2}$					
Capital	#4	$t_{4,1}$	$t_{4,2}$					
Land	#5	$t_{5,1}$	$t_{5,2}$					
Resident	#6			$t_{6,3}$	$t_{6,4}$	$t_{6,5}$		$t_{6,7}$
Government	#7							
Capital	#8						$t_{8,6}$	$t_{8,7}$
Indirect tax	#9	$t_{9,1}$	$t_{9,2}$					
Direct tax	#10			$t_{10,3}$	$t_{10,4}$	$t_{10,5}$		
Tariff	#11	$t_{11,1}$						
Rest of the world	#12	$t_{12,1}$						
Total		Subtotal by column #1	Subtotal by column #2	Subtotal by column #3	Subtotal by column #4	Subtotal by column #5	Subtotal by column #6	Subtotal by column #7

Continued

		Capital	Indirect tax	Direct tax	Tariff	Abroad	Total
		#8	#9	#10	#11	#12	
Commodities	#1	$t_{1,8}$				$t_{1,12}$	Subtotal by column 1
Conversion	#2	$t_{2,8}$					Subtotal by column 2
Labor	#3						Subtotal by column 3
Capital	#4						Subtotal by column 4
Land	#5						Subtotal by column 5
Resident	#6						Subtotal by column 6
Government	#7		$t_{7,9}$	$t_{7,10}$	$t_{7,11}$		Subtotal by column 7
Capital	#8					$t_{8,12}$	Subtotal by column 8
Indirect tax	#9						Subtotal by column 9
Direct tax	#10						Subtotal by column 10
Tariff	#11						Subtotal by column 11
Rest of the world	#12						Subtotal by column 12
Total		Subtotal by column #8	Subtotal by column #9	Subtotal by column #10	Subtotal by column #11	Subtotal by column #12	

Resident expenditures mainly include residents' product consumption ($t_{1,6}$), consumption of land use conversion ($t_{2,6}$) and savings investments ($t_{8,6}$).

As the regulator of macroeconomic and relevant policies, the government plays an important role in the process of economic operation and land use conversion. Therefore, it is necessary to introduce the government account into the SAM dataset of the CGELUC model. The revenue of government account #7 mainly comes from various taxes, including indirect taxes ($t_{7,9}$), direct taxes ($t_{7,10}$) and tariffs ($t_{7,11}$). Government expenditure mainly includes government consumption of commodities ($t_{1,7}$), the consumption of land use conversion ($t_{2,7}$), transfer payments to residents, social welfare ($t_{6,7}$) and government savings investments ($t_{8,7}$).

Capital account #8 obtains capital from household savings ($t_{8,6}$), government savings ($t_{8,7}$) and foreign capital inflows ($t_{8,12}$). This capital is converted into investments and then finally provides the investment demand for commodities ($t_{1,8}$) and land use conversion ($t_{2,8}$). Investment and consumption are two key indicators of China's economic development, or the dynamic CGELUC model.

Indirect tax #9, direct tax #10 and tariff account #11 are further separated from the government account. These accounts are independent in order to account for and classify the influence of various government taxes on land use conversion in the CGELUC model. Indirect taxes are mainly charged for the process of commodity production ($t_{9,1}$) and land use conversion ($t_{9,2}$). A direct tax is charged for various production factors (labor, capital and land) ($t_{10,3}$, $t_{10,4}$ and $t_{10,5}$). A tariff is charged on imported commodities ($t_{11,1}$). Income of the three types of tax accounts eventually enters the government account as an integral part of government income ($t_{7,9}$, $t_{7,10}$ and $t_{7,11}$).

Foreign account #12 is mainly used to account for the inflow and outflow of capital in regions outside the study area. This account receives income from the payment of imported commodities in the study area ($t_{12,1}$) and pays for exported commodities from the study area ($t_{1,12}$) and investment consumption of the regional capital account ($t_{8,12}$).

In the SAM table above, the subtotal by row i equals the subtotal by column i; the total investment equals total output. The method used to construct the SAM table is described in detail in the next section.

3.2.3 Preparation of the SAM Parameters

The prices of products and factors are generally set to the same unit since the transaction values involved in the SAM dataset of the CGELUC model are expressed as values. Most of the parameters in the model can be calculated by incorporating equations of the CGELUC model, and the few parameters that cannot be calculated in this way are determined with the quantitative analysis module.

3.2.3.1 Proportion Parameters of the Product Production Module

The consumption coefficients of products $ax_{d,c}$ and $al_{l,c}$ can be directly obtained from the ratios of the intermediate input of commodities and land factor input and the total department output in the SAM $al_{l,c} = LK_{l,c}/Z_c$. The parameter $al_{l,c} = t_{4,1}/\text{COL1}$ is calculated with data in the SAM table mentioned above.

The share of factor f in the production process of the intermediate product c is $\beta_{f,c}(t)$ can be determined from the ratio of the proportion of the quantity of factor f input into the quantity of all factors in the production process of product c in the SAM matrix.

The production scale coefficient of the intermediate product c, or $b_c(t)$, can be calculated with the following formula:

$$b_c(t) = Y_c(t) \Big/ \prod_f Fc_{f,c}(t)^{\beta_{f,c}(t)} \tag{3.46}$$

In the integrated products of domestic sales, the share parameters of imported products $\delta m_c(t)$ and locally produced products $\delta d_c(t)$ can be determined by the ratio of the quantity of imported and locally produced products and the total quantity of domestic sales. The elasticity of substitution $\eta_c(t)$ between the locally produced product c and imported product c cannot be directly obtained through the SAM. These need to be estimated with econometric methods; the setting of these parameters is further described as follows. After obtaining $\delta m_c(t)$, $\delta d_c(t)$ and $\eta_c(t)$, the scale parameter of the Armington function, $\gamma_c(t)$, can be determined with the following formula:

$$\gamma_c(t) = Q_c(t) \Big/ \left(\delta m_c(t) M_c(t)^{\eta_c(t)} + \delta d_c(t) DK_c(t)^{\eta_c(t)}\right)^{1/\eta_c(t)} \tag{3.47}$$

Relevant parameters of the total quantity of domestic products mainly include the share parameter $\xi e_c(t)$ of the export c, share parameters $\xi d_c(t)$ of product c produced and sold at home, the elasticity of conversion $\Phi_c(t)$ between the domestic product c and exported product c and the scale parameter $\theta_c(t)$ of the transfer function. These parameters are calculated based on processes and approaches similar to those of the integrated products sold at home.

3.2.3.2 Proportion Parameters of the Land Use Conversion Module

In the CGELUC model, land use conversion participates in economic activities as an independent sector similar to other commodity productions. Relevant parameters mainly include the consumption coefficient $axl_{c,zl}(t)$ of the intermediate product c in the land use conversion zl, consumption coefficient $ayl_{zl}(t)$ of other types of land, share of the factor f $\beta l_{f,zl}(t)$ in the production process of intermediate products in land use conversion zl and scale parameter $bl_{zl}(t)$ of the zlth newly-increased land. The calculation is similar to that of $ax_{d,c}(t)$, $al_{l,c}(t)$, $\beta_{f,c}(t)$ and $b_c(t)$.

3.2.3.3 Proportion Parameters of the Demand Module

The proportion parameters of the demand module mainly involve the consumption demand for different products, investment demand, land demand and demand for other factors of economic entities (government and residents). Government consumption should strictly conform to the implemented financial budget in the model. $\mu_c(t)$ is the proportion of the expense of the product c account in total government expenditures, and $\alpha_c(t)$ is the proportion of the expense of consumer good c in total household expenditures.

3.2.3.4 Parameters of the Product Price Module

The price of the product is directly related to the type of production function selected in the production module. In the top-level nest of the CGELUC model, the Leontief linear production function is adopted. The amount of intermediate inputs in the final products will directly affect the price of the final product.

3.3 Methods of SAM Compilation

In general, SAM is the final result of a national economic accounting system, and therefore, the structure and data of SAM are closely related with this accounting system. The SAM that supports CGELUC incorporates three land types (arable land, economic forest and grassland), which clarify the relationship with sectors in the national economy accounting system. National economic accounting is macro-accounting with the country as the main body. Its statistical range covers all of society, the survey method is diverse, the data sources are multiple and the various data are difficult to coordinate. Therefore, the kinds of information collected from different perspectives are complicated and distorted if they are not arranged and coordinated following certain theoretical systems and scientific methods. SAM can be used to appropriately process fragmented and unsystematic data to provide a better overview of the national economy. SAMs not only provide diverse indexes of the national economic accounting system, but also describe the interdependent and mutually-constraining relationship between subsystems in the national economy to provide a scientific basis for macroeconomic system management.

Generally, there are three steps to compile the SAM. First, a highly centralized macroscopic SAM account is established to provide a consistent macroeconomic framework to subdivide SAM in the next step. Second, sector accounts are subdivided based on the issues to be analyzed. In the process of subdividing the macroscopic SAM, data for the unit item in the macroscopic

SAM become the control numbers of the vectors or sub-matrices following the subdivision process. Third, if the disaggregated SAM account does not balance, certain assumptions or processing technologies are adopted to balance it, including the RAS and cross-entropy (CE) methods. The data used to compile the SAM are mainly from the national or regional IO tables, government summary table of annual financial accounts, national income and expenditure statistics, annual tax data, statistical yearbooks, import and export data and surveys of urban and rural residents.

Two methods are widely used to compile SAM. One is a top-down method; the other is a bottom-up method.

Top-down

The top-down method advocates compiling the SAM based on the known total amount and decomposition of the SAM. The data come from national or regional IO tables and national economy and accounting information. The macroscopic SAM provides a description of all macroeconomic activities. However, it is necessary to subdivide this information to obtain the disaggregated SAM to obtain more reliable data to analyze policies (Cramb et al., 2009; Sohl et al., 2010). Supporters of this method, such as Hayden and Round (1982), believe that when the classification level of the country is given, it is unlikely to define the detailed data used to compile the SAM. Clearly, the starting point for compiling the SAM must be the SAM of national economic accounting of a country. In addition, more detailed feedback depends on decomposition of institutional accounts and production departments in the SAM. The 1988 SAM of the United States and the 1987 SAM of China compiled by the State Council Development Research Center were both complied using the top-down method.

Bottom-up

The bottom-up method makes full use of existing information and classifies and summarizes the information to compile the SAM. In contrast with the top-down method, this approach advocates the starting point to be the various detailed data from different sources. It emphasizes data accuracy. However, as detailed data are difficult to obtain, this method is used far less frequently than the top-down method (Brown et al., 2008). Keuning and de Ruijter (1988) support the use of the bottom-up method; they regard it as controversial that the SAM compilation should be based on disaggregated data or aggregate accounting data. However, because the SAM of the national economic accounting data must be available in a timely manner at the end of the year, the information provided is always less than the information SAM should include. Therefore, we are prone to support the use of the top-down method. In this case, the SAM can be used to revise the SAM of national economic accounting rather than have the total quantity deciding the subdivided quantity. Clearly, inconsistencies obtained from initial estimates would feed back to statistical agencies of the country. Therefore, interactions of the construction of the SAM, improvements in basic data and the compilation of the SAM (every 5 years) are iterative processes.

It is necessary to note that the national economic accounts of some countries are unreliable. In such cases, information gained through elaborately designed surveys (such as living standards surveys or multiple-objective surveys) not only provides useful data, but also improves the reliability of the SAM of the national economy. In addition, an elaborately designed, multiple-objective survey also makes an amendment of the national economic account possible. Jabara and Lundberg (1992) used the bottom-up method when compiling the SAM of Gambia, and they believed that inconsistencies existed in the data of the national economic accounting. The SAM based on these data would result in an imbalance between the column and row totals.

As previously mentioned, the bottom-up method is an important method in summarizing relevant collected information, while the top-down method can be seen as a deductive method since it starts with the controlled total amount and divides each total amount to obtain the SAM. An excellent SAM should be based on adequate and accurate data, but since detailed and accurate data are difficult to obtain, the bottom-up method is used more frequently. To some extent, the SAM is a result of multiple iterations between prior continuity and later accuracy.

Supporters of the two methods both start with data. In other words, the key to compiling the SAM lies in the availability and usability of data. It is generally believed that the choice of method should be based on the issues analyzed for the countries and regions that have good databases. Presently in China, the top-down method is more feasible due to restrictions in statistical capacity (Huang et al., 2002).

3.3.1 Compilation of the Macroscopic SAM

Operation of the actual national economic accounting system is an extremely complicated process, the complexity of which is represented as the diversity of economic activities, sectors and products. It is extremely complicated to show all economic activities with the SAM. Generally, a macroscopic SAM should first be compiled, and then the disaggregated SAM is compiled according to research needs. A simple example of structure and compilation methods of a macroscopic SAM is shown below.

First, to form a general macroscopic SAM, all economic activities are defined as activities, all products of economic activities are defined as commodities, all capital and labor inputs are defined as factor inputs, all institution sectors, such as corporations and residents, are defined as sectors and all kinds of product uses are defined as final usage, including activity, product, factor, sector and final usage accounts. Doing so can produce a 5×5 macroscopic SAM, which is the simplest SAM, yet still reflects the process from production to distribution of the final products, and consequently the economy of a country. The specific form of the macroscopic SAM is shown in Table 3.3.

This SAM table includes five types of information. (i) Activity account. Columns indicate inputs of intermediate products and factors in economic activities, i.e., total inputs. Rows indicate the total income of industrial activities from revenues of product sales, i.e., total product outputs. (ii) Product account. Columns indicate that the aggregate supply is from economic activities, and rows indicate that the aggregate demand is from intermediate need and the final usage of the products. (iii) Factor account. Columns indicate factor income distributed to departments, i.e., factor distribution. (iv) Institution account. Columns indicate products the institutions consume, i.e., final use, and rows indicate that the income of the institutions is from factor revenue. (v) Final usage account. Columns indicate final consumed commodities, i.e., final product supply or use. Rows indicate that the final use comes from final demand or consumption of the institutions.

A series of important macroeconomic balances are gained using the macroscopic SAM mentioned above. These gains include balances of the regional total input, total demand, factor income, sector income and final usage.

- Total input = total output = intermediate input+ added value
- Total demand = total supply = intermediate consumption + final product
- Factor income = factor distribution = added value
- Sector income = income usage = added value
- Final usage = final demand = added value

The entire macroeconomy operation process can be described by reflecting macroeconomic account data with the SAM, which makes it superior to the traditional 'T' type of account. One method for compiling a macroscopic SAM is to use a descriptive statement, i.e., by obtaining the data that the macroscopic SAM needs using a circular account system of the national economic account. Another method involves directly compiling the SAM through a simplified IO table and some relevant macroeconomic data. The specific case depends on availability of the national economic account data of each country. Generally, the former method can be used if the national economic account system is complete; if it is incomplete or is mainly shown in table form, the latter method can be used.

The SAM of different dimensions may be compiled according to specific conditions. Generally, the fundamental structure of the macroscopic SAM with complete systems for the CGE model is 8×8, i.e., activity, product and factor accounts are retained, and then the sector and final usage accounts are subdivided into the five departments (resident, corporation, government, savings and foreign). With an increase in the number of accounts, the content indicated by these accounts is richer than that of the 5×5 SAM. The activity account indicates the input and output of domestic activities. In the product account, rows indicate the total domestic demand including intermediate demand, resident demand, government demand, investment and

Table 3.3 Structure of a simple SAM

		1	2	3	4	5	
		Activity	Product	Factor	Sector	Final Use	Total
1	Activity		Total Output				Total Input
2	Product	Intermediate				Final Product	Total Demand
3	Factor	Added Value					Factor Income
4	Sector			Added Value			Sector Income
5	Final Use				Final Product		Final Demand
	Total	Total Input	Total Product Supply	Factor	Income Use	Final Use	

import. Columns indicate the total supply including total domestic output and import. The factor account mainly indicates factor input and distribution of factor revenue. In the resident account, rows indicate disposable income including factor income and transfer income, and columns indicate resident expenditure, product consumption, tax and family savings. In the corporation account, which indicates business income and expenditures, rows indicate business capital income and transfer income, and columns indicate business profit distribution and tax. In the government account, rows indicate government revenue such as production tax and income tax, and columns indicate government expenditures and transfer payments. In the investment-savings account, rows indicate resident, corporation and government savings and overseas investment, and columns indicate that the investment comes from commodities. In the foreign account, rows indicate domestic payments to foreign countries, i.e., the foreign exchange expenditure manifested by the import, foreign factor expenditures, the surplus corporations pay abroad and government transfer expenditures. Columns indicate foreign payments to the domestic country, i.e., the foreign exchange income presented as the export, overseas factor income, transfer of foreign currency and foreign transfer expenditures to corporations and foreign investments. The specific SAM structure is listed in Table 3.4.

3.3.2 Subdivision of the Macroscopic SAM

The macroscopic SAM is subdivided into subaccounts. The setting of the subaccounts often differs among countries and has no standard form. This is because (i) the statistical bases and availability of data differ among countries; and (ii) the purposes of policy analysis and forms of established economic models vary, which results in different requirements for subdivision levels.

Two different methods are always available to subdivide an account. The first is to subdivide the entire economic class into unit classes. The activity account and the product account are first subdivided according to industrial and product sectors, respectively, which stand for the IO relationship of production, i.e., the production matrix and usage matrix in IO technology. Consequently, some regard the SAM as an extension of an IO table. In fact, the IO table only describes the relationship between product and institutional sectors, while the SAM describes both the relationship between product and institutional sectors and the relationship between institutional sectors. After the activity and product accounts are subdivided, the factors are then subdivided into labor, capital and land. The business account is then subdivided. Finally, the enterprises are subdivided into state-owned enterprises, shareholding enterprises and foreign-owned enterprises according to ownership, or large-scale enterprises, medium-scale enterprises and small-scale enterprises according to size. Other methods of subdivisions exist and

Table 3.4 Basic structure of SAM

			Expenditure				
			1	2	3	4	5
			Activity	Product	Factor	Resident	Corporation
Income	1	Activity		Market output		Resident self-production and self-consumption	
	2	Product	Intermediate input	Transaction costs		Private consumption	
	3	Factor	Added value				
	4	Resident			Resident factor income	Transfer expenditure among residents	Surplus corporations pay to residents
	5	Corporation		Corporation factor income			
	6	Government	Production tax, value added tax	Sales tax, customs, export tax	Factor income of the government, factor tax	Individual income tax, income tax	Corporation income tax, surplus submitted by corporations
	7	Savings-investment account				Resident savings	Corporation savings
	8	Foreign		Import	Foreign factor income		Surplus corporations pay abroad
		Total	Total input	Total supply	Factor expenditure	Resident expenditure	Business expenditure

Continued

			Expenditure			
			6	7	8	Total
			Government	Savings-investment account	Foreign	
Income	1	Activity				Total output
	2	Product	Government consumption	Investment	Export	Total demand
	3	Factor			Factor income from abroad	Factor income
	4	Resident	Transfer of the government to residents		Transfer of abroad to residents	Total resident income
	5	Corporation	Transfer of the government to corporations		Transfer of abroad to corporations	Total corporation income
	6	Government				Total government income
	7	Savings-investment account	Government savings		Overseas savings	Total savings
	8	Foreign	Payment of the government abroad			Foreign exchange expenditure
		Total	Government expenditure	Total investment	Foreign exchange income	

are based on national statistical status and research purpose. In addition, the subdivision of residents is also an important part of the subdivision of the SAM. Residents can be subdivided into rural and urban residents according to living area or income levels and can even be subdivided according to two standards simultaneously. The foreign account is sometimes subdivided into different countries or country groups in studies focusing on the economic communication between one country and the rest of the world. The accumulation account is subdivided according to institutional sectors and introduces a financial account to expand the SAM into a financial SAM. The assets and liabilities account can even be introduced to expand SAM to combine the flow and the stock. This is an expansion account method in the compilation method of the macroscopic SAM, i.e., a subdivision of the account system.

The other method used to expand the SAM is to subdivide the trade types. Regular transfers among institutional sectors can be subdivided according to differences among regular transfers. For example, resident income tax can be separated from regular transfers of residents to the government. This method directly extracts different transactions separately from the general national economic account. When there are a large number of data, it may be difficult to balance the SAM in the compiling process.

In the compilation of SAM, a disaggregated SAM is obtained by combining the two methods, subdividing the industrial activity and kinds of products and incorporating the macroscopic economic data with the subdivided data of relevant institutions.

The disaggregated SAM, which includes the relationships between product activities and transactions among sectors at the sector level, is ideal to describe mid-level economic flows and can provide large amounts of valuable data for policy analysis and model building.

3.3.3 Balancing the SAM

According to the principles of social accounting, expenditures should equal income, which is shown when the row sum equals the column sum in the SAM. But in the process of compiling the SAM, row sums are usually not equal to column sums due to differences in data sources and the following statistical errors. (i) Inequalities often occur between the row and column accounts in the SAM with the same data source, which defies the principle that the row sum and the corresponding column sum should be equal. (ii) Abnormal data do exist in the table, e.g., negative numbers are input in the intermediate sector in the previous section. (iii) When data items are updated, it is necessary to update the original SAM. It is possible to only add one error account in the SAM to keep the error or to regulate the data in the accounts to balance the SAM.

Generally, three steps are needed to compile the SAM to ensure equality between the row and corresponding column subtotals. (i) The macroscopic SAM is first compiled followed by the more specific SAM. Data in the macroscopic SAM are taken as control numbers for each sub-matrix to ensure that the sum of the data in the sub-matrixes equals the control number. (ii) Inconsistent data are analyzed, a judgment is made according to auxiliary information and data are adjusted. The SAM gathers many different accounts together, the data of which should come from different sources, and a payment of one account must be expenditure for another. The process of analyzing and judging differences in the data also serves as a check for the acquired statistical data. (iii) Data of the SAM are adjusted using mathematical methods such as RAS, CE and least squares to balance the SAM. The theory and steps of RAS and CE are introduced in the following sections (Duan, 2004).

3.3.3.1 The RAS Method

RAS, which is also called the biproportional method, was put forward by Stone (1961), an English economist. RAS was originally used to amend the direct consumption coefficient in the IO table but has gradually extended to balance other matrices. The essence of adjusting the SAM with RAS is to use two main diagonal matrices, namely the alternative multiplier matrix and the manufacturing multiplier matrix. The alternative multiplier matrix is used to left multiply the SAM to reach the required row goal, and the manufacturing multiplier matrix is used to right multiply the SAM to reach the required column goal. The process is repeated until the row and the column in the SAM meet accuracy requirements. The formula for RAS is as follows:

$$\begin{cases} R_i^{(K)} &= u_i^* / \sum\limits_{j=1} t_{ij}^{(k-1)} x_j^{(1)} \\ S_i^{(k)} &= v_j^* / \sum\limits_{i=1} R_i^{(k)} t_{ij}^{(k-1)} x_j^1 \\ a_{ij}^{(k)} &= R_i^{(k)} t_{ij}^{(k-1)} S_j^1 \end{cases} \quad (i = 1, 2, \cdots, n; j = 1, 2, \cdots, n) \tag{3.48}$$

where $R_i^{(k)}$ represents the alternative multiplier matrix left multiplied in the kth step; $S_i^{(k)}$ represents the manufacturing multiplier matrix right multiplied in the kth step; u_i^* and v_j^* represent the sum of the known row vector and the sum of the known column vector in the SAM, respectively; $a_{ij}^{(k)}$ represents the data items in the kth step in the SAM table; $x_j^{(1)}$ stands for the row sum or the column sum of the final SAM.

Adjusting the SAM with RAS balances the row and the column mechanically and forcibly, which may change most data in the original matrix. Therefore, some accurate data in the original SAM may also change, and some reliable information might be lost. To retain the accurate data in the original SAM, some treatment is conducted on the SAM when RAS is used. The accurate data in the original SAM are extracted from the matrix before adjustment, and the corresponding blanks in the matrix are set to zero. RAS is then applied to adjust the matrix. After the adjustment, the extracted data are returned to the adjusted SAM. Row and column sums in the treated SAM remain both accurate and balanced.

RAS can be used to adjust both the full SAM table and the sub-matrix in the SAM. An advantage of RAS is that it does not require complicated software tools. Microsoft Office Excel is capable of easily and simply converting RAS into a planning problem to find the solution. However, RAS is a purely mathematical leveling method; its logic is short of real economic meaning. Therefore, there are many disadvantages of using RAS to adjust the SAM. First, the assumption regarding the consistency of the alternative multiplier and the right multiplied manufacturing multiplier among sectors is dubious and inconsistent with facts. Second, RAS cannot adjust a matrix with negative numbers. Third, the error of the SAM adjusted with RAS is generally very large. To surmount these disadvantages, Byron (1978) put forward an improved RAS method, and Liu (1996) came up with the RAS-weighted amendment method called the RTALS method. These methods are good at balancing the SAM.

3.3.3.2 The Cross Entropy Method

The CE method was originally put forward and applied in statistics and economics by Theil (1967), who was inspired by the theory of information entropy proposed by Shannon (1948). Shannon defined information entropy as $-\ln\frac{p_i}{q_i} = -[\ln p_i - \ln q_i]$, in which p_i and q_i represent the prior probability and the later probability of event E_i, respectively. Therefore, the expectations of the information for event E_i are:

$$-I(p:q) = -\sum_i p_i \ln\frac{p_i}{q_i} \tag{3.49}$$

where $I(p{:}q)$ is the mutual entropy distance between the two probabilities defined by Kullback and Leibler (1951). Theil (1967) subsequently applied this concept to balance the IO table.

CE is mainly used to update the original SAM after gaining the updated sector summary data. Its core idea is to embed the new information into the SAM and to minimize the difference between the updated SAM and the original SAM. The difference is measured by the CE distance suggested by Kullback and Leibler (1951).

Suppose the original SAM is T^0, and all data in the matrix is t_{ij}^0; the updated SAM is T^1, and each data item of the corresponding matrix is t_{ij}^1. Therefore, the CE method can be represented as a nonlinear optimization problem solver; its arithmetic expression is as follows:

$$\min H = \sum_i\sum_j a_{ij}^1 \ln\frac{a_{ij}^1}{a_{ij}^0} = \sum_i\sum_j a_{ij}^1 \ln a_{ij}^1 - \sum_i\sum_j a_{ij}^1 \ln a_{ij}^0 \tag{3.50}$$

$$\sum_j a_{ij}^1 T_j^1 = T_i^1, \quad \sum_j a_{ij}^1 = 1 \tag{3.51}$$

where a_{ij}^0 and a_{ij}^1 represent the coefficient matrix before and after the adjustment, respectively; i.e., $a_{ij}^0 = \frac{t_{ij}^0}{\sum_i t_{ij}^0}$, $a_{ij}^1 = \frac{t_{ij}^1}{\sum_i t_{ij}^1}$, T_j^1 and T_i^1 represent the sum of rows and the sum of columns in the updated SAM table, respectively. The objective of the optimization problem mentioned above is to minimize the distance. The constraint conditions indicate that row sums and column sums in the updated SAM table are still equal and are also equal to the updated row sums (or column sums). The EXCEL VBA program of the RAS program code is illustrated in Appendix 1.

3.4 Summary

The CGELUC model selects the framework of CGE to analyze the influence of socioeconomic factors in an equilibrium economic system such as the industrial structure, trade environment, economic policies and institutional arrangements on the structure of regional land use. This model can be used to simulate principles of regional land use structural changes due to constraints and influences at the policy level. The model can also conduct relevant research pertaining to land use such as simulations, predictions, assessments and analyses. The CEGLUC model uses the price signal to organically link the factor market, commodity market and land use subject and forms an equilibrium analysis system covering multiple markets and sectors.

Economic activities are the main driving factors behind structural changes in land use and are also constrained by the structure of regional land use. The CGELUC model analyzes factors that influence the types of regional land use based on macroscopic quantitative analysis, revealing the relationships between economic variables and changes in the area of cultivated, economic forest and pasture lands. Then constructing mechanism-based models to analyze the dynamic laws for the succession of land use structure at the regional scale.

References

Adelman I and Robinson S. 1978. Income Distribution Policy in Developing Countries. Stanford: Stanford University Press.

Armington P A. 1969. A theory of demand for products distinguished by place of production. IMF Staff Papers, 16(1): 159–178.

Böhringer C and Löschel A. 2006. Computable general equilibrium models for sustainability impact assessment: Status quo and prospects. Ecological Economics, 60, 49–64.

Brown D G, Robinson D T, An L, Nassauer J I, Zellner M, Rand W, Riolo R, Page S

E, Low B, Wang Z F. 2008. Exurbia from the bottom-up: Confronting empirical challenges to characterizing a complex system. Geoforum, 39(2): 805–818.

Byron R P. 1978. The estimation of large social account matrices. Journal of the Royal Statistical Society, 141(3): 359–367.

Conrad K. 2001. Computable general equilibrium models in environmental and resource economics. In: Tietenberg T, Folmer H. Eds. The International Yearbook of Environmental and Resource Economics 2002/2003.

Conway T M and Lathrop R G. 2005. Modeling the ecological consequences of land-use policies in an urbanizing region. Environmental Management, 35(3): 278–291.

Cramb R A, Colfer C J P, Dressler W, Laungaramsri P, Trung L Q, Mulyoutami E, Peluso N L, Wadley R L. 2009. Swidden transformations and rural livelihoods in Southeast Asia. Human Ecology, 37(3): 323–346.

Deng X Z, Huang J K, Rozelle S, Uchida E. 2006. Cultivated land conversion and potential agricultural productivity in China. Land Use Policy, 23(4): 372–384.

Deng X Z, Huang J K, Rozelle S, Uchida E. 2008. Growth, population and industrialization and urban land expansion of China. Journal of Urban Economics, 63(1): 96–115.

Deng X Z, Jiang Q O, Zhan J Y, He S J, Lin Y Z. 2010a. Simulation on the dynamics of forest area changes in Northeast China. Journal of Geographical Sciences, 20(4): 495–509.

Deng X Z, Huang J K, Rozelle S, Uchida E. 2010b. Economic growth and the expansion of urban land in China. Urban Studies, 47(4): 813–843.

Deng X Z, Su H B, Zhan J Y. 2008. Integration of multiple data sources to simulate the Dynamics of Land Systems. Sensors, 8(2): 620–634.

Dervis K. 1975. Substitution, employment and intertemporal equilibrium in a nonlinear multi-sector planning model for turkey. European Economic Review, (6): 77–96.

Dixon P B, Parmenter B R, Powell A A. 1984. The role of miniatures in computable general equilibrium modelling: Experience from ORANI. Economic Modelling, 1(4): 421–428.

Duan Z G. 2004. Research on the Modelling and Applications of Chinese. Wuhan: Huazhong University of Science and Technology.

Fu B J, Ma K M, Zhou H F, Chen L D. 1999. The effect of land use structure on the distribution of soil nutrients in the hilly area of the Loess Plateau, China. Chinese Science Bulletin, 44(8): 732–736.

Gelan A. 2002. Trade liberalisation and urban-rural linkages: A CGE analysis for Ethiopia. Journal of Policy Modeling, 24(7–8): 707–738.

Haberl H, Batterbury S, Moran E. 2001. Using and shaping the land: A long-term perspective. Land Use Policy, 18(1): 1–8.

Hanasaki N, Kanae S, Oki T, Masuda K, Motoya K, Shirakawa N, Shen Y, Tanaka K. 2008. An integrated model for the assessment of global water resources Part 2: Applications and assessments. Hydrology and Earth System Sciences, 12(4): 1027–1037.

Hayden C and Round J I. 1982. Developments in social accounting methods as applied to the analysis of income distribution and employment issues. World Development, 10: 451–465.

Hietel E, Waldhardt R, Otte A. 2004. Analysing land-cover changes in relation to environmental variables in Hesse, Germany. Landscape Ecology, 19(5): 473–489.

Huang C C, Pang J L, Li P H. 2002. Abruptly increased climatic aridity and its social impact on the Loess Plateau of China at 3100 a BP. Journal of Arid Environments, 52(1): 87–99.

Irwin E G and Geoghegan J. 2001. Theory, data, methods: Developing spatially explicit economic models of land use change. Agriculture Ecosystems and Environment, 85(1–3): 7–23.

Jabara C L, Lundberg M, Jallow A S. 1992. A social accounting matrix for the Gambia. Working Paper No. 20, Ithaca, NY: Cornell Food and Nutrition Policy Program.

Johanson L. 1960. A Multisectoral Study of Economic Growth. Amsterdam: North-Holland.

Keuning S J and de Ruijter W A. 1988. Guidelines to the construction of a Social Accounting Matrix. Journal of the International Association, 34(1): 71–100.

Krausmann F, Haberl H, Schulz N B, Erb K H, Darge E, Gaube V. 2003. Land-use change and socio-economic metabolism in Austria—Part I: Driving forces of land-use change: 1950—1995. Land Use Policy, 20(1): 1–20.

Kullback S and Leibler R A. 1951. On information and sufficiency. The Annals of Mathematical Statistics, 22(1): 79–86.

Lambin E F, Turner B L, Geist H J, Agbola S B, Angelsen A, Bruce J W, Coomes O T, Dirzo R, Fischer G, Folke C, George P S, Homewood K, Imbernon J, Leemans R, Li X, Moran E F, Mortimore M, Ramakrishnan P S, Richards J F, Skånes H, Steffen W, Stone G D, Svedin U, Veldkamp T A, Vogel C, Xu J. 2001. The causes of land-use and land-cover change: Moving beyond the myths. Global Environmental Change, 11(4): 261–269.

Lehtonen H, Aakkula J, Rikkonen P. 2005. Alternative agricultural policy scenarios, sector modelling and indicators: A sustainability assessment. Journal of Sustainable Agriculture, 26(4): 63–93.

Leip A, Marchi G, Koeble R, Kempen M, Britz W, Li C. 2008. Linking an economic model for European agriculture with a mechanistic model to estimate nitrogen and carbon losses from arable soils in Europe. Biogeosciences, 5(1): 73–94.

Liu J X and Yi H Y. 1996. Weighted modification and generalization of RAS method on Input-Output Analysis—RTALS Method and its Mathematical Model. Journal of Chongqing University, 19(4): 49–52.

Liu J Y, Zhuang D F, Luo D, Xiao X. 2003. Land-cover classification of China: Integrated analysis of AVHRR imagery and geo-physical data. International Journal of Remote Sensing, 24(12): 2485–2500.

Rozelle S and Rosegrant M W. 1997. China's past, present, and future food economy: Can China continue to meet the challenges? Food Policy, 22(3): 191–200.

Scarf H and Hansen T. 1973. The Computation of Economic Equilibrium. New Haven, Conn: Yale University Press.

Shannon C E. 1948. A mathematical theory of communication. Bell System Technical Journal, 27: 379–423 & 623–656.

Sohl T L, Loveland T R, Sleeter B M, Sayler K L, Barnes C A. 2010. Addressing foundational elements of regional land-use change forecasting. Landscape

Ecology, 25(2): 233–247.

Stone R. 1961. Input-Output and National Accounts. Paris: Organisation for European Economic Co-operation.

Theil H. 1967. Economics and Information Theory. Amsterdam: North-Holland.

Veldkamp A and Verburg P H. 2004. Modelling land use change and environmental impact. Journal of Environmental Management, 72(1–2): 1–3.

Verburg P H and Veldkamp A. 2001. The role of spatially explicit models in land-use change research: A case study for cropping patterns in China. Agriculture Ecosystems and Environment, 85(1–3): 177–190.

Wong G Y and Alavalapati J R R. 2003. The land-use effects of a forest carbon policy in the US. Forest Policy and Economics, 5(3): 249–263.

Chapter 4 The DLS Model and Its Application

The model of Dynamics of Land System (DLS) is a collection of programs that simulates pattern changes in land uses by conducting scenario analysis of the area of land use change. Results reveal the driving mechanisms of land use change and simulate the balance between supply and demand of land at the pixel level (Deng et al., 2008). The model analyzes causes of the dynamics of land use patterns, simulates the process of land use changes, and assists land use planning and land management decisions (Deng et al., 2010a). The DLS model can export a macroscopic pattern changes map of land uses at high spatial and temporal resolution by estimating the effects of driving factors of spatial pattern changes, formulating land use conversion rules and scenarios of land use change and simulating dynamic spatiotemporal processes of land use changes. Driving factors include natural environmental conditions, socioeconomic factors and land use management policies, all of which are closely linked to pattern changes in land uses (Lambin et al., 2001; Lambin et al., 2003; Haberl et al., 2004; Burgi et al., 2004; Aguiar et al., 2007; Turner II et al., 2007; Veldkamp and Verburg, 2004; Verburg, 2006).

4.1 Principles and Function Modules of the DLS Model

The DLS model is theoretically based on restrictions of the distribution of land use types. The model dynamically simulates the macroscopic pattern changes in land uses by classifying the driving factors that influence this pattern (Deng et al., 2008). The simulation spatially allocates the area change in land use and is based on spatial statistics, predicting the probabilities of different land use types and incorporating the probability of distribution of different land use types at the pixel level.

4.1.1 Fundamental Definition

Simulating the macroscopic pattern changes in land uses involves simulating the spatiotemporal processes of changing area and the distributions of regional land use types. This is done by quantitatively measuring flow and stock in the conversion processes of various land use types (Turner II, 1997; Veldkamp and Lambin, 2001; Burgi and Turner, 2002). To realize this goal, it is necessary to first understand the target and features of the simulated dynamics of the land use pattern.

Simulating the macroscopic pattern changes in land uses is targeted at the human-modified land system, which is closely related to land use. The land system is an open, complex system consisting of two subsystems, the geographic environment and human activities, inside which are certain structures and functions (Verburg et al., 2002; Wang et al., 2010). At the core of simulated land use pattern changes are interactions among the natural environment, human society and area of land use change. Accordingly, to produce a macroscopic simulation of a land use pattern, it is necessary to explore new approaches to simulate the dynamics of land system spatial distribution, temporal processes, change in organization, bulk effect and complementary synergies (Veldkamp and Verburg, 2004; Liu et al., 2005).

Changes in the area of regional land use types are closely related to other factors at different scales in the land system. The relationship between them generally includes features such as mechanisms, feedbacks, complexities and systematizations, which are specifically represented as follows.

(i) Natural controlling factors, represented by terrain, climate, soil and vegetation, play a dominant role in changing the regional land use pattern in the long-term and in controlling the direction and degree of change in the regional land use pattern. (ii) Socioeconomic driving factors, including population change, economic development, technical progress and institutional changes, interact with the area of land use change and play a decisive role in the pattern changes in regional land uses in the short-term. (iii) Various nonlinear relationships exist between natural controlling factors and socioeconomic factors, which often conceal the real reasons for the pattern changes in land uses.

Many limitations still exist in current research on simulating the pattern changes in land uses. Systematic analysis and expression of mechanisms of pattern changes in land uses are difficult to conduct (Dai et al., 2005; Pontius et al., 2007). Pattern changes in land uses are closely related to land use decisions, and therefore, simulating pattern changes in land uses needs to comprehensively consider factors such as socioeconomic development, cultural traditions, natural conditions and historic trends in pattern changes in land uses to improve the reliability and accuracy of simulation results.

4.1.2 Features of the DLS Model

Recent research has made progress in the analysis of driving forces behind pattern changes in land uses with economic models and empirical statistical methods (Liu, 2002; Veldkamp and Verburg, 2004; Li et al., 2005; Liu et al., 2005). Shi et al. (2000) analyzed natural and human factors driving land use change in Shenzhen with regression analysis; Chen et al. (2000) built a multiple regression model of land use change using a multi-scale statistical method. Researchers at the Institute of Agricultural Resource and Planning, Chinese Academy of Agricultural Sciences cooperated with scholars at Wageningen University, the Netherlands, to build a model of land use change in China with assistance from a geographic information system (GIS). This was a good attempt at creating a comprehensive evaluation model of land use change (Verburg et al., 2000). Simulations of pattern changes in land uses have focused on regional and microscopic aspects; however, in-depth research has involved the utility of using the models mentioned above with these two aspects, but many limitations still exist.

Conventional models capable of simulating the macroscopic pattern changes in land uses are limited to simulation of only one or several land use types (Ge and Dai, 2005); however, the DLS model differs from these models because it comprehensively simulates the spatiotemporal pattern of all kinds of land use types at the regional scale. It has solved the problem of discriminating between endogenous and exogenous driving factors of land use changes. In addition, the DLS model quantitatively analyzes the effects of different driving factors by building a spatially-explicit statistical model of the distribution of land use types and driving factors at the pixel level, and it sees the pattern changes in land uses as a dynamic spatiotemporal process. Also, different scenarios of changing area of regional land use types are designed in the DLS model based on comprehensive measurements of factors such as features of regional socioeconomic development, cultural traditions, natural conditions and history of land use. Thus, the DLS model has improved the scientific and rational nature of predicted and estimated results.

4.1.3 Framework of the DLS Model

The DLS model fully considers the links among related models of nature, ecology and economy. It also extracts decision-making reference information used in land use planning, environmental planning and management of natural resources by designing different scenarios of changing regional land use area. Users of the DLS model can input nonlinear demand change, different conversion rules and driving factors at different pattern changes in land uses to simulate and analyze the complex changes in regional land use patterns. The DLS model also considers the influence of macroscopic factors such as topography, environment, trade and institutional arrangement and land management policies to more accurately simulate possible scenarios of pattern changes in land uses.

The DLS model presumes that land use pattern change is influenced by both historic pattern changes in land uses and driving factors within the pixel and neighboring pixels. Decisions of land use planners have important influence on the pattern changes in land uses, especially at the regional level (Fig. 4.1).

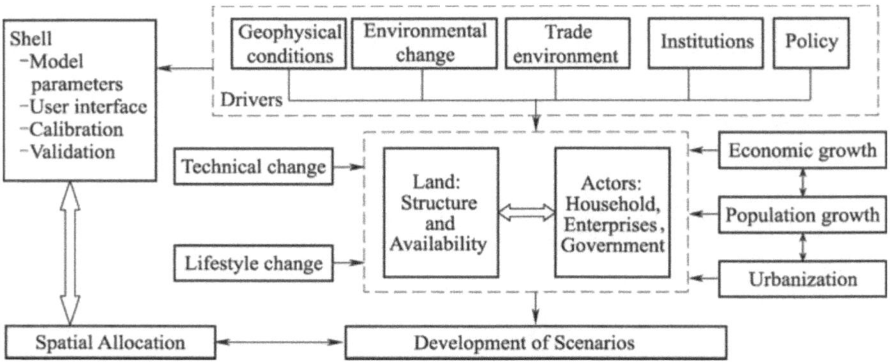

Fig. 4.1 Modeling framework of the DLS model.

In addition, the DLS model considers regional restrictions on the distribution of land use types. For example, the model sets regions where it is impossible for a certain land use type to appear as restricted regions and removes these regions so that they are not input into the model. Moreover, the input parameters and exogenous variables may change with time due to influences from conversion rules of regional land use types and nonlinear demand change. Therefore, it is still necessary to consider uncertainties of simulation results in the DLS model.

4.1.4 Application

The DLS model effectively simulates spatiotemporal pattern changes in land uses. Regarding data integration, the DLS model represents various land use types in a grid format, which spatially expresses the characteristics of the distribution of regional land use types with a high resolution. The DLS model takes information from the basic grid unit as observed data and performs a spatiotemporal simulation of the pattern changes in land uses at the pixel level.

The DLS model fully considers the complexity of the driving mechanisms of pattern changes. It reveals dynamic spatiotemporal rules of land use changes by considering regional restrictions on changing land use area based on a comprehensive analysis of factors that influence land use changes. Researches have indicated that as an auxiliary tool to analyze changes in regional land use area, natural environmental effects of these changes, land use planning and land management decision-making, the DLS model has truly realized the dynamic simulation of pattern changes in land uses with scenarios of changing land use area at the regional scale. It also analyzes mechanisms driving the distribution of land use types at the grid scale (Deng et al., 2008; Deng et al., 2010b).

4.1.5 Function Modules of the DLS Model

The DLS model is based on quantitative analysis of land use pattern changes at the pixel level, interactions among driving factors and spatiotemporal distribution of land use pattern change. It simulates the pattern changes in regional land uses by analyzing the driving forces of land distribution at the grid scale and allocation of changing land use areas. Analyzing both the driving forces behind land distribution and the spatial allocation of land use change is the most important component of the DLS model (Deng et al., 2008).

Mechanism analysis of the DLS model aims to estimate the statistical relationship between the pattern changes in land uses and its driving factors. Theoretically, mechanistic analysis provides a reaction function of each land use type. Corresponding weights are given to all driving factors according to principles that can be assumed to be fixed for a short period, but driving factors change over time. With the reaction function determined, reasons for differences between simulated and observed distribution of land use types can be summarized as follows: values of some driving factors have changed, such as population growth or temperature; competition exists among different land use types; and restrictions occur between local historic conditions and current demand. Driving factors behind land use patterns can be analyzed with the explanatory linear model of land use pattern (ELMLUP) and explanatory nonlinear model of land use pattern (ENMLUP) built at the pixel level. The two models can be used to research restrictions on the distribution of land use types at the pixel level with different backgrounds and goals, and they can be used flexibly to reveal in-depth driving mechanisms of pattern changes in land uses at the pixel level.

4.1.6 Explanatory Linear Model of Land Use Pattern

Linear regression is the model most commonly used in researching the driving mechanisms of land use patterns as it explores driving factors at wide ranges and with high spatial resolution (Verburg et al., 2002; Zhang et al., 2003). The explanatory linear model of land use patterns at the pixel level, or ELMLUP, is introduced in this chapter.

4.1.6.1 Model Hypothesis

The ELMLUP contains a demanding and a distribution module. The target variable of the ELMLUP is the proportion of the area of land use type $k(k = 1, 2, \cdots, M)$ in grid $i(i = 1, 2, \cdots, n)$ at time t abbreviated as Q_i^{kt}. The explanatory variable of the model is a covariant vector of driving factors composed of a series of natural environmental conditions and socioeconomic factors that are tightly related to the pattern changes in land uses (with a significance level of 5%).

$$X_i^t = (x_{i1}^t, x_{i2}^t, \cdots, x_{il}^t, \cdots, x_{iL}^t)^T \tag{4.1}$$

To measure the impact of spatially autocorrelated land use types, several variables, including $\hat{Q}_i^{kt}$ and $\hat{X}_i^t$, are defined in the ELMLUP. Let $\hat{Q}_i^{kt} = \sum_{j \neq i} w_{ij}^k Q_i^{kt}$, where w_{ij} is the spatial weight function of the impact of grid j on grid i. The definition of $\hat{X}_i^t$ is similar to that of $\hat{Q}_i^{kt}$, which is the weighted average of X_i^t. According to the first law of geography, the spatial weight function is usually defined as the reciprocal of the distance between grid j and grid i.

$$W_{ij}^k = \begin{cases} 1/D_{ij} \\ 0 \end{cases} \tag{4.2}$$

where D_{ij} can be the Euclidean distance, the absolute distance, or the Minkowski distance (Tobler, 1970).

4.1.6.2 Model Inference

Spatial autocorrelation

The quantitative relationship between $\hat{Q}_i^{kt}$ and $\hat{X}_i^t$ is developed through the following multiple linear regression model.

$$\hat{Q}_i^{kt} = a_0^k + a^k \hat{X}_i^t \tag{4.3}$$

where $a^k = (a_1^k, a_2^k, \cdots, a_L^k)$ is the coefficient matrix of $\hat{X}_i^t$, and a_0^k is a constant term. Regarding grid i at time t, the result $reg(\hat{Q}_i^{kt})$ estimated by the model is naturally employed to reflect the average proportion of area of land use type k under natural and socioeconomic conditions $\hat{X}_i^t$.

Apparently, $reg(\hat{Q}_i^{kt})$ does not equate with deviation of the actual observed value $real(\hat{Q}_i^{kt})$. If the demanding area of land use type k changes in the demanding module, the relative stability of Land use pattern will be broken. Therefore, we can hypothesize that a certain relationship exists between the land pattern change and the value difference between $reg(\hat{Q}_i^{kt})$ and $real(\hat{Q}_i^{kt})$: when estimated value, $reg(\hat{Q}_i^{kt})$, is smaller than the observed value, $real(\hat{Q}_i^{kt})$, the area proportion of land use type k will increase; when estimated value, $reg(\hat{Q}_i^{kt})$, is larger than the observed value, $real(\hat{Q}_i^{kt})$, the area proportion of land use type k will decrease.

When the demanding module of the ELMLUP requires the area proportion of land use type k to change to $DEMAND^{k(t+1)}$ at time $t+1$ in grid

i, the area proportion of land use type k will vary.

$$\hat{Q}_i^{k(t+1)} = real(\hat{Q}_i^{kt}) + [reg(\hat{Q}_i^{kt}) - real(\hat{Q}_i^{kt})] \cdot F_i \tag{4.4}$$

where $\hat{Q}_i^{k(t+1)}$ is the area proportion of land use type k in grid i at time $t+1$; F_i is the changing coefficient of the area of the land use type regulated by the general demanding equation:

$$DEMAND^{k(t+1)} = \sum_{i=1}^{n} \{real(\hat{Q}_i^{kt}) + [reg(\hat{Q}_i^{kt}) - real(\hat{Q}_i^{kt})] \cdot F_i\} \tag{4.5}$$

An iteration adjustment is then needed until the proportion of the area of the land use type k increases to $DEMAND^{k(t+1)}$.

Conversely, if the demanding area of land uses type decreases, the trends for the changes in the land uses types will be dissimilar.

ELMLUP

In the same way, the quantitative relationship between $\hat{Q}_i^{kt}$ and $\hat{X}_i^t$ is developed through the following regression equation:

$$Q_i^{kt} = b_0^k + b^k X_i^t \tag{4.6}$$

where $b^k = (b_1^k, b_2^k, \cdots, b_L^k)$ is the regression coefficient matrix of X_i^t, and b_0^k is a constant term. $reg(\hat{Q}_i^{kt})$ is the area proportion of land use type k at time t, estimated by the multiple linear regression model; $real(\hat{Q}_i^{kt})$ is the actual observed value of the area proportion of land use type k at time t. When the demanding module requires the proportion of the area of land use type k to change to $DEMAND^{k(t+1)}$ at time $t+1$ in grid i, the area proportion of land use type k will vary correspondingly.

$$Q_i^{k(t+1)} = real(Q_i^{kt}) + [reg(Q_i^{kt}) - real(Q_i^{kt})] \cdot F_i' \cdot R_i^{kt} \tag{4.7}$$

where the definition of F' is similar to that of F_i; R_i^{kt} is the influence function that stands for the influence of the spatial autocorrelation factors on grid i that change with $\hat{Q}_i^{kt}$. If the change in area of land use type k in grids near grid i is frequent, there will be correspondingly great changes in Q_i^{kt} and R_i^{kt} due to spatial autocorrelation.

By contrast, if land use type k in grids near grid i are relatively steady, the change in Q_i^{kt} would be correspondingly little. This is the explanatory model for land use patterns in linear form, or the ELMLUP, which considers the effect of spatial autocorrelation.

4.1.6.3 Model Estimation

Many approaches exist to estimate the coefficient of the two multiple linear regression functions in ELMLUP. In this chapter, we introduce one of the most commonly used methods, the least squares method.

The least squares method produces a line that has the minimum sum of the deviations squared (least square error) from a given set of data (Gao et al., 2005). For the two multiple linear regression functions in the ELMLUP, the minimum sums of the deviations squared are respectively defined by the following two equations:

$$\hat{Q}(a_0^k, a^k) = \sum_{i=1}^{n} [real(\hat{Q}_i^{kt}) - reg(\hat{Q}_i^{kt})]^2 = \sum_{i=1}^{n} [real(\hat{Q}_i^{kt}) - (a_0^k + a^k \hat{X}_i^t)]^2 \tag{4.8}$$

$$Q(b_0^k, b^k) = \sum_{i=1}^{n} [real(Q_i^{kt}) - reg(Q_i^{kt})]^2 = \sum_{i=1}^{n} [real(Q_i^{kt}) - (b_0^k + b^k \hat{X}_i^t)]^2 \tag{4.9}$$

4.1.6.4 Model Test

It is still unknown whether linear relationships exist between the change in land use pattern and the natural and socioeconomic factors after the regression coefficient of the multiple linear functions is obtained in the ELMLUP. Therefore, a significance test is needed for the estimated multiple linear regression function. Here, we introduce the approach of using variance analysis to test the significance of the regression function. In this approach, the total variance is decomposed into two parts.

$$\begin{aligned}\sum_{i=1}^{n} (Q_i^{kt} - \bar{Q}^{kt})^2 &= \sum_{i=1}^{n} [Q_i^{kt} - reg(Q_i^{kt})]^2 + \sum_{i=1}^{n} [reg(Q_i^{kt}) - \bar{Q}^{kt}]^2 \\ &= ESS + MSS\end{aligned} \tag{4.10}$$

where $\bar{Q}^{kt}$ is the average of Q_i^{kt}; *ESS* is the sum of variance of regression function; *MSS* is the sum of variances of the errors. Then, a new statistic is defined as follows:

$$F = \frac{MSS/f}{ESS/g} = \frac{MMS}{EMS} \tag{4.11}$$

where statistic F has a distribution of $F(f, g)$, and f and g are the degrees of freedom of the regression function and error, respectively.

By calculating statistic F and the significance probability, we can judge the significance of the multiple regression function. If the value of the significance probability is relatively small, or smaller than the significance level (for instance 0.01), we can conclude that the regression function accurately simulates the relationships between land use patterns and their driving factors.

4.1.7 Explanatory Nonlinear Model of Land Use Pattern

The driving force analysis model for land use patterns in nonlinear form is built based on land use area percentage grid data.

4.1.7.1 Grid Area Percentage Data

Percentage data were first proposed by Ferrers (1866) and is becoming increasingly important in statistical analysis. It is usually expressed as the following vector set:

$$S = \left\{ (s_1,\ s_2,\ \cdots,\ s_m)^T \in R^m \middle| \sum_{i=1}^{m} s_i = 1,\ 0 < s_i < 1 \right\} \tag{4.12}$$

$$s_i = S_i \Big/ \sum_{j=1}^{m} S_j \tag{4.13}$$

where s_i is the ith element of the percentage data, and S_i is the original observed value of s_i, or the area of cultivated land and the area of developed land.

Area percentage data are derived from grid data at a certain grid pixel scale. Area percentage data are constrained by two restriction conditions as follows:

$$\sum_{i=1}^{m} s_i = 1, \quad 0 < s_i < 1 \tag{4.14}$$

$$\sum_{i=1}^{m} S_i = \Omega \tag{4.15}$$

where Ω is constant and represents the area of the grid pixel.

Three main problems must be solved before regression analysis can be conducted using area percentage data. One problem is that the range of values of area percentage data should be located in the interior (between 0 and 1). However, one or several elements usually exist that have values equal to zero. Another problem is that the existence of perfect multicollinearity among variables of area percentage data indicates that the ordinary least squares method is invalid. The final problem is that the regression model must account for the restriction conditions, Eqs. (4.14) and (4.15). We have designed a scheme to overcome these three problems using methods of zero suppression handling and symmetric log-ratio transformation.

Theoretically, it is impossible for the area of some land use types to equal zero if areas are counted at a high enough resolution, that is, areas of some types of land use categories are too small to be detected (Bacon-Shone, 2003). Thus, if the area of one land use category is equal to zero, the area of this type of land use category is assigned a minimal value. Consequently, the sample vector is in the following form

$$\left(s_1',\ s_2',\ \cdots,\ s_p'\right)^T \in [0,\ 1]^p \tag{4.16}$$

where s'_j is the area proportion of the jth land use category in the total area of grid pixels. If $s'_j = 0$, it is assigned a new minimal value $s'_j = \varepsilon$ and $y_i = s'_j \Big/ \sum\limits_{i=1}^{p} s'_i$. The grid area percentage data are then obtained for land use categories:

$$Y = \left\{ (y_1, y_2, \cdots, y_p)^T \in R^p \middle| \sum_{j=1}^{p} y_j = 1,\ 0 < y_j < 1 \right\} \tag{4.17}$$

where y_j is the area proportion of the jth land use category in the total area of grid pixels.

Symmetric log-ratio transformation is conducted after the grid percentage data are treated to stretch the values of area percentage data from (0, 1) to $(-\infty, +\infty)$ (4.18).

$$Z = (z_1, z_2, \cdots, z_p)^T, \quad z_j = \ln\left(y_j \Big/ \sqrt[p]{\prod_{i=1}^{p} y_i} \right), \quad j = 1, 2, \cdots, p \tag{4.18}$$

where $z_j \in (-\infty, +\infty)$. Let $s_j = z_j - z_p$, $j = 1, 2, \cdots, p-1$, and through the inverse transformation we can get Eq. (4.19).

$$y_j = \frac{e^{s_j}}{1 + \sum\limits_{i=1}^{p-1} e^{s_i}}, \quad y_p = \frac{1}{1 + \sum\limits_{i=1}^{p-1} e^{s_i}}, \quad j = 1, 2, \cdots, p-1 \tag{4.19}$$

Symmetric log-ratio transformation not only solves the essential zero problem and the problem of constrained total land area, but also linearizes the non-linear relationships between land use patterns and their driving factors. In addition, the transformation retains the symmetry of the original percentage data, and the newly generated variables can be used directly to explore characteristics of the percentage data, making estimation results easily explainable (Paustian et al., 1997; Wang et al., 2008).

4.1.7.2 Partial Least Squares Analysis

Multicollinearity among variables in regression analysis is a problem that must be addressed, as is analysis of driving mechanisms of land use pattern changes. Since its discovery in the 1930s by Frisch (1934), multicollinearity has received increasing attention. Multicollinearity among independent variables always causes deviations of regression estimates, preventing accurate and robust estimations of the coefficients. Without exception, analysis of driving mechanisms of land use patterns faces the same problem. Wold et al. (1983) proposed partial least squares (PLS) regression to tackle the problem. This approach, based on factor analysis, maximizes the covariance between the predicted matrix and the independent matrix composed of factors in the reductive space.

Suppose $X = (X_1, X_2, \cdots, X_q)^T$ is the independent vector variable, and $Z = (Z_1, Z_2, \cdots, Z_q)^T$ is the dependent vector variable. The standardized observed data matrixes of the dependent and independent vector variables after log-ratio transformation are respectively as follows:

$$Z_0 = \begin{bmatrix} z_{11} & \cdots & z_{1p} \\ z_{21} & \cdots & z_{2p} \\ \vdots & & \vdots \\ z_{n1} & \cdots & z_{np} \end{bmatrix}, \quad X_0 = \begin{bmatrix} x_{11} & \cdots & x_{1q} \\ x_{21} & \cdots & x_{2q} \\ \vdots & & \vdots \\ x_{n1} & \cdots & x_{nq} \end{bmatrix} \tag{4.20}$$

The first pair of PLS components

The first pair of components is defined as U_1 and V_1, where U_1 is a linear combination of the independent vector variable X:

$$U_1 = \omega_{11}X_1 + \cdots + \omega_{1q}X_q = \omega_1^T X \tag{4.21}$$

and V_1 is a linear combination of the independent vector variable Z:

$$V_1 = \upsilon_{11}Z_1 + \cdots + \upsilon_{1p}Z_p = \upsilon_1^T Z \tag{4.22}$$

The score-vector of the first pair of components U_1 and V_1 can be calculated and denoted as u_1 and v_1, respectively.

$$u_1 = X_0\omega_1 = \begin{bmatrix} x_{11} & \cdots & x_{1q} \\ x_{21} & \cdots & x_{2q} \\ \vdots & & \vdots \\ x_{n1} & \cdots & x_{nq} \end{bmatrix} \begin{bmatrix} \omega_{11} \\ \omega_{12} \\ \vdots \\ \omega_{1q} \end{bmatrix} = \begin{bmatrix} u_{11} \\ u_{21} \\ \vdots \\ u_{n1} \end{bmatrix} \tag{4.23}$$

$$\nu_1 = Z_0\upsilon_1 = \begin{bmatrix} z_{11} & \cdots & z_{1p} \\ z_{21} & \cdots & z_{2p} \\ \vdots & & \vdots \\ z_{n1} & \cdots & z_{np} \end{bmatrix} \begin{bmatrix} \upsilon_{11} \\ \upsilon_{12} \\ \vdots \\ \upsilon_{1p} \end{bmatrix} = \begin{bmatrix} \nu_{11} \\ \nu_{21} \\ \vdots \\ \nu_{n1} \end{bmatrix} \tag{4.24}$$

The covariance of the first pair of components U_1 and V_1 can be calculated by the inner-product of the score-vectors u_1 and ν_1. Thus the constrained extremum problem, Eq. (4.25), is used to calculate the unit vectors ω_1 and υ_1, which satisfy the qualification that: (i) the first pair of PLS components U_1 and V_1 extracts as much information from the standard observed data matrix as possible; and (ii) the covariate between U_1 and V_1 receives a maximum value.

$$\begin{cases} \max\{\langle u_1,\ v_1\rangle\} = \max\left\{\omega_1^T X_0^T Z_0 \upsilon_1\right\} \\ \omega_1^T\omega_1 = \|\omega_1\|^2 = 1,\ \upsilon_1^T\upsilon_1 = \|\upsilon_1\|^2 = 1 \end{cases} \tag{4.25}$$

The constrained extremum problem is solved by calculating the eigenvalue and its corresponding eigenvector of the matrix $Q = X_0^T Z_0 Z_0^T X_0$. The eigenvector of maximum eigenvalue $(\omega_1^T X_0^T Z_0 \upsilon_1)^2$ is the solution of vector ω_1. Vector υ_1 is calculated using Eq. (4.26).

$$\upsilon_1 = \frac{1}{\omega_1^T X_0^T Z_0 \upsilon_1} Z_0^T X_0 \omega_1 \tag{4.26}$$

Regression equations based on the first pair of PLS components

Suppose the regression model with independent variable U_1 and dependent variables X_0 and Z_0 is defined as follows:

$$\begin{cases} X_0 = u_1 \alpha_1^T + S_1 \\ Z_0 = u_1 \beta_1^T + T_1 \end{cases} \tag{4.27}$$

where u_1 is the nth dimension score vector of U_1; $\alpha_1^T = (\alpha_{11}, \alpha_{12}, \cdots, \alpha_{1q})$, and $\beta_1^T = (\beta_{11}, \beta_{12}, \cdots, \beta_{1q})$ are the parameter vectors of the regression model; S_1 and T_1 are the residual matrices. Therefore, the least squares estimates of the regression coefficient vectors α_1 and β_1 are calculated according to Eq. (4.28).

$$\begin{cases} \alpha_1^T = \left(u_1^T u_1\right)^{-1} u_1^T X_0 \\ \beta_1^T = \left(u_1^T u_1\right)^{-1} u_1^T Z_0 \end{cases} \tag{4.28}$$

Final regression equation

Let $X_0' = u_1 \alpha_1^T$ and $Z_0' = u_1 \beta_1^T$, then the residual matrices are illustrated as $S_1 = X_0 - X_0'$ and $T_1 = Z_0 - Z_0'$. Replacing the standard observed data matrices X_0 and Z_0 with S_1 and T_1, respectively, and repeating the above mathematical operation, the weights of the second pair of PLS components, S_2 and T_2, are obtained:

$$\omega_2 = (\omega_{21}, \ \cdots, \ \omega_{2q})^T, \quad \upsilon_2 = (\upsilon_{21}, \ \cdots, \ \upsilon_{2p})^T \tag{4.29}$$

Then, $\upsilon_2 = T_1 \upsilon_2$ and $u_2 = S_1 \omega_2$ are the score vectors of the second pair of components S_2 and T_2, respectively, and can be calculated. The load capacity of the second pair of PLS components can be calculated with Eq. (4.30).

$$\begin{cases} \alpha_2^T = \left(u_2^T u_2\right)^{-1} u_2^T S_1 \\ \beta_2^T = \left(u_2^T u_2\right)^{-1} u_2^T T_1 \end{cases} \tag{4.30}$$

The generic form of the area percentage data model can then be written as Eq. (4.31)

$$\begin{cases} X_0 = u_1 \alpha_1^T + u_2 \alpha_2^T + S_2 \\ Z_0 = u_1 \beta_1^T + u_2 \beta_2^T + T_2 \end{cases} \tag{4.31}$$

Suppose the rank of data matrix $n \times q$ of X_0 is r, which satisfies $r \leqslant \min(n-1, q)$. The r components and the standardized observation data matrices X_0 and Z_0, can be obtained and further disassembled as shown in Eq. (4.32).

$$\begin{cases} X_0 = u_1\alpha_1^T + \cdots + u_r\alpha_r^T + S_r \\ Z_0 = u_1\beta_1^T + \cdots + u_r\beta_r^T + T_r \end{cases} \tag{4.32}$$

Given that $X_i^*(i = 1, 2, \cdots, q)$ and Z_j^* $(j = 1, 2, \cdots, p)$ are the standardized variables, the values of U_k and Z_j^* can easily be obtained according to Eqs. (4.33) and (4.34).

$$U_k = \omega_{k1}X_1^* + \cdots + \omega_{kq}X_q^* \,, \quad k = 1, \cdots, r \tag{4.33}$$

$$Z_j^* = \beta_{1j}U_1 + \beta_{2j}U_2 + \cdots + \beta_{rj}U_r \,, \quad j = 1, \cdots, p \tag{4.34}$$

After substituting Eq. (4.33) into Eq. (4.34), the PLS regression equation, Eq. (4.35), is obtained.

$$\hat{Z}_j^* = a_{j1}^*X_1^* + \cdots + a_{jq}^*X_q^* \,, \quad j = 1, \cdots, p \tag{4.35}$$

The PLS regression model of original variables, which are included in Eq. (4.36), can be generated by replacing the standardized variables X_i^* and Z_j^* with the original variables X_i and Z_j in Eq. (4.34).

$$\hat{Z}_j = a_{j0} + a_{j1}X_1 + \cdots + a_{jq}X_q \,, \quad j = 1, \cdots, p \tag{4.36}$$

The PLS regression model can also be verified to follow restriction conditions, Eqs. (4.14) and (4.15), and Eq. (4.37) should always hold for any $i = 0, 1, 2, \cdots, q$

$$\sum_j^p a_{ji} = 0 \tag{4.37}$$

Determining of the number of PLS components

Generally, it is not always necessary to obtain all PLS components, which is time consuming when establishing the PLS regression model. The first several PLS components are always enough to explain the regression model. Approaches including leave-one-out, batch-wise cross-validation, split-sample cross-validation and random sample cross-validation are widely used to ascertain the number of obtained components. These methods differ from each other in cross-validation datasets.

The leave-one-out approach leaves ith $(i = 1, 2, \cdots, n)$ observations as the validation data, and the remaining $n-1$ observations are used to build the PLS regression model.

The batch-wise cross-validation approach follows the same strategy as the leave-one-out approach, except that it uses a sequence of j ordinal observations as the validation dataset. When $j = 1$, the batch-wise cross-validation approach is retrogressed to the leave-one-out approach.

The split-sample cross-validation approach follows the same strategy as the batch-wise cross-validation approach, except that it does not strictly require the observation to be set in an ordinal sequence but is separated by a certain span in the original observation sequence.

In the random sample cross-validation approach, the validation data are randomly chosen.

The estimation result $z'_{j(i)}(k)(i \in I)$ of observation $Z_j(j = 1, 2, \cdots, p)$ can be obtained when the cross-validation dataset $I \subset$ is included in the PLS regression equation with k components. Regarding I, after repeating the above operations, the predictive residual error sum of square of the jth independent variable $Z_j(j = 1, 2, \cdots, p)$ can be calculated using Eq. (4.38) when the kth components have been extracted.

$$PRESS_j(k) = \sum_{I \subset \{1, \cdots, n\}} \sum_{i \in I} \left(z_{ij} - \hat{z}_{j(i)}(k)\right)^2 \tag{4.38}$$

Furthermore, the predicted residual error sum of square of $Z = (Z_1, Z_2, \cdots, Z_p)^T$ is calculated from Eq. (4.39).

$$PRESS(k) = \sum_{j=1}^{p} PRESS_j(k) \tag{4.39}$$

The k that minimizes the predicted residual error sum of square of Z is the number of components to obtain.

4.1.7.3 Neighborhood Effect

Neighborhood enrichment reflects the relative enrichment of one certain land use type in neighbor grids, which can be calculated with the following formula:

$$F_{i,k,d} = \frac{P_{i,k,d}}{P_k} \tag{4.40}$$

where $F_{i,k,d}$ represents the neighborhood enrichment factors; i is the grid number; k is the number of land use types; d stands for the radius of the neighborhood, which is determined with prior knowledge; $P_{i,k,d} = n_{i,k,d}/n_{i,d}$ is the percent of the grid number of the kth land use type in the total grid number in the neighborhood of grid i; $P_k = N_k/N$ is the percent of the grid number of the kth land use type in the total grid number of the study area; $n_{i,k,d}$ is the grid number of the kth land use type in the neighborhood of grid i; $n_{i,d}$ represents the total grid number in the neighborhood of grid i; N_k is the total grid number of the kth land use type in the whole study area; and N is the total grid number in the region

When $F_{i,k,d} = 1$, $F_{i,k,d} < 1$ and $F_{i,k,d} > 1$, the grid enrichment of the kth land use type in the neighborhood with a radius of d of grid i is equal to, or smaller than or larger than that of the whole region, respectively.

Average neighborhood enrichment is an indicator that quantitatively represents the mutual promotion or inhibition effects of different land use types in different neighborhood ranges and is calculated with the following formula:

$$G_{l,k,d} = \frac{1}{N_l} \sum_{i \in l} F_{i,k,d} \tag{4.41}$$

where $G_{l,k,d}$ indicates the average neighborhood enrichment of the lth and kth land use type; N_l is the total grid number of the lth land use type in this region; $i \in l$ indicates the grids that belong to the range of the lth land use type; and $\sum F_{i,k,d}$ represents the sum of neighborhood enrichment of the kth land use type within the domain of the lth land use type. When $G_{l,k,d} > 1$, there are mutual promotion effects in the spatially statistical sense between the lth and kth land use types within the neighborhood with a radius of d, indicating the presences of inhibition effects. The interaction between two land use types in different neighborhood ranges can be quantitatively analyzed by regulating the neighborhood radius d and calculating the average neighborhood enrichment of the lth and kth land use types in different neighborhood ranges.

4.1.8 Spatial Allocation of the Changing Area of Land Uses

4.1.8.1 Decision Rules

In the process of spatially allocating changes in land use area, it is necessary for the DLS model to set certain decision rules for the various land use types with different degrees of stability to restrict the actions of land use change in the model according to historical changes in various land use types and land use planning. If historical data and future land use planning indicate that a certain land use type is prone to converting to another land use type, it is set to be easily converted to other land uses; otherwise, it can be set to relatively stable or hard to be converted to other land uses. Spatial allocation of changes in land use area simulates the actual stability of various land use types by assigning proper values to the stability parameters, which constitute the following stability parameter matrix.

$$A = \begin{pmatrix} a_{11} & a_{12} & \cdots & a_{1i} & \cdots & a_{1p} \\ a_{21} & a_{22} & \cdots & a_{2i} & \cdots & a_{2p} \\ \vdots & \vdots & & \vdots & & \vdots \\ a_{j1} & a_{j2} & \cdots & a_{ji} & \cdots & a_{jp} \\ \vdots & \vdots & & \vdots & & \vdots \\ a_{p1} & a_{p2} & \cdots & a_{pi} & \cdots & a_{pp} \end{pmatrix} \tag{4.42}$$

where a_{ji} is the stability parameter of conversion of land use type j to land use type i; a_{ii} is the stability parameter of the area of land use type i that remains unchanged. Three conditions are usually met when values are assigned to stability parameters. First, for the conversion of one land type to another that has been historically stable and unrelated to land planning, the corresponding stability parameter in the model is assigned to 1. Second, for land use types that are prone to conversion, the corresponding stability parameters in the model are assigned to 0. Third, for most land use types, the possibility of conversion is between the two extremes, and the stability parameters in the model are assigned values between 0 and 1. The larger the stability parameter, the more stable the corresponding land use type and the lower the possibility of mutual conversion. In addition, it is necessary to further verify and regulate the process of checking the model because the configuration of stability parameters in the model mainly depends on experts' experience and researchers' understanding of actual conditions of the study area.

In the process of spatially allocating changes in land use area, the stability of certain land use types defined with stability parameters in the model is restricted by two aspects, i.e., when one land use type is not prone to convert to other land use types and when other land use types are not prone to convert to this land use type. Many uncertainties exist in land use change. In fact, in model simulations, it may be very difficult or impossible for land use change to occur in a certain direction, but conversion in the reverse direction may be very common (Deng et al., 2008). For example, it is costly and uncommon to convert water areas to cultivated land, but in southern China, where the demand for aquatic produce is high and the price continues to rise, many paddy fields are converted into fish or shrimp ponds. Under these conditions, the spatial allocation of changing land use area defines the decision rules of these conversions by constructing the land use conversion rule matrix.

4.1.8.2 Allocation Steps

The input parameters used in the module for spatially allocating changes in land use area reflect local, regional and historical characteristics of the pattern changes in regional land uses (Fig. 4.2). Specific steps are shown in the following figure.

The spatial allocation module of land use first calculates the number of grids to allocate according to the conversion rules set for each pixel and the land areas to be allocated over space. It then calculates the allocation probability L_{ik} of different land use types for the grid to allocate. Finally, it allocates the land use pattern with the obtained allocation probability L_{ik} and obtains the change rules for the regional land use pattern.

Generally, the allocation probability of different land use types L_{ik} is determined based on the following three situations:

(i) If a certain land use type existed in the previous simulation year, and its stability is less than 1, the spatial allocation module will calculate the distribution probability, sum of the compensation factor and stability factor,

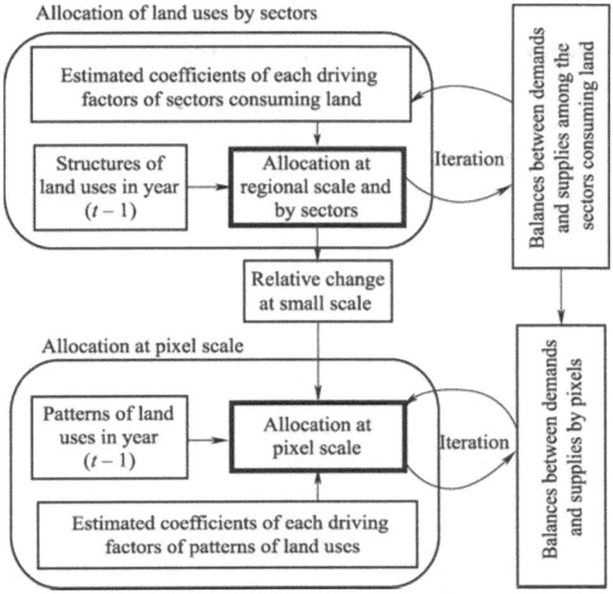

Fig. 4.2 Steps of spatial allocation of area change in land use in the DLS model.

which are used as the allocation probability:

$$L_{i,k} = P_{i,k} + C_k + S_k \tag{4.43}$$

where L_{ik} is the allocation probability of the kth land use type in grid i; P_{ik} is the distribution probability of the kth land use type in grid i; C_k and S_k are the compensation and stability factors, respectively.

(ii) When the compensation factor C_k is nearly 0, L_{ik} consists of the distribution probability P_{ik} and stability factor S_k as follows:

$$L_{i,k} = P_{i,k} + S_k \tag{4.44}$$

(iii) Within each spatial allocation step, the DLS model excludes those pixels with a decreasing trend for a certain kind of land use type from obtaining new areas of that kind of land use type. If the spatial allocation module does not allow the configuration of stability, then the land use type with the largest L_{ik} is allocated to the grids without enough area of land use types (Fig. 4.3).

When the area of the study site is small and the geophysical conditions are relatively consistent, the area change can be directly allocated with the method mentioned above. Conversely, if the area of the study site is large and there is significant spatial difference in regional geophysical conditions, it is more feasible to first zone and then allocate the area change based on the spatial distribution of geophysical conditions (Gao and Deng, 2002; Deng et al., 2008).

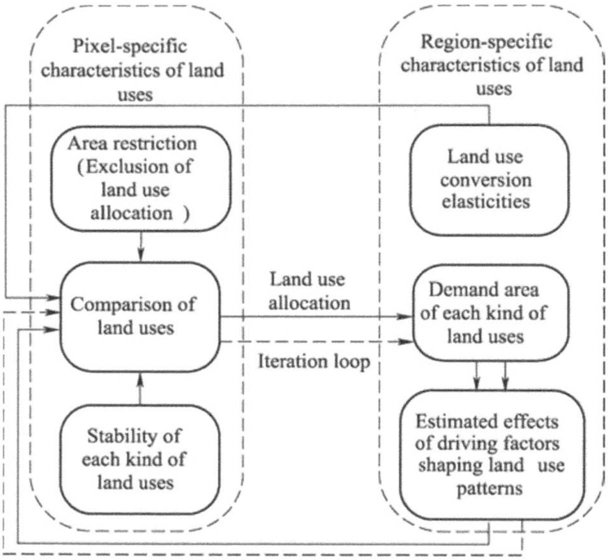

Fig. 4.3 Schematic representation of the spatial allocation of land use changes at the regional and pixel scales.

In summary, the DLS model is an effective tool to identify various factors that influence the distribution of regional land use types, reveal driving mechanisms of land use pattern changes and reflect the pattern changes in land uses in grids at certain scales.

4.2 DLS Installation and Configuration

Installation and configuration of DLS software are two main steps before development of the DLS model.

4.2.1 DLS Installation

DLS Software is a software tool for the dynamic simulation of the land use pattern which was developed based on the DLS model. The latest version of DLS was released in 2007. It has developed into a program package that can be installed independently. DLS in version 2007 can be used in Microsoft Windows and was developed for Windows XP Professional. However, the software has passed testing in Windows 9x, Me, 2000/NT, 2003 Server and XP Home environments.

In the Windows operating system, insert the installation program CD in the CD-ROM, click "DLS MODEL setup program" in the root directory, enter the installation directory, double-click the installation file "Setup.exe" and then enter the installation interface. Follow the instructions to complete the installation.

4.2.2 Configuring the DLS Operating Environment

After installation, the DLS model interface (Fig. 4.4) can be opened by clicking "Start" → "All Programs" → "DLS MODEL." The DLS user interface is user friendly, and the user can directly configure the model operating environment and input the parameters and variables in the main interface.

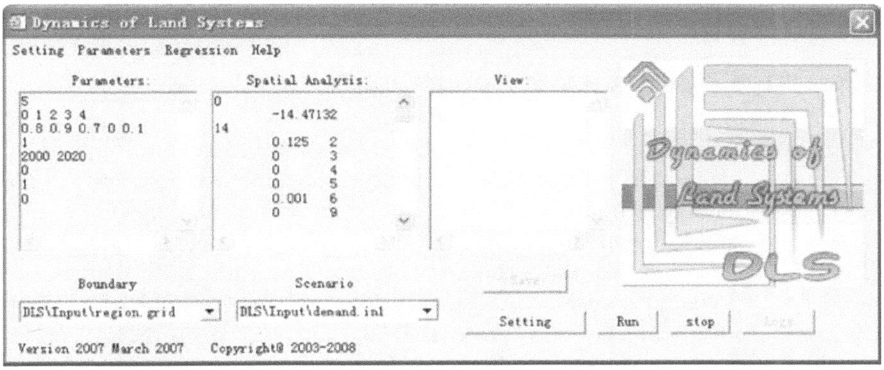

Fig. 4.4 User interface of DLS.

The operating system can be configured either in the Settings pull-down menu or the Settings button in the main interface. After starting the DLS model, set the file allocation running path and the name of the control file (Fig. 4.5). Select the control file allocation input parameters, the storage path of the output results and the names of the restricted zone data and those of land demand scenario data (Fig. 4.6).

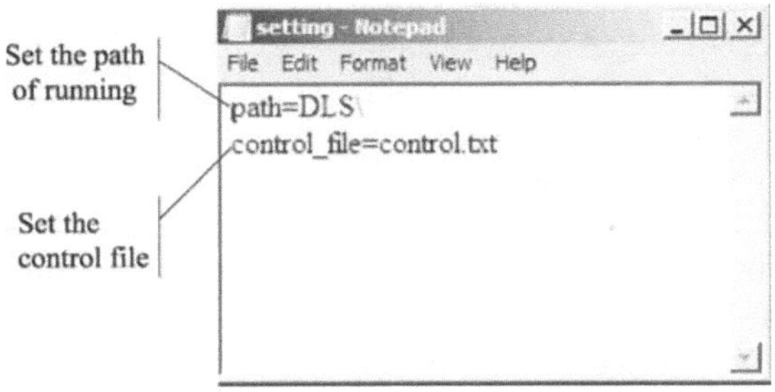

Fig. 4.5 Setting of running environment of DLS.

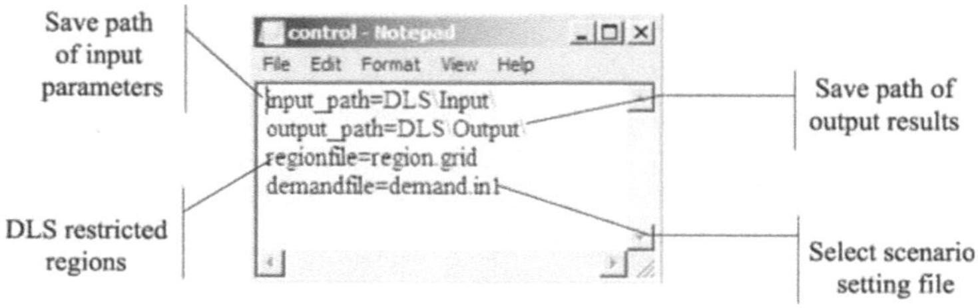

Fig. 4.6 Configurations of input and output parameters for running the DLS model.

If DLS is installed in the Linux operating system, it is necessary to use "/" when setting the file path, while "\" is used in a Windows system. All configuration files are saved in the file folder in the installation directory.

4.3 DLS Input Parameter Preparation

Six kinds of parameters are needed for DLS, i.e., simulation condition setting parameters, driving factor data, spatial analysis parameters, restricted region code, land demand scenario data and binary data of land types. The main DLS interface is convenient for the user to input and change the parameters (Fig 4.5). Meanwhile, to make the DLS program automatically read the related files, the user can use an ASCII data file prepared in another software environment and directly copy it to the DLS installation directory or the simulation directory set by the user.

4.3.1 Simulation Condition Setting Parameters

Parameters in the "Parameters" window at the far left can be edited through the "Input" menu under the "Parameters" menu. Once the user begins to edit the parameters, the "Parameters" window will change from a grey inactive window to an active window where the user can edit the parameters. After editing parameters, the user can store changes in the parameters in the simulated pattern changes in land uses by clicking the "Save" button.

Parameters in the "Parameters" window, which the user can also edit with Notepad software or a text editor, are included in the "main.1" file under the installation directory "DLS\Input." The user can also create a new file in Notepad software or a text editor, save it as a file in "main.1" format and put it under the installation directory "DLS\Input." The main parameters are included in the following figure (Fig. 4.7).

Line 1: Number of land use types;

Line 2: Land use type codes, starting from 0;

Line 3: Decision rules corresponding with the land use type;

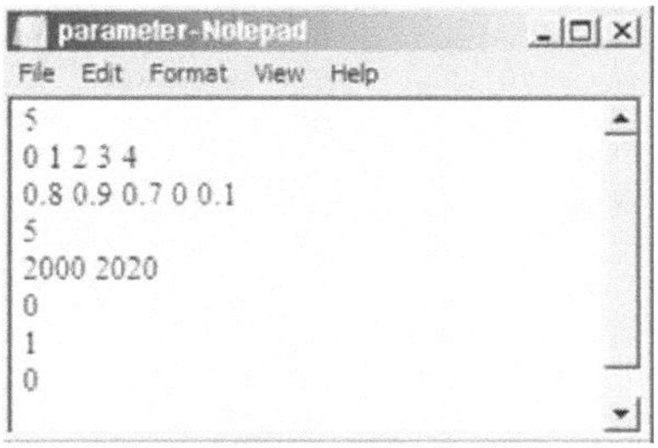

Fig. 4.7 Compilation of main file for running DLS.

Line 4: Condition for convergence: the permissible error when the land demand changes and actual allocated land converge;

Line 5: Initial and ending year of simulation;

Line 6: Number of driving factors for the distribution of land use types;

Line 7: Record format mark of the main file: 1 indicates that the ArcView header file will be exported in the output file; 0 indicates that it will not.

4.3.2 Spatial Analysis Parameters

The main component of the user interface is the Spatial Analysis window, which contains regression equations of different land use types and driving factors. The user can edit this file by clicking "Modify" under the "Regression" menu. Another option is to open and modify the "allocl.reg" file under the installation directory "DLS\Input."

The regression coefficients between different land types and driving factors are calculated with the following steps.

(i) Resample the GRID data of land types and driving factors at a certain spatial scale with the "SAMPLE" order in the Arc module of ArcGIS software. Save the result in a text file, the first line of which records the variable names of the corresponding land type and driving factors (Fig. 4.8).

(ii) Calculate the coefficients of determination between the land type and driving factors with statistical software capable of logistic regression analysis (e.g., SPSS software) and ENMLUP with the following procedures: open the logistic regression dialog box from the menu Analyze → Regression → Binary Logistic. Select the independent variables and related parameters, and perform the calculation to obtain the regression coefficients between the land type and driving factors (Table 4.1). Estimate the correlation between the land types and driving factors according to "S.E.". An S.E. larger than 0.2 indicates that the correlation is not strong, and the coefficient of determination can be deleted.

(iii) Delete the parameters with weak correlation, and create a file named "allocl.reg" in the following format shown in Fig. 4.9. Save it under the installation directory "DLS\Input."

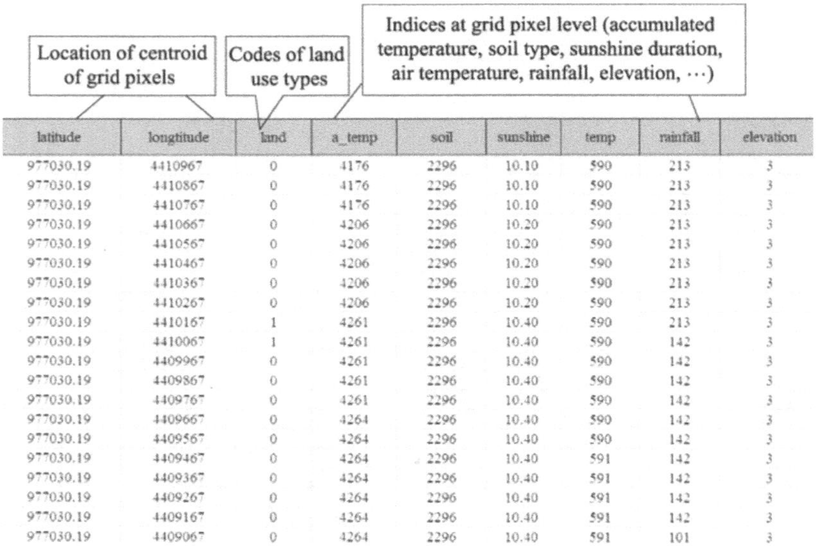

latitude	longtitude	land	a_temp	soil	sunshine	temp	rainfall	elevation
977030.19	4410967	0	4176	2296	10.10	590	213	3
977030.19	4410867	0	4176	2296	10.10	590	213	3
977030.19	4410767	0	4176	2296	10.10	590	213	3
977030.19	4410667	0	4206	2296	10.20	590	213	3
977030.19	4410567	0	4206	2296	10.20	590	213	3
977030.19	4410467	0	4206	2296	10.20	590	213	3
977030.19	4410367	0	4206	2296	10.20	590	213	3
977030.19	4410267	0	4206	2296	10.20	590	213	3
977030.19	4410167	1	4261	2296	10.40	590	213	3
977030.19	4410067	1	4261	2296	10.40	590	142	3
977030.19	4409967	0	4261	2296	10.40	590	142	3
977030.19	4409867	0	4261	2296	10.40	590	142	3
977030.19	4409767	0	4261	2296	10.40	590	142	3
977030.19	4409667	0	4264	2296	10.40	590	142	3
977030.19	4409567	0	4264	2296	10.40	590	142	3
977030.19	4409467	0	4264	2296	10.40	591	142	3
977030.19	4409367	0	4264	2296	10.40	591	142	3
977030.19	4409267	0	4264	2296	10.40	591	142	3
977030.19	4409167	0	4264	2296	10.40	591	142	3
977030.19	4409067	0	4264	2296	10.40	591	101	3

Fig. 4.8 Snapshot of the variables used by the DLS model to estimate the land use conversion elasticity.

Table 4.1 Output results of the ENMLUP estimation

	Variables in the equation						
		B	S.E.	Wald	df	Sig.	Exp(B)
Step 1[a]	*Ctemp*	.002	.001	3.860	1	.049	1.002
	Erosion	−.009	.007	1.493	1	.222	.992
	shining_hr	−1.052	.336	9.801	1	.002	.349
	Temp	.046	.002	704.854	1	.000	1.047
	Rainfall	−.018	.000	3.047E3	1	.000	.982
	Elevation	.758	.017	2.041E3	1	.000	2.134
	Loam	−.464	.018	653.227	1	.000	.629
	Splain	−.003	.000	3.360E3	1	.000	.997
	d2expway	.005	.009	.232	1	.630	1.005
	Landform	.009	.001	72.306	1	.000	1.009
	Organic	−1.763	.029	3.799E3	1	.000	.172
	d2hwy	.081	.005	295.466	1	.000	1.084
	d2pvcap	−.046	.008	36.404	1	.000	.955
	d2pvway	.188	.013	222.260	1	.000	1.207
	d2road	.019	.006	10.530	1	.001	1.019
	Popdensity	.064	.008	66.277	1	.000	1.066
	GDP	−.001	.000	479.715	1	.000	.999
	Constant	−31.984	14.830	4.651	1	.031	.000

a. Variable(s) entered in step 1: *ctemp, erosion, shining_hr, temp, rainfall, elevation, loam, splain, d2expway, landform, organic, d2hwy, d2pvcap, d2pvway, d2road, popdensity, GDP.*

Line 1: Codes of each land type;

Line 2: Constant of spatial regression results of each land type;

Line 3: Number of driving factors for the distribution of land types;

Line 4 (and subsequent lines): Codes of the regression coefficients and driving factors.

The next land types after the regression coefficients of one land type are listed, and the regression coefficients of all land types that need to be calculated will be listed in this file.

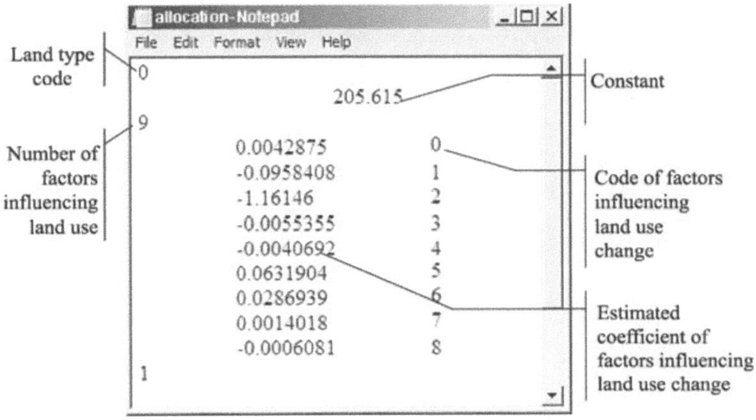

Fig. 4.9 Formatted parameters exported from the ENMLUP estimation.

4.3.3 Driving Factor Data

Driving factor data are saved in the files under the installation directory "DLS\Input." All factors that affect the distribution of land types such as natural variables, socioeconomic variables and policies are prepared with ArcGIS software according to characteristics of each variable. All data are disaggregated onto the spatial unit with a certain spatial resolution, and the final dataset is saved as ASCII data in "sclgr*.grd" format. The "*" in different driving force file names is replaced with a number corresponding to the code numbers of the impact factors. The process of transforming the data in ArcView and ArcGIS software is as follows. (i) Transform the GRID data into text data with the File → Export Data Source tool; (ii) Select the output data format; as the output data are GRID data, the ASCII Raster format is selected; (iii) Select the GRID data file that needs to be output from the storage directory of the GRID data; (iv) Choose the save file path, input the name of the output text data and save the text file in the selected path.

4.3.4 Land Demand Scenario Data

The land demand scenario data are saved under the installation directory "DLS\Input." The land demand scenario file is named in the "demand.*" format the corresponding selection list of which is displayed in the "Scenario Design" pull-down menu in the main interface. This can be opened and edited with a text editor such as Notepad, and each line of this file records the demand of different land types in the simulation period (Fig. 4.10).

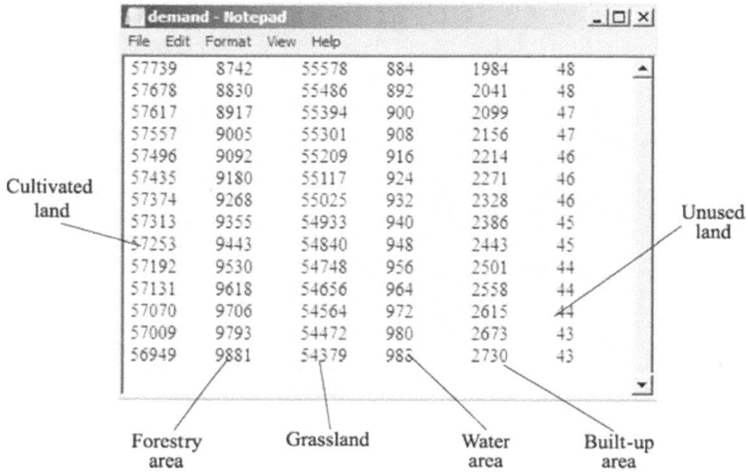

57739	8742	55578	884	1984	48
57678	8830	55486	892	2041	48
57617	8917	55394	900	2099	47
57557	9005	55301	908	2156	47
57496	9092	55209	916	2214	46
57435	9180	55117	924	2271	46
57374	9268	55025	932	2328	46
57313	9355	54933	940	2386	45
57253	9443	54840	948	2443	45
57192	9530	54748	956	2501	44
57131	9618	54656	964	2558	44
57070	9706	54564	972	2615	44
57009	9793	54472	980	2673	43
56949	9881	54379	988	2730	43

Fig. 4.10 Scenario-based land demands for running DLS.

The land demand scenario data are prepared as follows: estimate the rate of change for each land type according to land use planning data for the subsequent 20 years and statistical data of land types of recent years. Then calculate the land type data of each year with a rate of change with $N_{i+1} = N_i^*(1+b)$.

The area sum of all land types should be equal to the regional total area prior to performing the calculation. Thus, it is necessary to make adjustments according to the regional total area and land use pattern.

4.3.5 Restricted Region Code Data

The restricted region files under the installation directory "DLS\Input" are named in the "regi*.*" format, and their names appear in the region selection box "Area restriction." The GRID files included in the restricted region files are in a rectangular format; only these active grids located in non-restricted areas can participate in simulations of land use changes, where the value "0" stands for the active grid and "−9999" null and "−9998" stand for restricted regions (Fig. 4.11). The sort order of values in this file corresponds with that of the actual grids. Preparation of the restricted region code data are similar to that of the driver data, which can be realized by saving the GRID data as a text file with the Export Data tool.

```
__++__ simulation for year    1 __+__
   0    205.6150     9
   1   -116.2159     9
   2   -36.26043     9
   3    85.94983     9
   4    153.8026     8

demand direction for cove 0 is -1; demand:32568.7
demand direction for cove 1 is 1; demand:120236.
demand direction for cove 2 is 1; demand:21463.6
demand direction for cove 3 is 1; demand:19147.6
demand direction for cove 4 is -1; demand:28510.6

 1 ①40725.50 .............. ②0.5006190 .............. ③25.04491 .............. ④76.79225
 2   40717.50 ..............   0.5010777 ..............   25.02034 ..............   76.75047
 3   40701.50 ..............   0.5013463 ..............   24.97122 ..............   76.66692
 4   40681.50 ..............   0.5018201 ..............   24.90982 ..............   76.54158
 5   40673.50 ..............   0.5021290 ..............   24.88526 ..............   76.54158
 6   40665.50 ..............   0.5026180 ..............   24.86069 ..............   76.47891
 7   40665.50 ..............   0.5026758 ..............   24.86069 ..............   76.47891
 8   40665.50 ..............   0.5044107 ..............   24.86069 ..............   76.45803
 9   40637.50 ..............   0.5047202 ..............   24.77472 ..............   76.31180
10   40625.50 ..............   0.5051681 ..............   24.73788 ..............   76.20735
11   40629.50 ..............   0.5054268 ..............   24.75016 ..............   76.16558
12   40629.50 ..............   0.5056825 ..............   24.75016 ..............   76.16558
13   40353.52 ..............   0.5059981 ..............   23.90278 ..............   73.80512
14   40337.52 ..............   0.5070848 ..............   23.85365 ..............   73.63800
15   40317.52 ..............   0.5073349 ..............   23.79224 ..............   73.55444
16   40305.52 ..............   0.5081456 ..............   23.75540 ..............   73.47089
17   40289.53 ..............   0.5083910 ..............   23.70628 ..............   73.26199
18   40257.53 ..............   0.5086447 ..............   23.60803 ..............   73.05311
19   40249.53 ..............   0.5094516 ..............   23.58347 ..............   72.92777
20   40241.53 ..............   0.5097812 ..............   23.55891 ..............   72.90688
21   40233.53 ..............   0.5115739 ..............   23.53435 ..............   72.82333
```

Fig. 4.11 Representation of the null value, restricted and active grid pixels by evaluating −9999, −9998 and 0, respectively.

4.3.6 Land Use Type Data

Many methods can be used to prepare the land-type binary data. The method used in the Workstation program in the ArcGIS software environment will be introduced in Chapter 6. Another method with ArcView software is introduced as follows.

First, open the grid data for the land type and boundary. Select Analysis → Property to open the dialog box, and select the boundary grid data in Analysis Mask.

Then, open the dialog box through Analysis → Map Calculation, and input the calculation formula to extract the binary grid data with the land type codes 1, 2, 3, 4, 5 and 6, respectively.

Save the calculation results as follows: open Theme → Storage Data Set, select the storage path and input the storage file name.

Finally, transform the binary data into text data named in the "cov1_#.0" format, and then save it under the installation directory "DLS\Input."

4.4 DLS Operation and Results Output

The model must be reconfigured when it is used in a new region and the model results are saved in two formats according to the year.

4.4.1 DLS Operation

After reconfiguration, select the restricted region and scenario files and click the "Run" button. The model will run automatically, and the results will be listed one by one in the view window. These can be saved in the file "DLS\Output," and the running process will be saved in the "Log" file under the output directory, which includes not only the running information but also the iteration parameters listed in every step of the operation. All these parameters are listed in the operation steps. The implication of the codes annotated is as follows. (i) Number of iterations; (ii) Allocated quantity of each land use type; (iii) Iteration parameters of each land use type; (iv) Gaps between the demanded quantity and allocated quantity; (v) Maximum gaps between the demanded quantity and allocated quantity.

4.4.2 Results Output

The results of each land type are saved as an "*out1_#.*" file where "#" is the land type code and "*" is the year to calculate. The results of all land types every year are saved as "out all.*" files, in which a single value of each land type is saved. The new values of all grids are also saved in these result files, which can be read by ArcView GIS software. ArcView GIS reads data as follows. (i) If the seventh line of the "main.1" file is 1, the ArcView title will be output in the output file, which can be directly saved in ASCII-GRID format. This kind of data can be imported through File (Import Data Source) in ArcView GIS software; (ii) Run this module, and select the input data type in the pop-up window. Here the ASCII Raster data type is selected; (iii) Select the name of the layer to convert (a single land type or all land types); (iv) Input the name of the output data. The output data will be saved in the selected path. "Integer" format is selected as the type of output grid unit data, which can be directly opened in the active window.

4.5 Summary

The DLS model is a powerful tool for simulating the dynamics of land use changes. It comprehensively considers the control of external demand and influences of various neighborhood driving factors, emphasizes internal suitability, controls random disturbance factors, has specific decision rules and constructs multiple objective functions. Therefore, it is robust for simulating land use pattern changes in terms of both the expression of mechanisms and simulation effects (Deng et al., 2008; Zhan et al., 2007).

DLS is a software tool developed based on the DLS model for the dynamic simulation of the land use pattern changes. This chapter introduces the main procedures of DLS including installation, parameter configuration, running steps and results output. It can measure the influence of driving factors that are closely associated with changes in the land use pattern, including natural conditions, socioeconomic factors and even land use management policies. It can simulate the spatiotemporal process of pattern changes in land uses and export maps of pattern changes in land uses with high spatial and temporal resolution by setting conversion rules of land use types and designing change scenarios.

References

Aguiar A P D, Câmara G, Escada M I S, 2007. Spatial statistical analysis of land-use determinants in the Brazilian Amazonia: Exploring intra-regional heterogeneity. Ecological Modelling, 209(2–4): 169–188.

Bacon-Shone J. 2003. Modelling structural zeros in compositional data. In S. Thió-Henestrosa and Martín-Fernández J A (Eds.), Proceedings of CODAWORK'03, The First Compositional Data Analysis Workshop. Spain: University of Girona. pp. 15–17.

Burgi M and Turner M G. 2002. Factors and processes shaping land cover and land cover changes along the Wisconsin River. Ecosystems, 5(2): 184–201.

Burgi M, Hersperger A M, Schneeberger N. 2004. Driving forces of landscape change—Current and new directions, Landscape Ecology, 19, 857–868.

Chen Y Q. 2000. Multilscale spatial characterization of land use/land cover in China. Scientia Geographica Sinica, 20(3): 198–202.

Dai E, Wu S, Shi W, Cheung C K, Sharker A. 2005. Modeling change-pattern-value dynamics on land use: An integrated GIS and artificial neural networks approach. Environmental Management, 36(4): 576–591.

Deng X Z, Su H B, Zhan J Y. 2008. Integration of multiple data sources to simulate the Dynamics of Land Systems. Sensors, 8(2): 620–634.

Deng X Z, Jiang Q O, Lin Y Z, Han J Z. 2010a. Simulation of changes of soil organic carbon stock of cropland in China. Geographical Research, 29(1): 93–101 (in Chinese).

Deng X Z, Huang J K, Rozelle S, Uchida E. 2010b. Economic growth and the expansion of urban land in China. Urban Studies, 47(4): 813–843.

Ferrers N M. 1866. An Elementary Treatise on Trilinear Coordinates. London: Macmillan.

Frisch R. 1934. Statistical Confluence Analysis by Means of Complete Regression Systems. Oslo: Universitetets Okonomiske Institute.

Gao Z Q and Deng X Z. 2002. Analysis on spatial features of LUCC based on remote sensing and GIS in China. Chinese Geographical Science, 12(2): 107–113.

Gao Z Q, Liu J Y, Cao M K, Li K R, Tao B. 2005. Impacts of land-use and climate changes on ecosystem productivity and carbon cycle in the cropping-grazing transitional zone in China. Science in China Series D—Earth Sciences, 48(9): 1479–1491.

Ge Q S and Dai J H. 2005. Farming and forestry land use changes in China and their driving forces from 1900 to 1980. Science in China Series D—Earth Sciences, 48(10): 1747–1757.

Haberl H, Wackernagel M, Wrbka T. 2004. Land use and sustainability indicators. An introduction. Land Use Policy, 21(3): 193–198.

Lambin E F, Turner B L, Geist H J, Agbola S B, Angelsen A, Bruce J W, Coomes O T, Dirzo R, Fischer G, Folke C, George P S, Homewood K, Imbernon J, Leemans R, Li X, Moran E F, Mortimore M, Ramakrishnan P S, Richards J F, Skanes H, Steffen W, Stone G D, Svedin U, Veldkamp T A, Vogel C, Xu J. 2001. The causes of land-use and land-cover change: Moving beyond the myths. Global Environmental Change, 11(4): 261–269.

Lambin E F, Geist H J, Lepers E. 2003. Dynamics of land-use and land-cover change in tropical regions. Annual Review of Environment and Resources, 28: 205–241.

Li L, Zhang P Y, Hou W. 2005. Land use/cover change and driving forces in Southern Liaoning Province since 1950s. Chinese Geographical Science, 15(2): 131–136.

Liu J Y, Deng X Z, Liu M L, Zhang S W. 2002. Study on the spatial patterns of land-use change and analyses of driving forces in Northeastern China during 1990—2000. Chinese Geographical Science, 12(4): 299–308.

Liu X H, Wang J F, Liu M L, Meng B. 2005. Spatial heterogeneity of the driving forces of cropland change in China. Science in China Series D—Earth Sciences, 48(12): 2231–2240.

Paustian K, Levine E, Post W M, Ryzhova I M. 1997. The use of models to integrate information and understanding of soil C at the regional scale. Geoderma, 79(1–4): 227–260.

Pontius R G, Walker R, Yao-Kumah R, Arima E, Aldrich S, Caldas M, Vergara D. 2007. Accuracy assessment for a simulation model of Amazonian deforestation. Annals of the Association of American Geographers, 97(4): 677–695.

Shi P J, Gong P, Li X B, Chen J, Qi Y, Pan Y Z. 2000. Method and Practice of Study on Land Use/Land Cover Changes. Beijing: Science Press.

Tobler W. 1970. A computer movie simulating urban growth in the detroit region. Economic Geography, 46(2): 234–240.

Turner B L II. 1997. The sustainability principle in global agendas: Implications for understanding land-use/cover change. The Geographical Journal, 163(2): 133–140.

Turner B L II, Lambin E F, Reenberg A. 2007. The emergence of land change science for global environmental change and sustainability. Proceedings, National Academy of Sciences of the United States of America, 104(52): 20666–20671.

Veldkamp A and Lambin E F. 2001. Predicting land-use change. Agriculture Ecosystems and Environment, 85(1–3): 1–6.

Veldkamp A and Verburg P H. 2004. Modelling land use change and environmental impact. Journal of Environmental Management, 72(1–2): 1–3.

Verburg P H. 2006. Simulating feedbacks in land use and land cover change models. Landscape Ecology, 21(8): 1171–1183.

Verburg P H, Chen Y Q, Veldkamp T A. 2000. Spatial explorations of land use change and grain production in China. Agriculture Ecosystems and Environment, 82(1–3): 333–354.

Verburg P H, Soepboer W, Veldkamp A, Limpiada R, Espaldon V, Mastura S S A. 2002. Modeling the spatial dynamics of regional land use: The CLUE-S model. Environmental Management, 30(3): 391–405.

Wang S Y, Liu J S, Ma T B. 2010. Dynamics and changes in spatial patterns of land use in Yellow River Basin, China. Land Use Policy, 27(2): 313–323.

Wang X D, Zhong X G, Liu S Z, Li M H. 2008. A non-linear technique based on fractal method for describing gully-head changes associated with land-use in an arid environment in China. Catena, 72(1): 106–112.

Wold S, Albano C, Dunn W J III, Esbensen K, Hellberg S, Johansson E, Sjõstrõm M. 1983. Pattern recognition: Finding and using patterns in multivariate data. In: Martens H and Russwurm H Jr (Eds.), Food Research and Data Analysis. London: Applied Science Pub, pp. 147–188.

Zhan J Y, Deng X Z, Jiang Q O, Shi N N. 2007. The application of system dynamics and CLUE-S model in land use change dynamic simulation: A case study in Taips County, Inner Mongolia of China. Proceedings of the 2007 Conference on Systems Science, Management Science and System Dynamics: Sustainable Development and Complex Systems, 1–10: 2781–2789.

Zhang X Q, Ge Q S, Zheng J Y. 2003. Analysis of driving forces on the change of historical farmland use in Shandong Province during the Qing Dynasty (1644—1911). Chinese Geographical Science, 13(3): 207–215.

Chapter 5 Estimation System for Land Productivity and Its Applications

The land resource is a multifunctional natural resource, which is in continuously growing demand under a background of rapid population growth and fast economic development (Lin and Ho, 2003; Veldkamp and Verburg, 2004; Deng et al., 2006). This is especially the case in China, where the economy is developing rapidly and land use patterns are undergoing unprecedented change due to pressure from these demands (Ash and Edmonds, 1998; Liu et al., 2004). Structural change and pattern succession in land systems undoubtedly leads to changes in the suitability and quality of different kinds of land types and directly influences agricultural productivity (Fischer, 1998; Seto et al., 2000; Albersen et al., 2002; Deng et al., 2005; Deng et al., 2008). In the context of the debate "Who will feed China" and the global food safety crisis, the issue of loss of land resources has caused much concern in governmental and academic circles (Husle, 1993; Fan, 1997; Fisher et al., 2001). Consequently, the structural change in land systems and the change in land productivity resulting from land pattern succession have become a hotspot for academic research (Dumanski, 2000; Liu and Chen, 2000; Fischer and Sun, 2001; Foley et al., 2005; Deng et al., 2006).

The sustainable exploration and use of land resources are crucial to all levels of a government and land users, and the protection of land resources is related to current and future benefits for humans (DeFries et al., 2004; Deng, 2008a). Decision-makers and land users are often confronted with two challenges: (i) restore degraded cultivated land by improving the environment and soil fertility; and (ii) make full use of the land with appropriate planning to maintain land productivity, reduce soil erosion and prevent further degradation of land resources (Fischer, 1998). Only by developing a set of comprehensive methods to inform land use planning and management, can these two challenges be met. These methods are required to direct land use planning and solve the in-depth contradictions around land use to regulate the structure of land use and guarantee maximum benefit with the premise of sustainable development.

It is necessary to estimate the effects of land system change to maximize the use of the land. The DLS model provides an important way to predict scenarios for future land productivity (Deng et al., 2008). When combined with associated models, the DLS can analyze trends in land productivity under various hypotheses and provide decision-making information support for land use planning and land resource management.

5.1 Estimation System for Land Productivity

Land productivity generally refers to the overall productivity related to various combinations of the natural characteristics of the land and socioeconomic factors. Land productivity is determined by radiation, heat, water and soil, the biological characteristics of the crop, and input levels and management. These factors restrain and interact with each other and form a stepwise series of land productivity: photosynthetic productivity—thermal potential productivity—climate potential productivity—land potential productivity—land productivity (Deng et al., 2009).

5.1.1 Fundamental Principles

The Estimation System for Land Productivity (ESLP) is a collection of several applications, including land suitability assessment, and the evaluation of land productivity, and some advanced applications which use the stock of land resources as fundamental input information (Deng et al., 2009). The outputs from the ESLP include agro-ecological zoning maps, land suitability assessment maps, and attribute data such as cropping area and crop production. These outputs provide basic decision-making information for the assessment of land degradation, simulation of land productivity, assessment of land carrying capacity, and optimal allocation of regional land use (Deng, 2008b).

The agro-ecological zoning in the ESLP is concerned with features of soil, terrain and climate, with driving factors that influence crop growth such as climate, soil and reclamation intensity forming the basis for agro-ecological zones (Deng et al., 2009). The environment and conditions for crop growth are basically the same in a given agro-ecological zone and vary between agro-ecological zones. Land use information can be combined with ecological parameters and agro-ecological zones to form a complete database by superimposing land ownership, land use conditions, land suitability, the nutritional characteristics of host population and livestock, ground production facilities, and the cost of crops in the agro-ecological zones. This database can be used to estimate land productivity for each pixel (Fig. 5.1).

The core modules of the ESLP include the estimation of the cumulative amount of land resources, the determination of land use types and land use intensity, the demands of crop growth on climatic resources such as effective radiation, temperature and rainfall, and the assessment of land suitability which includes the maximum potential crop yield and limiting factors of

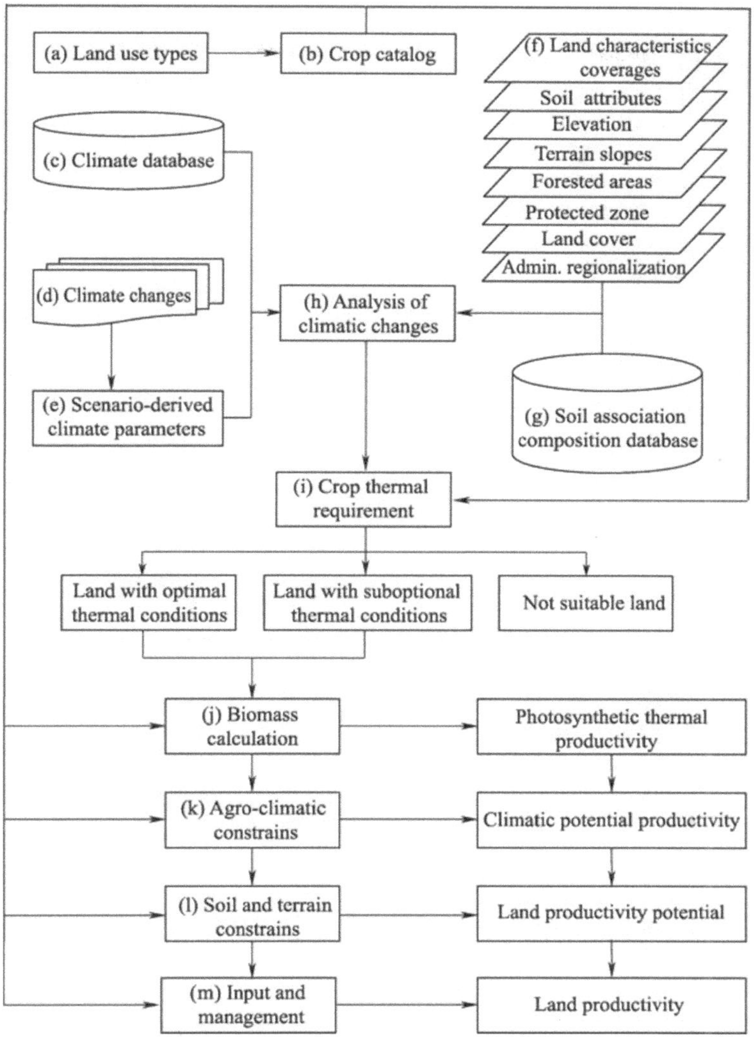

Fig. 5.1 Flow chart of the ESLP.

crop production (Deng et al., 2009). The substitutability of land use and crop types, and multi-objective planning methods are introduced into the ESLP to improve the accuracy of the estimation results. Input and management information are incorporated into the operating parameters of the ESLP to form an open and scalable decision-support system, which integrates the theory and methods of eco-economic planning and can be applied to the management of sustainable agriculture.

The innovations in the ESLP include: (i) innovative methods for the characterization of land use types by hierarchical and one kilometer grid components; (ii) the use of a hydrothermal growing period and water balance model for every one kilometer grid; (iii) revisions to soil maps using soil profile data; (iv) development of a calculation model for the allocation of land use area to determine the cultivated land area in each agro-ecological zone; (v) a crop rotation system that calculates productivity in the context of a multi-cropping system; (vi) the construction of a set of mathematical models for assessing efficient productivity; (vii) the assessment of land quality, productivity and potential population supporting capacity; (viii) innovative calculation methods for potential land productivity and land productivity which are applicable at different input levels, at the province, county and city scales, and at large, medium and small scales.

5.1.2 Parameters

Parameters in the ESLP are introduced as following, and they include growing period, thermal zoning, soil properties, land resource stocks, climate parameters under different scenarios and input levels.

5.1.2.1 Growing Period

The growing period for crops, influenced by seasons, is one of the important parameters in the ESLP. As a comprehensive indicator of changes to the agro-ecological conditions, the growing period is defined as the period from the time when moisture and temperature conditions are suitable for crop growth until the crops mature (Parry et al., 2004; Webb et al., 2005; Fischer et al., 2005). The accuracy of land productivity estimation is improved with the introduction of the growing period into the ESLP and consideration of the influence of factors such as air temperature, precipitation, and evapotranspiration and climate disasters.

It is important to consider the balance between precipitation and potential evaporation when determining the length of the growing period. Calculation of the start of the growing period involves temperature, the ratio of precipitation and potential evaporation, and the end of the crop growth period (Marlon et al., 2008). The growing period generally starts during the rainy season. In some regions, especially where there are several peaks in precipitation, there may be several growing periods, and consequently there may be a variety of combinations of crop growing periods in these regions. There are various combinations of crop growing periods in China with a complex layout. The main combinations of crop growing periods in China include: the annual dry-type growth period; the intermediate-type hydrothermal growth period; the double-intermediate hydrothermal growth period; the middle of the normal water-hot growth period; the normal type.

5.1.2.2 Thermal Zoning

The thermal zone is one of the important parameters in agro-ecological zoning

(Fischer et al. 2000). The thermal zone indicates the total heat available during the growing period which can usually be represented by the heat available for the crop during each day of the growing period.

5.1.2.3 Soil Properties

The soil property information is the basis of soil mapping. At a regional scale, the basic unit of soil mapping is the different types of soil. Soil types are classified as different soil genus or soil species. Soil properties are influenced by the soil quality, land management and even the habits of the planted crops. Although the classification and composition of the basic soil mapping unit may appear complex, it can still be seen as an independent micro system (Lambin et al., 2001).

5.1.2.4 Land Resource Stocks

The land resource stock is characterized by the combined status of land use types, and constitutes the basis of agro-ecological zoning. It includes comprehensive information such as the growing period, heat zone and soil properties, and single-factor indexes such as the climate. Land use types can be classified into one of six classes and 25 sub-classes to provide the foundation for land suitability assessment (Liu et al., 2002; Liu et al., 2004; Deng et al., 2006).

5.1.2.5 Climate Parameters under Different Scenarios

It is useful to simulate and predict the spatiotemporal changes in land productivity under different scenarios, which can be extended with climate parameters. At least four climate parameters need to be exported from the general circulation model to get the basic climatic condition for one pixel (Kaufmann et al., 2007). Each scenario then has its own characteristics because the CO_2 density (Δ CO_2) in the air and the water use efficiency of crops are different. The parameters used in these climate scenarios have an impact on the evaporation coefficient of reference crops and the estimation of crop biomass.

5.1.2.6 Input Levels

An effective way to increase productivity is to raise the input levels, which can include the financial investment by governments, collectives or individual farmers in fixed and current assets. The ESLP can estimate and simulate changes in land productivity for different input levels (Veldkamp and Verburg, 2004).

5.1.3 Function Modules

The ESLP estimates land productivity through an iterative method. The calculation procedure includes five steps: potential photosynthetic productivity, potential thermal productivity, potential climate productivity, potential land production, and land productivity.

5.1.3.1 Potential Photosynthetic Productivity

The potential photosynthetic productivity is the potential land productivity as determined solely by the photosynthetically active radiation, based on the assumption that the temperature, water, soil, breeds and other agricultural inputs are all in optimal condition. It is calculated as following:

$$\begin{aligned} Y_1 = Cf(Q) = K\Omega\varepsilon\phi(1-\alpha)(1-\beta)(1-\rho)(1-\gamma)(1-\omega) \\ \cdot(1-d)sf(L)(1-\eta)^{-1}(1-\delta)^{-1}q^{-1}\textstyle\sum Q_j \end{aligned} \tag{5.1}$$

where Y_1 is the potential photosynthetic productivity, with the unit kg/ha; C is the unit conversion factor; K is the area coefficient; $\sum Q_j$ is the total solar radiation during the growing period (MJ/m^2); Ω is the crop solar radiation utilization efficiency; ε is the percentage of effective radiation in the total radiation; Φ is the photon conversion efficiency; α is the reflectivity of the plant groups; β is the transmittance of the luxuriant plant groups; ρ is the proportion of radiation intercepted by non-photosynthetic organs of plants; γ is the proportion of the light that exceeds the light saturation point; ω is the proportion of respiration in the photosynthate; d is the crop leaf abscission rate; s is the economic crop coefficient; $f(L)$ is the corrected value of the crop leaf area dynamics; η is the moisture content of the ripened grain; δ is the percentage of ash; and q is the heat content of the dry matter (MJ/kg). The main values for these parameters with different crops are listed in Table 5.1.

5.1.3.2 Potential Thermal Productivity

The potential thermal productivity, the upper limit of irrigated agricultural production, refers to the land productivity determined by the natural thermal condition when water, soil, breeds and other agricultural inputs are all in optimal conditions. It is calculated as following:

$$Y_2 = f(T) \cdot Y_1 \tag{5.2}$$

where Y_2 stands for the potential thermal productivity, in units of kg/ha; $f(T)$ is the temperature revision function for crop photosynthesis. $f(T)$ is identified from three cardinal temperatures for major crop plants at which crops can grow and high yield can be achieved and used as a benchmark in this study. $f(T)$ is calculated using the following equations:

$$f(T) = \frac{(T-T_1)(T_2-T)^B}{(T_0-T_1)(T_2-T_0)^B} \tag{5.3}$$

$$B = (T_2-T_0)/(T_0-T_1) \tag{5.4}$$

Table 5.1 Parameters used to calculate the potential photosynthetic productivity in the ESLP and their values

Parameters	Physical Significance	Corn	Bean	Sorghum	Millet	Rice
Ω	Proportion of the ability of CO_2 fixing in crop photosynthesis	0.783	0.783	1	1	0.9
E	Proportion of the photosynthetic active radiation to the total radiation	0.49	0.49	0.49	0.49	0.49
Φ	Photon conversion efficiency	0.229	0.229	0.224	0.224	0.224
α	Reflectivity of the plant groups	0.08	0.1	0.09	0.08	0.06
ρ	Proportion of radiation intercepted by the non-photosynthetic organs of plants	0.1	0.1	0.1	0.1	0.1
γ	Proportion of light that exceeds the light saturation point	0.1	0.05	0.1	0.1	0.1
ω	Proportion of respiration to photosynthate	0.3	0.35	0.3	0.3	0.33
D	Crop leaf abscission rate	0.1	0.1	0.1	0.1	0.1
S	Crop economic coefficient	0.4	0.35	0.35	0.35	0.45
$F(L)$	Corrected value for crop leaf area dynamics	0.58	0.5	0.52	0.44	0.56
H	Moisture content of the ripened grain	0.15	0.15	0.15	0.15	0.14
Δ	Percentage of ash	0.08	0.08	0.08	0.08	0.08
Q	Heat content per unit dry matter (MJ/kg)	17.2	23.1	17.8	20.0	16.9

where T is the average temperature for one period, which is an asymmetric parabolic function in the range of 0–1 determined by T_1, T_2 and T_0 which are the lower, upper and optimum temperatures for crop growth and development, respectively. In this study, the crop growth period is divided into five stages: seedling, vegetative, nutrition and reproduction, nutrition and grain-filling, and maturity stages. $f(T)$ is calculated separately for each stage. The values of T_0, T_1 and T_2 for each stage are determined with reference to Table 5.2.

The number of growing days is revised using the following formula:

$$F(N) = 1 + (N - N_0)/1.7 \cdot N_0 \tag{5.5}$$

where N is the number of days when the temperature is above 10℃ during May and September; N_0 is 153, the number of the days from May to September inclusive.

5.1.3.3 Potential Climate Productivity

The potential climate productivity is calculated by further revising the water

Table 5.2 Three cardinal temperatures for major crops

Month	Growth period	Corn, sorghum, millet			Rice			Bean		
		T_0	T_1	T_2	T_0	T_1	T_2	T_0	T_1	T_2
May	Seedling stage	20.0	8.0	27.0	21.0	9.0	28.0	18.5	7.5	26.0
June	Vegetative stage	24.5	11.5	30.0	25.0	12.5	32.0	23.5	10.0	30.0
July	Nutrition and reproduction period	27.0	14.0	33.0	27.8	15.0	33.0	26.0	13.0	32.0
August	Nutrition and grain-filling stage	25.5	14.0	32.0	26.3	15.0	33.0	24.5	14.0	30.5
September	Maturity stage	19.0	10.0	30.0	19.3	10.5	30.0	18.0	10.0	30.0

indicator based on the potential thermal productivity. It differs from previous studies in that this study considers not only natural precipitation but also irrigation water. Therefore, the potential thermal productivity here is called the potential climate productivity which is calculated as following:

$$Y_w = Y_T \cdot f(W)(1 - I_r) + Y_2 \cdot I_r \tag{5.6}$$

where I_r is the irrigation coefficient; Y_2 is the potential thermal productivity; Y_w is the potential climate productivity. The study of the potential thermal productivity can be summed up as research on the function of water. There are no authoritative models for the water calculation at this time, so the model recommended by the United Nations Food and Agriculture Organization is used here:

$$f(W) = 1 - K_y \times (1 - Pe/ET_m) \tag{5.7}$$

where K_y is the reactive yield coefficient; ET_m is the maximum evapotranspiration (mm); Pe is the effective precipitation, which can be calculated from the model designed by the US Department of Agriculture Soil Conservation Service:

$$Pe = R/125 \cdot (125 - 0.2 \cdot R) \quad (\text{If R} < 250 \text{ mm}) \tag{5.8}$$

$$Pe = 125 + 0.1 \cdot R \quad (\text{If R} > 250 \text{ mm}) \tag{5.9}$$

where R is the total precipitation; and ET_m is the maximum evapotranspiration during the crop growing period, which can be calculated from:

$$ET_m = K_1 \cdot ET_0 \tag{5.10}$$

where K_1 is the crop coefficient, which is related to the season, the crop breed and the crop colony structure; ET_0 is the reference evapotranspiration, which is calculated using the improved Penman-Monteith model:

$$ET_0 = \frac{0.408\Delta(R_n - G) + \gamma\dfrac{900}{T+273}u_2(e_s - e_a)}{\Delta + \gamma(1 + 0.34u_2)} \tag{5.11}$$

where Δ is the slope of the saturated vapor pressure – temperature curve (kPa℃$^{-1}$); R_n is the net radiation from the crop canopy surface (MJm^{-2}h^{-1});

G is the soil heat flux ($MJm^{-2}h^{-1}$); γ is the hygrometer constant; T is the daily average temperature (℃); u_2 is the wind speed at 2 m height; e_s is the saturation vapor pressure (kPa); e_a is the actual vapor pressure; the soil heat flux G is calculated from the following formula:

$$G = 0.1 \times R_n \tag{5.12}$$

J is the ordinal number of each day in the year. The average climate potential productivity for these days is used.

Table 5.3 Ordinal numbers for days during May to September

	May	June	July	August	September
Ordinal Number	136	167	197	228	258

Table 5.4 K_y and K_l values for major crop plants

	Corn	Millet	Bean	Sorghum	Rice
K_y	1.25	0.8	0.85	0.9	1.25
K_l	0.9	0.825	1.22	0.9	1.05

5.1.3.4 Potential Land Productivity

The potential land productivity can be obtained from the potential climate productivity (Y_w) and the validity coefficient for soil:

$$Y_L = f(s) \cdot Y_w \tag{5.13}$$

Twelve factors that influence soil properties are selected and their weighting coefficients (W_i) are determined by establishing a comparison matrix based on their relative importance to soil effectiveness, soil properties and soil nutrients. The factors are each divided into a number of levels based on their beneficial or restraining effects on crop growth and production, and are assigned different scores to establish the soil effectiveness factor classification and scoring system①. The ESLP calculates the soil effectiveness coefficients using the following formula:

$$f(s) = \sum_i A_i \cdot W_i \tag{5.14}$$

5.1.3.5 Land Productivity

The potential productivities described previously analyze land productivity only from the perspective of the natural properties of the land. However,

① China has a vast land territory with different soil types and various land use types. All the soil types cannot be accurately summarized with a single classification and scoring system. However, given that this study is more concerned about the overall distribution and variation pattern of soil macro-properties, then the soil was classified based on soil property standards used in the second national general detailed soil survey and with reference to *China's Soil* and other published research, to develop this national classification and scoring system of soil effectiveness factors.

land productivity is also affected by socioeconomic factors such as input levels, field management and planting structure (Bolliger et al., 2008). Land productivity is an indicator of the production capacity of a unit land area considering many socioeconomic factors and based on potential land productivity.

Table 5.5 Soil effectiveness factor classification and scoring system

Soil effectiveness	Categories	Classification					
		1	2	3	4	5	6
Soil properties	Soil texture	L	LS, SL	LC, CL	SLC, SCL	SC, C	S
	pH	6.5–7.5	5.5–6.5	7.5–8.5	4.5–5.5	8.5–9.0	$<4.5, \geqslant 9.0$
	Tillage layer thickness	$\geqslant 20$	16–20	12–16	8–12	4–8	< 4
	Score	1	0.9	0.7	0.6	0.5	0.4
Soil nutrient	Organic Carbon	$\geqslant 40$	30–40	20–30	10–20	6–10	< 6
	TN	$\geqslant 2.0$	1.5–2.0	1.0–1.5	0.75–1.0	0.5–0.75	< 0.5
	TP	$\geqslant 2.0$	1.5–2.0	1.0–1.5	0.7–1.0	0.4–0.7	< 0.4
	TK	$\geqslant 30$	20–30	15–20	10–15	5–10	< 5
	Alkali-hydrolyzable Nitrogen	$\geqslant 150$	120–150	90–120	60–90	30–60	< 30
	AP	$\geqslant 40$	20–40	10–20	5–10	3–5	< 3
	AK	$\geqslant 200$	150–200	100–150	50–100	30–50	< 30
	Score	1	0.9	0.8	0.7	0.6	0.4
Site condition	Slope	$\leqslant 3$	3–7	7–15	15–25	25–35	> 35
	Score	1	0.9	0.8	0.6	0.4	0.1
	Aspect	Gentle	South	Southeast Southwest	Northeast Northwest slope	North	East West
	Score	1	0.9	0.8	0.7	0.6	0.75

The inputs can be divided the fundamental inputs to improve land conditions and the conventional production inputs for specific production processes. The fundamental inputs include activities such as land terracing on hilly slopes, and land consolidation and drainage on the plains, while process related inputs include fertilizers, breed selection and the use of agricultural machinery.

The ESLP uses the Cobb-Douglas function to estimate land productivity influenced by fundamental inputs and conventional production inputs as follows:

$$Y = AK_1^{\alpha}K_2^{\beta}YL^{\gamma} \tag{5.15}$$

where Y is the land productivity; A is the scaling parameter of the Cobb-Douglas function; K_1 is the fundamental input for improving land conditions;

K_2 is the routine productive input for specific production processes; YL is the potential land productivity; α, β and γ meet the following conditions:

$$\alpha + \beta + \gamma = 1 \tag{5.16}$$

The total investment is allocated between the fundamental inputs and conventional production inputs based on the profit maximization principle. Assuming that the total investment amount is M, then

$$M = K_1 P_1 + K_2 P_2 \tag{5.17}$$

where P_1 and P_2 are the prices of fundamental inputs and productive inputs, respectively. So the allocation of the total investment between the fundamental inputs and productive inputs satisfies the optimum condition:

$$\text{MAX } W = AK_1^{\alpha} K_2^{\beta} YL^{\gamma} P - K_1 P_1 - K_2 P_2 \tag{5.18}$$

where W is the production profit, and P is the product price. The optimum investment program is found by solving the equations above, so that:

$$K_1 = \left(\frac{1}{Y_L^{\gamma}}\right)^{\frac{1}{\alpha+\beta-1}} \left(\frac{P_1}{\alpha}\right)^{\frac{1-\beta}{\alpha+\beta-1}} \left(\frac{P_2}{\beta}\right)^{\frac{\beta}{\alpha+\beta-1}} \tag{5.19}$$

$$K_2 = \left(\frac{1}{Y_L^{\gamma}}\right)^{\frac{1}{\alpha+\beta-1}} \left(\frac{P_1}{\alpha}\right)^{\frac{\alpha}{\alpha+\beta-1}} \left(\frac{P_2}{\beta}\right)^{\frac{1-\alpha}{\alpha+\beta-1}} \tag{5.20}$$

The estimation of land productivity is found by substituting K_1 and K_2 into the land productivity calculation formula.

5.2 Operation of the Estimation Model

The land productivity estimation contains eight operational steps shown in Fig. 5.2. The first four operations mainly include the preparation of the parameters: temperature interpolation, identifying the length of the growing period (LGP), and determining the radiation surface and effective radiation. The final four operations determine the potential thermal productivity, potential climate productivity, potential land productivity and potential agricultural productivity. The potential thermal productivity operation includes the calculation of the photosynthetic productivity and potential thermal productivity (Deng et al., 2009).

First, it is necessary to set the data path for convenient operation as there are numerous parameters involved in the ESLP. Click "setting" in the main interface to set the data path and then the data paths for the other interfaces are converted to the chosen path (Fig. 5.3).

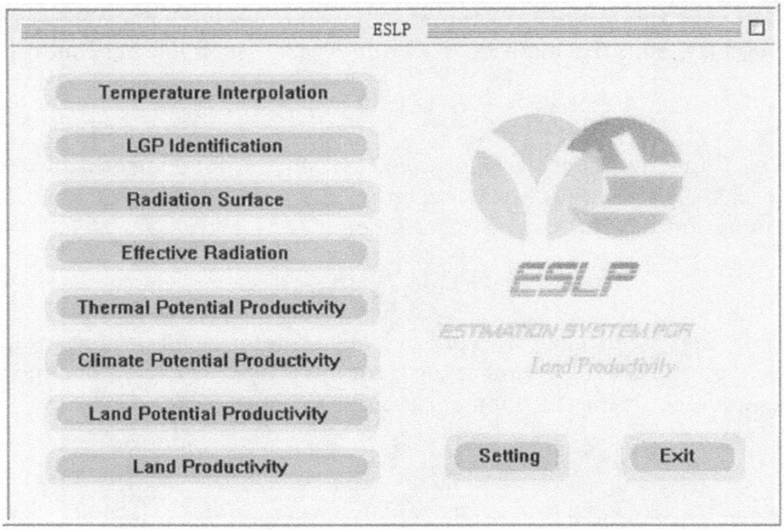

Fig. 5.2 User interface of the ESLP.

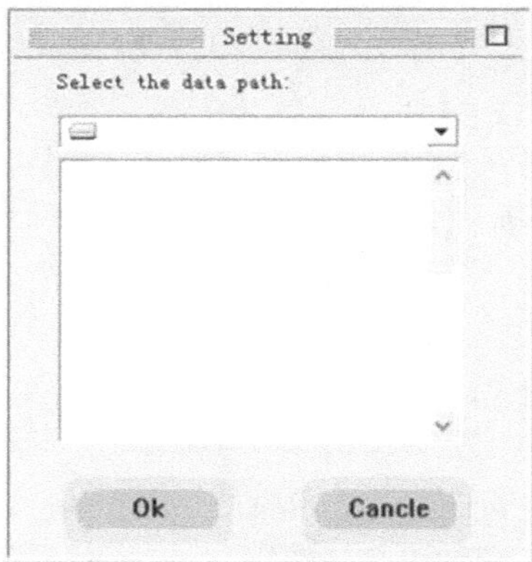

Fig. 5.3 Load the parameters into the ESLP.

5.2.1 Temperature Interpolation

The ESLP can link climate data stored in a dbf format to a spatial distribution map of meteorological observation stations and then interpolate the vector data into spatial grid data. The input parameters needed include the workspace, the year of interpolation, the storage path for the temperature text data, and the output path for the temperature grid data (Fig. 5.4). The temperature data are obtained from meteorological data in 10-day units as observed by the meteorological stations.

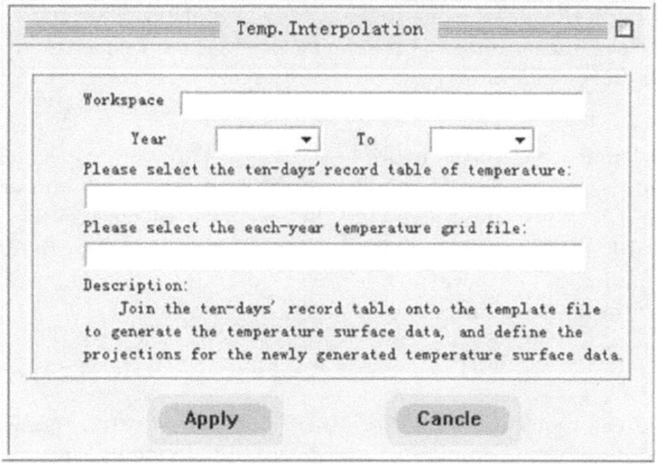

Fig. 5.4 Interface for interpolating the air temperature module.

There are many methods for the spatial interpolation of temperature, and the distance weighting method is used to spatially interpolate climate data in the ESLP. The interpolation process considers the effects of the vertical lapse rate of temperature and location of every observation station on climatic factors as shown in Fig. 5.4.

The interpolation model operates on each individual pixel, assuming that there is no correlation between the pixels. The ESLP has designed a four-point interpolation method for obtaining daily meteorological data for each pixel, which involves the correction of temperature with digital elevation model and the adjustment of the coefficient of precipitation based on data coming from the four closest weather stations. The specific steps in spatial interpolation are described below.

(i) Calculate the order and distances from the four closest weather stations to each grid point

Calculate the distance from the grid center to all the meteorological stations based on its geodetic coordinates in the program. Because of the edge effect of spatial data interpolation, the actual data for the meteorological stations is chosen and the internal ID numbers of the four stations are obtained using the bubble sort algorithm.

Assume that meteorological station S_i has the same attributes (abscissa (meter) x, ordinate (meter) y, annual precipitation line (millimeter) incline), as grid point G, then the square of the distance from grid points to the four sites is as follows:

$$d_i^2 = (S_i x - Gx)^2 + (S_i y - Gy)^2 \tag{5.21}$$

(ii) Calculate the weighting of each site on the grid points

It is necessary to determine whether the data are valid before a weight determination can be made as not every station will provide effective climate information. If the data from meteorological station S_i is invalid (there is obvious lack of measurement or incorrect data), its weight is 0; if the data are valid, and its weight is:

$$W_i = 1/d_i^2 \tag{5.22}$$

(iii) Calculate the temperature

The temperature decreases as the height increases. The temperature data are adjusted to the temperature at the sea level as with every increase in altitude of 100 m, the average daily temperature decreases by 0.6℃, the daily extreme maximum temperature decreases by 0.9℃, and the daily extreme minimum temperature decreases by 0.4℃ as follows:

$$S_iT^* = S_iT + r \times S_ielv/100.0 \tag{5.23}$$

where S_i is the meteorological station $i; T^*$ is the adjusted temperature (including the maximum, minimum and average daily temperatures); T is the original data; *elv* is the altitude (meter). The temperature of the grid point at sea level is then calculated by the following formula:

$$G.T^* = \frac{\sum_{i=1}^{4}(W_i \times S_iT^*)}{\sum_{i=1}^{4} W_i} \tag{5.24}$$

Finally, the temperature at the actual elevation is determined by:

$$G.T = G.T^* - r \times G.elv/100.0 \tag{5.25}$$

5.2.2 LGP Identification

The LGP identification module is used to determine the length of the growing period. The input parameters include the workspace, the estimated number of years and the output paths for the LGP identification results (Fig. 5.5). Temperature is the basis for the determination of the LGP. The ESLP uses the spatially interpolated temperature grid data to determine the initial and final ten-day periods with the average temperature above 5℃ for each year and consequently determines the LGP for crops.

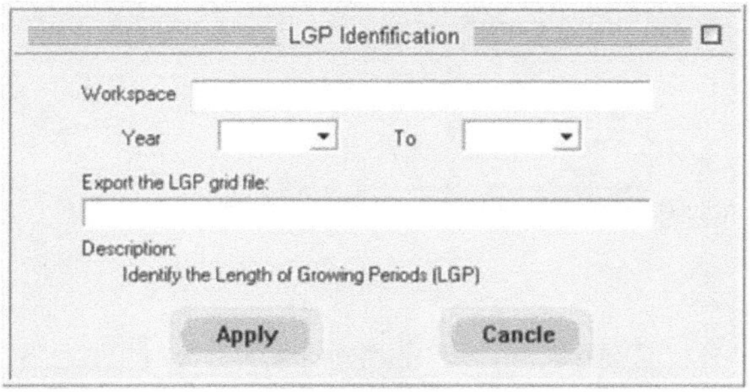

Fig. 5.5 Exportation of the estimated LGP grid.

5.2.3 Radiation Data Preparation

The radiation data preparation module transforms the radiation data from text data to spatial grid data. The input parameters include the workplace, input path for site-based radiation observation data, estimated year, and the storage path of output data (Fig. 5.6). The site-based radiation observation data come from surface meteorological observations.

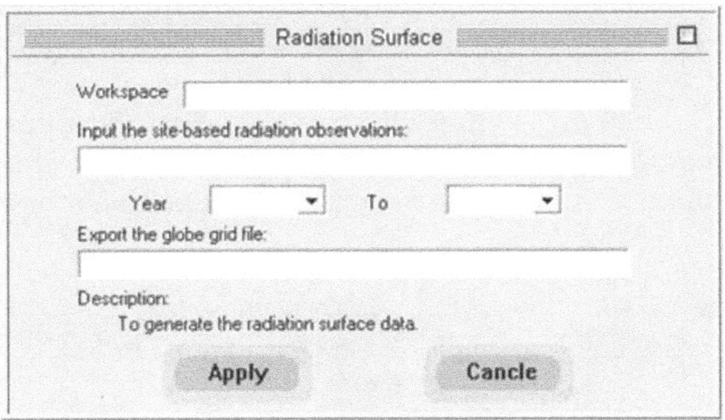

Fig. 5.6 Exportation of the estimated radiation grid.

5.2.4 Estimation of Effective Radiation

The effective radiation estimation module is used to determine the effective radiation during the LGP for crops based on the radiation data and the LGP for crops. The input parameters include the LGP for crops, estimated years, output path for effective radiation data and input path for radiation data (Fig. 5.7). The parameters of this module are all sourced from the estimation results of preceding modules.

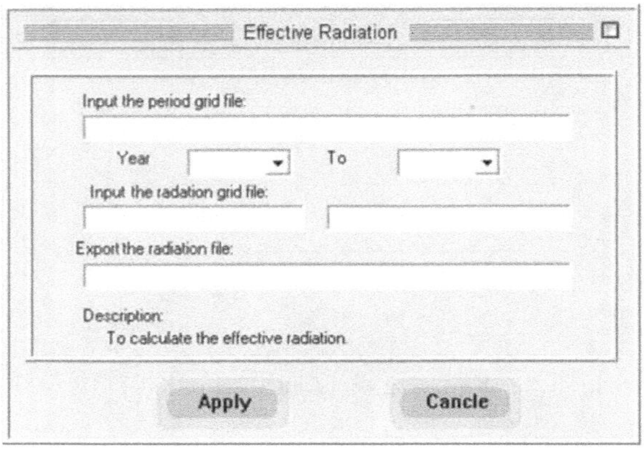

Fig. 5.7 Estimation and export of the effective radiation grid.

5.2.5 Potential Thermal Productivity

The potential thermal productivity module estimates the maximum potential productivity of crops under certain temperature and light conditions. The parameters required for this module include the input path for temperature data, estimated years, input paths for the effective radiation data and land use data, and the output path for the potential thermal productivity (Fig. 5.8). The temperature and effective radiation data are from the estimation results described above. The land use data are sourced from remote sensing image data, with operator-computer interactions to extract land use information.

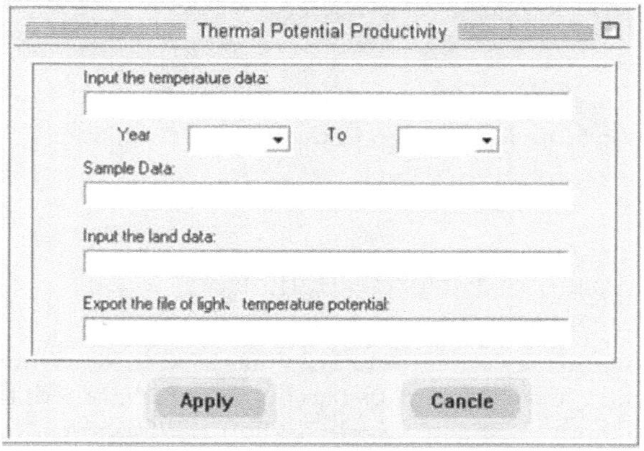

Fig. 5.8 Estimation and export of the thermal potential productivity grid.

5.2.6 Potential Climate Productivity

The potential climate productivity module estimates how restrictions in precipitation affect the potential productivity. The input parameters include the elevation, effective radiation, average, maximum and minimum temperatures, wind speed at 2 m above ground level, average relative humidity, precipitation and the *kc* coefficient (Fig. 5.9). The elevation data are obtained with the following steps. First, a topographic map is scanned and saved as a raster data image. GIS-based software is then used to digitize the map, and a contour layer is extracted with the contour and point elevation feature information (mainly peak elevations). Finally, the contour layer is used as the source file and interpolated to get an elevation map in GRID format with the use of the Kriging interpolation software tool. The climate data, such as effective radiation and precipitation, are obtained from ground-based observations at meteorological stations, with the original data stored in ASCII format and then interpolated into GRID format.

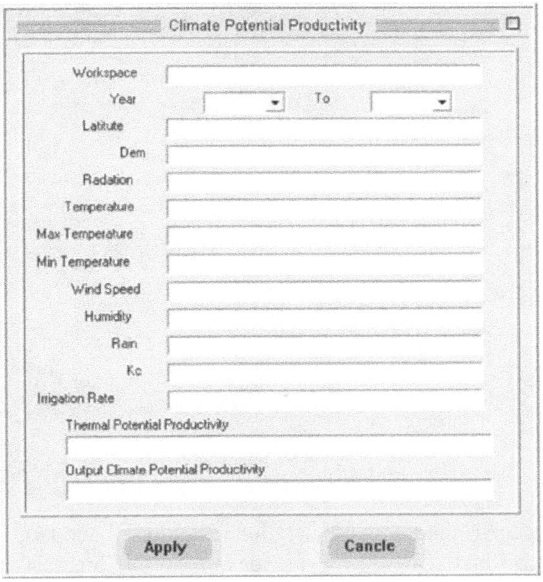

Fig. 5.9 Estimation and export of the climate potential productivity grid.

5.2.7 Potential Land Productivity

The potential land productivity module estimates the controlling effects of soil characteristics on potential productivity. There are numerous parameters in this module, including 12 parameters related to three main aspects, the site conditions, soil properties and soil nutrients (Fig. 5.10). The site condition parameters include the slope and aspect, which can be obtained by estimation from the elevation data using GIS application software. Soil property parameters include soil texture, pH, and topsoil depth. For the pH and topsoil depth, soil survey data can be used. The soil survey data are text data, which use points as the statistical unit and can be interpolated into grid data with the Kriging interpolation method. The soil nutrient data include soil organic matter, total nitrogen, total phosphorus, total potassium, available nitrogen, available phosphorus and potassium, all of which are also obtained from the soil survey data (China Soil Book 1993, 1994, 1995 and 1996).

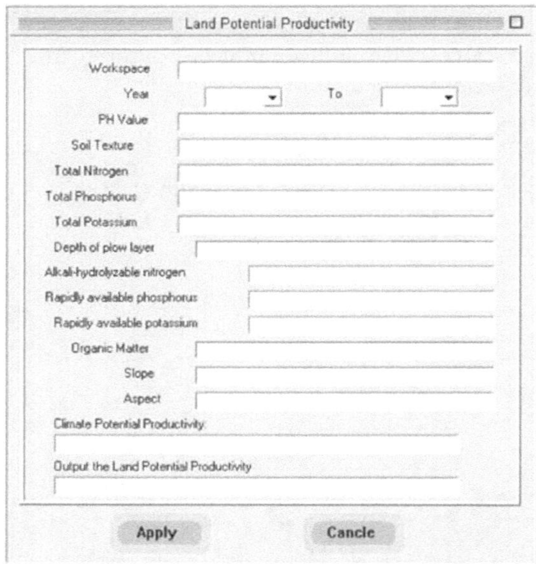

Fig. 5.10 Estimation and export of the land potential productivity grid.

The soil texture needs to be further classified based on the soil texture classification standard (Table 5.6) after interpolation. Soil texture is a soil physical property, which generally refers to the composition of mineral grains of different diameters in the soil. Soil texture is closely related to soil aeration, fertilizer retention, water holding capacity and ease of cultivation. Soil texture is an important property for identifying appropriate soil use, management and improvement, and therefore it is a vital factor for land productivity.

Table 5.6 Classification of soil texture in China

Soil texture	Particle composition (%)			
Texture group	Texture name	Sand (1–0.05 mm)	Coarse dust (0.05–0.01 mm)	Clay (0.001 mm)
Sand	Coarse sand	> 70		
	Fine sand	⩾ 60– ⩽70		
	Surface sand	⩾ 50– < 60		
Loam	Sandy silt	⩾ 20	⩾ 40	< 30
	Silt	< 20		
	Sandy Loam	⩾ 20	< 40	
	Loam	< 20		
	Sandy clay	⩾ 50		⩾ 30
Clay	Dust clay			⩾ 30– < 35
	Clay soil			⩾ 35– ⩽40
	Clay			> 40

5.2.8 Land Productivity

The land productivity module aims to estimate the land productivity at different management and input levels. The required parameters include the input level, contribution coefficients of investment in agricultural science, technology and management, estimated years, input paths for potential land productivity, and output paths of land productivity (Fig. 5.11). The contribution coefficients of investment in agricultural science, technology and management are obtained from weighted suitability estimates with the assumption that the investments will maximize the regional economic benefit.

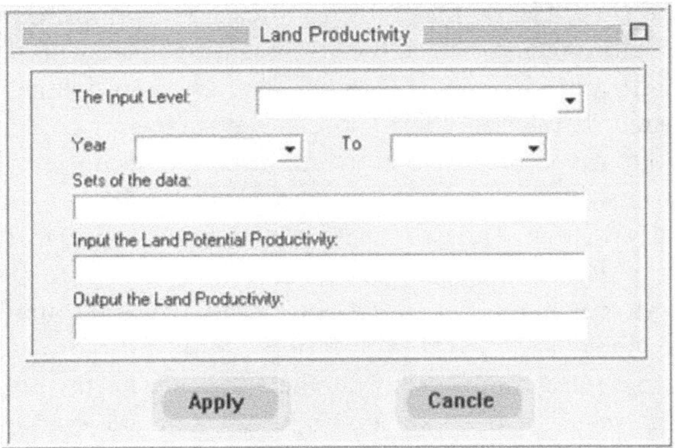

Fig. 5.11 Estimation and export of the land productivity grid.

The agricultural investment and management level data include the agricultural population, total power of farm machinery, fertilizer use, plastic film use, investment in agricultural infrastructure construction, and agriculture funding input, all of which are usually at a regional scale. It is necessary to disaggregate the data to a pixel scale to ensure the consistency of the research scales.

The agricultural population data are disaggregated in a different way from other data. Effectively, the demographic data at the county level are redistributed to obtain the population living in each 1 km^2, while ensuring that the population of the whole county remains the same. Briefly, a correlation analysis is undertaken between residential land (including both urban and rural residential land) in each 1 km^2 grid and the area of built-up land and rural residential land based on the spatial distribution of populations in the different land types. Models are then established to find the population living in 1 km^2 grids of different land use types in the county. The models are generally in the following form:

$$P_i = \sum_{j=1}^{n} a_j x_j = B_j \tag{5.26}$$

where P_i is the total population in the district i; a_j is the demographic distribution coefficient for the jth land use type in this district (person/km^2); x_j is the area of the jth land use type in this district (km^2); and n is the number of secondary land use types.

To improve the classification accuracy, spatial distribution models for population are established for each secondary area to generate the initial population distribution coefficients of different land use types in the district. The population in each sub-district is calculated after being disaggregated. The difference between the populations in the different sub-districts and the actual population (residual item) is revised for each sub-district. The specific data generation process is as follows.

(i) Generate three GRID files which indicate the populations living on the urban residential land, rural residential land and farmland, using the urban population coefficient, rural population coefficient and farming population coefficient of each district in the region as parameters.

(ii) Carry out a vector-raster conversion of the secondary land use types using the land use vector map to generate land use area percentage data for each 1 km^2 grid, i.e., the percentage of the secondary land use type per square kilometer. Each secondary land use type is a separate grid map.

(iii) Calculate the sum of the product of the urban population coefficient, urban area, product of the rural population coefficient, rural-residential area, product of the farming population coefficient and the farmland area in the 1 km^2 grid. The result is used as the population in a 1 km^2 grid.

The 1 km^2 population data, the digital elevation model data and the distribution map of residual land are overlaid for revision, and populations are removed from pixels exceeding certain slope. Regions where residential areas are identified on the distribution map but where there is no population data in the corresponding pixels are also revised to obtain the revised 1km grid population distribution data.

The processes used to disaggregate the total power of farm machinery, fertilizer use, plastic film use, investment in agricultural infrastructure construction and agricultural funding inputs are as follows:

(i) extract the boundary of the regional cultivated land to generate a mask template;

(ii) calculate the weight of unit cultivated land areas based on the collected corresponding index values and convert the area into the 1 km^2 grid data;

(iii) regard the cultivated land boundary as a masking template, and obtain the disaggregated data for the corresponding indices using a map algebra calculation.

The disaggregated data for incomes from farming, forestry, and fishing are prepared in similar ways, except that the masking template is the boundary of the regional cultivated land, forest or grassland.

THIESSEN polygons① are generated from residual regional rural land data and revised based on residual land data. These polygons are used as the basis for the spatial allocation of rural electricity consumption, total rural income and average per capita income to spatially disaggregate the three indices.

Adjustment processing is necessary for all the socioeconomic data after disaggregation. The index values for each sub-district in the region are calculated, and differences between the calculated and actual index values are distributed in the corresponding layers including the index to ensure data accuracy.

5.3 Summary

Land productivity is one of the important indices in the assessment of effects of the dynamics of land system change. Land productivity is estimated from the natural, social and economic properties of the land resource and based on the sunlight, temperature, water, soil, input level and management conditions through an integrated GIS technique, which estimates land productivity at the pixel scale. The ESLP is a collection of several application programs, including land suitability assessment, the evaluation of land productivity, and some advanced applications which use the stock of land resources as the fundamental input information. The outputs from the ESLP provide basic decision-making support for the assessment of land degradation, simulation of land productivity, assessment of population carrying capacity and optimal allocation of regional land use.

① THIESSEN polygons refer to polygons whose boundaries define the area that is closest to each point relative to all other points. It is widely used to define individual areas of influence around a set of points.

The ESLP involves numerous parameters in the process of land productivity estimation, and the calculation processes are lengthy and complex. This chapter describes the processes, parameters needed and methods of data preparation, which will improve the ability of readers to use this model and provide a foundation for its wide application.

References

Albersen P J, Fischer G, Keyzer M A, Sun L. 2002. Estimation of agricultural production relations in the LUC model for China. RR-02-03. Laxenburg, Austria; Amsterdam, International Institute for Applied Systems Analysis; Centre for World Food Studies of the Free University 51.

Ash R F and Edmonds R L. 1998. China's land resources, environment and agricultural production. The China Quarterly 156(Special Issue: China's Environment): 836–879.

Bolliger J, Hagedorn F, Leifeld J, Bohl J, Zimmermann S, Soliva R, Kienast F. 2008. Effects of land-use change on carbon stocks in Switzerland. Ecosystems, 11(6): 895–907.

Deng X Z, Su H B, Zhan J Y. 2008. Integration of multiple data sources to simulate the Dynamics of Land Systems. Sensors, 8(2): 620–634.

Deng X Z, Huang J K, Rozelle S, Uchida E. 2006. Cultivated land conversion and potential agricultural productivity in China. Land Use Policy, 23(4): 372–384.

Deng X Z, Zhan J Y, Chen R. 2005. The patterns and driving forces of urban sprawl in China. IGARSS 2005: IEEE International Geoscience and Remote Sensing Symposium, Vols 1–8: 1511–1513.

Deng X Z. 2008a. Analysis of Land Use Conversions. Beijing: China Land Press.

Deng X Z. 2008b. Simulation of Land System Dynamics. Beijing: China Land Press.

Deng X Z, Jiang Q O, Zhan J Y. 2009. Scenario analyses of land productivity in China. Ecology and Environmnet, 18(5): 1835–1843.

DeFries R S, Asner G P, Houghton R. 2004. Trade-offs in land-use decisions: Towards a framework for assessing multiple ecosystem responses to land-use changed. Ecosystems and Land Use Change, 153: 1–9.

Dumanski J. 2000. Land quality indicators — Preface. Agriculture Ecosystems and Environment, 81(2): 81.

Fan S. 1997. How fast have China's agricultural production and productivity really been growing? New measurement and evidence. Environment and Production Technology Division, International Food Policy Research Institute: Washington, U.S.A.

Fischer G. 1998. AEZWIN — An interactive multiple-criteria analysis tool for land resources appraisal. Interim Report, IR-98-051/October. Laxenburg, Austria, International Institute for Applied Systems Analysis.

Fischer G and Sun L X. 2001. Model based analysis of land-use development in China agriculture. Ecosystem and Environment, 85(1–3): 163–176.

Fischer G, Shah M, ubiello F N, van Velthuizen H. 2005. Socio-economic and climate change impacts on agriculture: An integrated assessment, 1990—2080. Philosophical Transactions of the Royal Society B — Biological Sciences, 360(1463): 2067–2083.

Fischer G, van Velthuizen H T, Nachtergaele F O. 2000. Global agro-ecological zones assessment: Methodology and results. Interim Report IR-00-064. Luxemburg, Rome, IIASA.

Hulse J H. 1993. Agriculture, food and the environment. Food Research International, 26(6): 55–469.

Foley J A, DeFries R, Asner G P, Barford C, Bonan G. 2005. Global consequences of land use. Science, 309: 570–575.

Kaufmann R K, Seto K C, Schneider A, Liu Z T, Zhou L M, Wang W L. 2007. Climate response to rapid urban growth: Evidence of a human-induced precipitation deficit. Journal of Climate, 20(10): 2299–2306.

Lambin E F, Turner B L, Geist H J, Agbola S B, Angelsen A, Bruce J W, Coomes O T, Dirzo R, Fischer G, Folke C, George P S, Homewood K, Imbernon J, Leemans R, Li X, Moran E F, Mortimore M, Ramakrishnan P S, Richards J F, Skånes H, Steffen W, Stone G D, Svedin U, Veldkamp T A, Vogel C, Xu J. 2001. The causes of land-use and land-cover change: Moving beyond the myths. Global Environmental Change, 11(4): 261–269.

Lin G C S and Ho S P S. 2003. China's land resources and land-use change: Insights from the 1996 land survey. Land Use Policy, 20(2): 87–107.

Liu M L and Chen B M. 2000. The analysis on correlevity grain yield fluctuation and its relation with agricultural natural disasters in China in the recent years. Journal of Catastrophology, 15(4): 78–85.

Liu J Y, Deng X Z, Liu M L, Zhang S W. 2002. Study on the spatial patterns of land-use change and analyses of driving forces in Northeastern China during 1990—2000. Chinese Geographical Science, 12(4): 299–308.

Liu J Y, Xu X L, Gao Z Q. Zhuang D F. 2004. Recent land use change and its impact on farmland productivity in China. Remote Sensing and Modeling of Ecosystems for Sustainability, 5544: 295–300.

Marlon J R, Bartlein P J, Carcaillet C, Gavin D G, Harrison S P, Higuera P E, Joos F, Power M J, Prentice I C. 2008. Climate and human influences on global biomass burning over the past two millennia. Nature Geoscience, 1(10): 697–702.

National general survey of soil office. China Soil Book (Volume 1). Beijing: China Agriculture Press, 1993.

National general survey of soil office. China Soil Book (Volume 2). Beijing: China Agriculture Press, 1994.

National general survey of soil office. China Soil Book (Volume 3). Beijing: China Agriculture Press, 1994.

National general survey of soil office. China Soil Book (Volume 4). Beijing: China Agriculture Press, 1995.

National general survey of soil office. China Soil Book (Volume 5). Beijing: China Agriculture Press, 1995.

National general survey of soil office. China Soil Book (Volume 6). Beijing: China Agriculture Press, 1996.

Parry M L, Rosenzweig C, Iglesias A, Livermore M and Fischer G. 2004. Effects of climate change on global food production under SRES emissions and socio-economic scenarios. Glob. Environ. Change. Global Environmental Change, 14: 53–67.

Seto K C, Kaufmann R K, Woodcock C E. 2000. Landsat reveals China's farmland reserves, but they're vanishing fast. Nature, 406: 121.

Veldkamp A and Verburg P H. 2004. Modelling land use change and environmental impact. Journal of Environmental Management, 72(1–2): 1–3.

Webb T J, Woodward F I, Hannah L, Gaston K J. 2005. Forest cover-rainfall relationships in a biodiversity hotspot: The Atlantic forest of Brazil. Ecological Applications, 15(6): 1968–1983.

Chapter 6 Simulation of Structural Change in Land Use in Jiangxi Province Using the CGELUC Model

Structural change in regional land use is both a cause and component of regional environmental change and a response to regional environmental change, and has therefore been a concern of the academic community. Structural changes in regional land use driven by socioeconomic factors have been a particular focus of research (Greenberg et al., 1998; Seto et al., 2000; Weinstoerffer and Girardin, 2000; Krausmann et al., 2003; Yue et al., 2005). Socioeconomic factors come from different socioeconomic sectors, and their impacts on structural changes in regional land use intertwine. Existing models and methods such as conversion of land use and its effects at small regional extent (CLUE-S) (Verburg et al., 2002), cellular automata (Stevens and Dragicevic, 2007; Dawn et al., 2008), and ABM (Fontaine and Rounsevell, 2009; Polhill, 2009) have provided a good foundation for the study of regional environmental change. However, there is no research that explores structural change in regional land use with the interactive and joint effects of the various socioeconomic factors from a whole system perspective (Haberl et al., 2001; Liu et al., 2002; Kerr et al., 2003; Haberl et al., 2003; Seto and Kaufmann, 2003).

Land is a basic production factor and an important means of macroeconomic regulatory control, and is closely related to economic behavior and government policies. The Computable General Equilibrium of Land Use Change (CGELUC) model quantifies the relationship between these different factors. The CGELUC model is an equilibrium analysis model of land use change based on the theory of computable general equilibrium analysis. Using economic theory, the CGELUC model retrieves the coupled relationship between industrial development and structural changes in land use by conducting an equilibrium analysis. The model also quantitatively represents the relationship between regional development and land use change, and studies laws of the structural change in regional land use caused by regulatory policies. The CGELUC model links the factor market, commodity market and land use with the land rent and forms an equilibrium system covering multiple markets and sectors to simulate and provide scenario forecasts of structural change in regional land use.

Jiangxi Province is an important commodity grain production base in China, and is in the process of rapid economic development and gradually accelerated urbanization. The province has also converted cultivated land into forestry and grassland to improve conservation. Therefore, the land system change in Jiangxi Province mainly includes the processes of agricultural production, and conversion from cultivated land to built-up areas, forestry and grassland. In this chapter, we mainly explore how the land use structure changes in Jiangxi Province, what factors affect it and explanations of the driving mechanisms. Another consideration is that approximately 97% of Jiangxi Province is part of the Poyang Lake watershed, which is one of the world's important wetlands and an ecological protection area, so this study is also of significance to global ecological and environmental protection.

6.1 Design of the SAM in Jiangxi Province

The Social Accounting Matrix (SAM) is the basis of the CGELUC model. Compiling the SAM of Jiangxi Province mainly involves accounting for the GDP cash flow (income distribution), national income, total social supply and demand, and land use changes.

6.1.1 Overview of Jiangxi Province

Jiangxi Province is located in the southeast of China, on the southern bank of the lower reaches of the Yangtze River. The project *Returning Land for Farming to Forestry* began in 1999 and the percentage of forestry land use has reached 60% to date in the area between 24°29′ and 30°04′ N and 113°34′ and 118°28′ E. Jiangxi Province has a total area of 166 900 km^2 and had a population of 44 million in 2008. Jiangxi Province is surrounded by mountains to the south, east and west, and is relatively flat to the north. The central part of the province is hilly, and the whole terrain resembles a huge basin leaning to Poyang Lake in the north. There are more than 2 400 rivers in Jiangxi Province, including five major rivers: the Gan, Fu, Xin, Xiu and Rao rivers, making Jiangxi Province an ideal location for river transportation.

Jiangxi Province is bordered by Zhejiang and Fujian provinces to the east, Guangdong Province to the south, Hunan Province to the west, and Hubei and Anhui provinces to the north. The province adjoins the Yangtze River, and is a hinterland of the Yangtze River Delta, the Zhujiang River Delta and the Fujian Delta. The distances to crucial cities and ports in Shanghai, Guangzhou, Xiamen, Nanjing, Wuhan, Changsha, Hefei and other cities are generally between 600 and 700 km. There are 2 206 km of highways in Jiangxi Province, and the main routes into the province are all major highways.

Jiangxi has a sound ecological environment and rich resources. Jiangxi

Province is an important commodity grain production base and is in the process of rapid economic development and gradually accelerated urbanization. In addition, the conversion of cultivated land to forestry and grassland has been carried out to improve environmental conservation in the process of economic development. Therefore, the land use change in Jiangxi Province mainly includes the processes of agricultural production, and the conversion of cultivated land to built-up areas or forestry and grassland.

6.1.2 Compilation of the SAM in Jiangxi Province for 2007

The SAM is the basis of the CGELUC model. The SAM for Jiangxi Province required for the CGELUC model includes GDP cash flow (income distribution), the use of national income, total social supply and demand, and land use and land cover change. In the process of compiling the SAM for Jiangxi Province, the IO table for Jiangxi Province in 2007 is used as the basis, while the national economic equilibrium account is used as the standard when there is inconsistency between data from different sources, since the data in the national equilibrium account is relatively precise as it comes from annual statistical reports.

In compiling the SAM, the row and column data for the "activities", "commodity" and "elements" accounts were directly obtained from the IO table. Data related to land use conversion and land factors were mainly acquired from comparisons between 1:100 000 remote-sensing land use survey data of Jiangxi Province in 2001 and 2007. Tax, transfer payments between accounts, savings, and other data between accounts in other parts of the world were obtained from the *Statistical Yearbook of Jiangxi Province* in 2008 and the statistical data, related economic surveys and census data released by relevant departments. Other data that cannot be obtained from statistical reports can be obtained by calculations based on the principle that the row and column subtotals in the SAM are equal.

The structure of the SAM for Jiangxi Province in 2007 used in the CGELUC model is presented in Table 6.1. Given that the CGELUC model is used to simulate structural changes in regional land use under certain economic development conditions, it is necessary to include accounts related to changes in land use types and land use structure in the configuration of production activity module, the commodity module and the factor module in the compilation of the relevant SAM. These accounts are assigned corresponding values and included in the regional socioeconomic activities so that the structural change in regional land use caused by changes in different land use types, with different prices, during different periods and under different scenario hypotheses can be modeled.

Table 6.1 Policy variables included in the environmental protection scenario for land use changes in Jiangxi Province

Policy variable	Year	Amount
Discounted subsidy for returning cultivated land (yuan/ha)	2010	2 589
	2015	2 859
	2020	3 273
Cultivated land with gradient over 15 degrees (%)	2010	0.36
	2015	0.29
	2020	0.24

6.1.2.1 Structure of the SAM of Jiangxi Province

(i) Production activities

Using the IO table with 42 sectors in Jiangxi Province in 2007 and with reference to the national economy sector classification and code tables (GB/T47542007), the SAM for Jiangxi Province in 2007 used in the CGELUC model includes a total of 46 production sectors. These 46 production sectors are:

- Agriculture, forestry, animal husbandry and fishing (#1);
- Coal mining and dressing (#2);
- Petroleum and natural gas mining (#3);
- Metallic mining (#4);
- Non-metallic mining (#5);
- Food manufacturing and tobacco processing (#6);
- Textile manufacturing (#7);
- Garment leather, eider down and related products production (#8);
- Wood processing and furniture manufacturing (#9);
- Paper printing and stationery (#10);
- Petroleum processing, coking and nuclear fuel processing (#11);
- Chemical industry (#12);
- Non-metallic mineral products industry (#13);
- Metal smelting and rolling processing (#14);
- Metal products industry (#15);
- General and special equipment manufacturing (#16);
- Transportation equipment manufacturing (#17);
- Electrical, machinery and equipment manufacturing (#18);
- Communications equipment, computers and other electronic equipment manufacturing (#19);
- Manufacture of measuring instruments and machinery for cultural activity and office work (#20);
- Other manufacturing industries (#21);
- Waste scrap (#22);
- Electricity, heat production and supply (#23);
- Gas production and supply (#24);
- Water production and supply (#25);
- Construction industry (#26);

- Transportation and warehousing (#27);
- Postal and telecommunication services (#28);
- Information transmission, computer services and software industry (#29);
- Wholesale and retail trade (#30);
- Accommodation and catering (#31);
- Finance and insurance (#32);
- Real estate (#33);
- Leasing and business services (#34);
- Tourism (#35);
- Scientific research business (#36);
- Comprehensive technical services (#37);
- Other social services (#38);
- Education (#39);
- Health, social security and social welfare sector (#40);
- Culture, sports and entertainment (#41);
- Public administration and social organizations (#42);
- Cultivated land conversion (#43);
- Economic forestry conversion (#44);
- Grassland conversion (#45);
- Other types of land use conversion (#46).

(ii) Commodities

The classification of commodities was conducted in the same way as the classification of production activities described above. The compilation of the SAM for Jiangxi Province in 2007 is based on the assumption of the "pure sector", i.e., production activities and commodities correspond directly to each other and a particular production activity produces only one type of commodity.

(iii) Factors

The factors are divided into labor, capital and land. As we have used the CGELUC model to simulate the structural change in land use in Jiangxi Province, it is necessary to explicitly discuss the conversions of various types of land use in the model, rather than simply divide the land into four categories: cultivated land, economic forests, grassland and other types of land use.

(iv) Institutions

Institutions are divided into three categories: residents, businesses and government.

(v) Others

The other accounts mainly include the capital account and account of other regions in the world.

6.1.2.2 Data Process for the SAM of Jiangxi Province

The most important task is to enter the economic statistical data in the appropriate place in the SAM table after developing the basic account structure. Entering the data is one of the most complex and difficult tasks in the process of compiling the SAM. The data sources and handling processes in the sub-matrixes involved in the SAM table are discussed below based on the account structure described above.

The SAM compiled in this chapter is based on the GDP accounts for Jiangxi Province in 2007, but the data sources can be inconsistent when comparing data from the IO table with the GDP accounts in Jiangxi Province, for two main reasons. First, financial services are handled in different ways. In the IO table, the resident consumption includes the virtual consumption of financial services, but in the national accounts, the services of the financial sectors are treated as intermediate inputs and not included in the residents' final consumption. Second, tariffs are handled in different ways. In the IO table, import tariffs are included in value of the imports as intermediate inputs for various sectors, and the import accounting corresponding to commodities in other regions of the world also includes tariffs, which are used to offset the tariffs of imports consumed in the intermediate input. Therefore, the IO table needs amending as there are fewer parts in its final use section than in the accounting of annual regional GDP. Additionally, because there are a few accounts associated with land conversion in the accounts of the SAM for the CGELUC model, the calculated results will be bigger than the annual regional GDP accounting data with corresponding statistical data added in the revised IO table. Therefore, the IO table needs to be adjusted in the following ways to obtain a more accurate SAM table for Jiangxi Province in 2007.

(i) Adjustment of financial accounts

Data related to residents' final consumption in the "financial" sector needs to be added into the intermediate inputs of various sectors in proportion with the intermediate consumption of financial products in various departments as a framework, so that the residents' final consumption of products from the "financial" sector becomes zero. It is necessary to subtract the corresponding data from the "operation surplus" counted in the added value to maintain the equilibrium of the IO table.

(ii) Adjustment of tariffs

The import tariffs of intermediate inputs in the various departments need to be removed from the IO table and added into the "net tax on production" of added value. Similarly, it is necessary to add the corresponding tariffs into the "import" columns to balance the IO table. In other words, the columns of import tariff data for each sector according to relevant statistical information of "foreign economic trade" in *Statistical Yearbook of Jiangxi Province* in 2008 need to be identified, the calculation method for the import tariff rate and corresponding import tariffs for the year is combined, and the import tariff matrix based on the structure of intermediate inputs of products in the IO table is obtained. Next, the import tariff matrix is subtracted from the intermediate input matrix in the IO table, and the import tariff data for each sector are subtracted from the columns of imports. Finally, the import tariff data for each sector are subtracted from the net taxes on production.

(iii) Adjustment of land use Conversion account

The land use Conversion account is a unique feature of the CGELUC model, and the adjustment of this account directly influences the accuracy and reliability of the simulation results. The intermediate input section solves the problem of accounting for intermediate inputs in the land use conversion process and the amount of land conversion needed for the production of other sectors. The amount of land conversion inputs in the production activities of various sectors in Jiangxi Province in 2007 can be obtained by comparing the 1:100,000 remote sensing land use survey data for Jiangxi Province in 2001 and that in 2007. Furthermore, the intermediate inputs in land use conversion activities can be obtained by comparing the relevant data from the *Statistical Yearbook of Jiangxi Province* in 2007 and 2008.

The added value section needs to consider the total investment in various land factors. The land factors are included as part of the fixed capital, which satisfies the condition that the sum of the adjusted depreciation of fixed assets and total investment in land factors and business surplus equals the total fixed asset depreciation in the original IO table. The input land area can be directly obtained from the statistical yearbooks; the corresponding land price is estimated by incorporating the benchmark land prices and parcel land prices based on relevant rules and regulations in the *Interim Procedures of Prices of State-owned Urban Land in Jiangxi Province.*

The following sections explicitly explain the data sources in the submatrixes of the SAM based on the adjusted IO table of Jiangxi Province in 2007. The balance sheet of the constructed SAM is shown in Appendix 2.

Activities × Commodities: 46 × 46 matrix. The SAM established here is based on the "pure sector hypothesis", so the matrix is a diagonal matrix. The data in this section is obtained from the total outputs in the *Statistical Yearbook of Jiangxi Province* in 2008 as the total amount control data using the ratio of the outputs of each sector and the total output in the IO table as the structure.

Commodities × Activities: 46 × 46 matrix. This represents the intermediate inputs for each commodity. The total amount of intermediate inputs in the capital flow table of Jiangxi Province (1998–2007) is used for the control data, which are disaggregated using the intermediate inputs of the adjusted IO table of Jiangxi Province in 2007 as the structure.

Commodities × Residents (or Commodities × Government): 46 × 1 matrix. This shows the residents' (or government's) consumption of various commodities and land use conversions. To conveniently address the issue, it is assumed that the residents' (or government's) consumption of various commodities and land use conversions are reflected in the intermediate input section, and the direct consumption is zero. The residents' (or government's) consumption of various commodities is redistributed proportionately based on data from the adjusted IO table and combining the total amount of the residents' (or government's) consumption (the real object commodity exchange) from the capital flow table of Jiangxi Province (1998–2007).

Commodities × Capital: 46 × 1 matrix. This matrix records the sum of the fixed capital generating in the production processes of various commodities and stock changes. It is obtained by the correct adjustment of data in the IO table using the total savings amounts at home and abroad in the funds flow table for Jiangxi Province (1998–2007) as the control data and the total amount of generating capital in the adjusted IO table for Jiangxi Province in 2007 as the structure.

Commodities × other regions in the world: 46 × 1 matrix. This matrix records the exports of different commodities. Here the sum of exported land use conversion is set to be zero as land use conversion generally happens at a regional scale. The export sums for all commodities are mainly sourced from the relevant statistical data in *Statistics Yearbook of China Customs* and statistical data on "foreign economic trade" in the *Statistical Yearbook of Jiangxi Province* in 2008. It is noted that the export data in the IO table for Jiangxi Province in 2007 uses the producer price, which is obtained from the conversion of the free on board (FOB) prices with the conversion coefficients. However, the SAM used in the CGELUC model requires FOB prices. Therefore, before entering the relevant data in the SAM, we calculated conversion coefficients for exports from Jiangxi Province in 2007 by combining the relevant data in *China's Customs Statistical Yearbook*, then depreciating the export data with the export conversion coefficients obtained previously to determine the export amount calculated with the FOB price. The sum of imported and exported commodities in the "Foreign Economic Trade" section in the *Statistical Yearbook of Jiangxi Province* in 2008 was used as the control data, and was disaggregated after combining the converted export structure in the IO table.

Labor × Activities: 1 × 46 matrix. This represents the payment the labor factors obtained from production activities in different sectors and land use conversion processes. The payments involved here cannot be obtained directly from the relevant statistics because land use conversion takes place among various sectors of the CGELUC model. This sub-matrix data are generally entered by splitting payment of the labor factor input into the production activities in other sectors when compiling the SAM for Jiangxi Province in 2007. First, the intermediate input in the IO table before and after adjustment is compared and the proportion of commodities input into different land conversion activities by various sectors to the total intermediate input is calculated. The proportion of the payment mentioned above is then subtracted from workers' payments in each sector respectively based on the proportion, and this is added to the workers' payment for land use conversion. Finally, payment of the labor factor in the SAM can be obtained by disaggregating the statistical sum of "employment and wages" in the *Statistical Yearbook of Jiangxi Province* in 2008 and combining the workers' payment item in the revised IO table.

(Capital + land use types) × Activities: 5 × 46 matrix. The adjustment method for the corresponding items in the IO table has been described in detail above. This sub-matrix is obtained by a simple adjustment using the sum of the capital gains obtained from the national economic accounting data as the structure.

Resident × labor: workers' payment. This matrix is obtained by summarizing the calculation results of the "Labor × activity" sub-matrix.

Resident × investment: residents' investment income. This includes the income from individuals and family businesses. In national accounting, the household sector is also a production account, the scope of which includes the production activities of farmers and individual business households. This item can be calculated based on "net business income" and "family business income" from the "average cash income and expenditure of urban household per month per person (2007)" and "country resident income and composition" in the *Statistical Yearbook of Jiangxi Province* in 2008 and combining the rural and urban population in "households and population (from 1978 to the end of 2007)".

Resident × (Corporation + Government): 1 × 2 matrix. This represents the sum of regular transfers and property expenditure by enterprises and the government to residents. The data come from surveys of urban and rural residents in the *Statistical Yearbook of Jiangxi Province* in 2008. The transfer payments from the government to residents mainly include: government pension and social welfare benefits of 992.79 million yuan[①], social security benefits expenditure of 3.217 87 billion yuan, policy-related subsidy expenditure of 1.152 59 billion yuan and administrative institution pensions of 1.303 99 billion yuan.

Resident × other regions in the world: regular transfers from other regions in the world to residents. This matrix is obtained from the "average cash income and expenditure of urban household per person per month (2007)" and "income and composition of rural household" in the *Statistical Yearbook of Jiangxi Province* in 2008 and incorporates the SAM balance theory.

Government × Activity: 1 × 46 matrix, representing the net amount of production tax. This sub-matrix is obtained by further adjusting the corresponding data items in the adjusted IO table in a similar way to the adjustment of worker payments because the land use conversion activities also need to pay some production tax.

Government × Commodities: import tariffs. If the import tariff on land use conversion is set at zero, the tariffs on other commodities can be adjusted with reference to the adjustments in the IO table described previously.

Government × Resident: the direct tax on residents including regular transfers such as individual income tax and social security contributions. Personal income tax is acquired from the "local revenue" in the *Statistical Yearbook of Jiangxi Province* in 2008 (767.73 million yuan). Social security contributions mainly include old-age insurance, unemployment insurance, medical insurance, industrial injury insurance and maternity insurance, which are included in statistical data for "finance, banking, insurance" (3.394 96 billion

① Renminbi (RMB/¥).

yuan).

Investment × Resident: household savings. This matrix is obtained based on "balance of savings deposits of urban and rural residents (1978–2007)" in the *Statistical Yearbook of Jiangxi Province* in 2008 (27.711 13 billion yuan).

Other regions in the world × Commodities: 1 × 46 sub-matrix, representing the importation of various commodities. It is important to note that imports in the SAM refer to freight liner terms, while the IO tables use producer price. The data are adjusted using similar methods to those of the export items.

6.2 Design of the CGELUC Model for Jiangxi Province

The CGELUC model links the factor market, commodity market and land uses with the price of commodities or services produced by consuming land, and forms an equilibrium system covering multiple markets and sectors to carry out a simulation and scenario analysis of the structural change in land uses. When the marginal cost of employing one type of land use is lower than that of employing others, expansion of this type of land use will result in more benefits.

6.2.1 GAMS Operating Environment

The general algebraic modeling system (GAMS) is application-oriented mathematical programming software developed by experts of the World Bank. It is an advanced modeling language. Statements in this language are concise and easy for the model constructer to understand, which greatly improves user efficiency and extends the applications of mathematical programming techniques in policy analysis and decision-making.

6.2.1.1 Basic Characteristics of the GAMS

General principles

The design of the GAMS incorporates relational database theory and mathematical programming methods. The relational database provides a structural framework for the general data organization and transformation, while the mathematical programming provides a way to state and solve problems. The basic ideas are as follows:

- Various algorithms can be applied without changing the representation of the models, and new problem solving methods can be added without modifying the existing model;
- The statement of optimization is independent of the data used, and the separation between the logical structure and data means that increasing

the scale of a problem will not increase the complexity of the statement;

- The application of a relational data model automates the allocation of computer memory, so the user does not have to worry about memory problems for large and complex models.

Universal documents

The statement of the GAMS program makes it easily understood by both users and the computer. The program itself is the model documentation and it is very similar to conventional mathematical methods. Its features are as follows:

- The program makes full use of the precision and compactness of mathematical expressions;
- Data input and result output reports both use the most conventional methods wherever possible;
- Descriptive language is a part of the definition of the corresponding symbols, and it can be displayed simultaneously when necessary;
- A document stores all the information for the model.

Portability

The GAMS can operate in different computer environments, and model data can be conveniently converted between different types of computers and operating systems.

Open interface

The GAMS itself is just a text file without any special editing procedures or graphic input and output functions. Users can generate the GAMS procedures using their own familiar word processing tools. This open structure guarantees the compatibility of the GAMS in existing and future user environments.

Model library

The GAMS encloses a large number of formulated model programs. Users can quote the existing models or conveniently reconstruct and apply formulated technology.

6.2.1.2 Model Structure

The GAMS provides a consistent modeling environment and supports different mathematical methods and algorithms. It can handle linear, nonlinear and mixed integer optimization problems. The model is generated independently of specific algorithms, and users follow the same rules for different issues. There are three types of products in the GAMS software family.

Basic modules of the GAMS

This module contains the GAMS software language, BDMLP① linear planning algorithms and the GAMS model library.

Integrated systems that combine modified specific algorithms, including:

- GAMS/CONOPT provides the independent high-performance CONOPT non-linear algorithm;
- GAMS/CPLEX includes the linear and mixed integer programming algorithms of CPLEX specially modified for GAMS;
- GAMS/DICCPT can solve large-scale non-linear mixed integer programming problems with many non-linear and MIP algorithms;
- GAMS/LAMPS uses the LAMPS linear and mixed-integer algorithm;
- GAMS/LOQO is a specially modified interior-point algorithm, which is used to solve large structural problems;
- GAMS/MILES is used to solve mixed complementary problems such as non-linear complementarities and variational inequalities;
- GAMS/MINOS contains the very mature and widely used MINOS algorithm, which is specially amended to a format acceptable to GAMS;
- GAMS/MPSGE is the programming language and solving method for the economic equilibrium model;
- GAMS/OSL provides simple linear, mixed integer programming and interior-point algorithms for solving big complex problems;
- GAMS/XA is a modified version of professional linear and mixed integer programming system XA;
- GAMS/ZOOM is a mixed-integer of ZOOM and linear algorithm of XMP;

Modules connected with special solving algorithms including:

- GAMS/CPLEX LINK for calling the CPLEX program;
- GAMS/MPSX LINKT for using GAMS as a modeling system for the MPSX linear and mixed-programming algorithm of IBM;
- GAMS/OSL LINK is used to connect optimization subroutines, including linear, mixed integer and interior-point algorithms;
- RGAMS/SCICONIC LINK is used to link the linear and mixed-programming algorithms of GAMS and SCI-CONIC;

6.2.2 Structure of the CGELUC Model for Jiangxi Province

Jiangxi is an important water and soil conservation area in China, so in large forested areas, the forestry policy has an important influence on structural

① GAMS/BDMLP is an LP and MIP solver that comes free with any GAMS software and is intended for small to medium sized models. GAMS/BDMLP was originally developed at the World Bank by Brooke, Drud and Meeraus (1985) and is now maintained by GAMS Development. GAMS/BDMLP is running on all platforms for which GAMS is available.

changes in local land use. Therefore, the CGELUC model structure in Jiangxi Province, described below, includes the following: quantitative thematic analysis of land use, macroscopic econometric modeling, spatial variations in land use, analysis of impacts of regional agricultural policy, and scenario analysis of regional forestry policy. The relationships between these basic functional structures reflect the way socioeconomic factors drive structural changes in regional land use (Fig. 6.1).

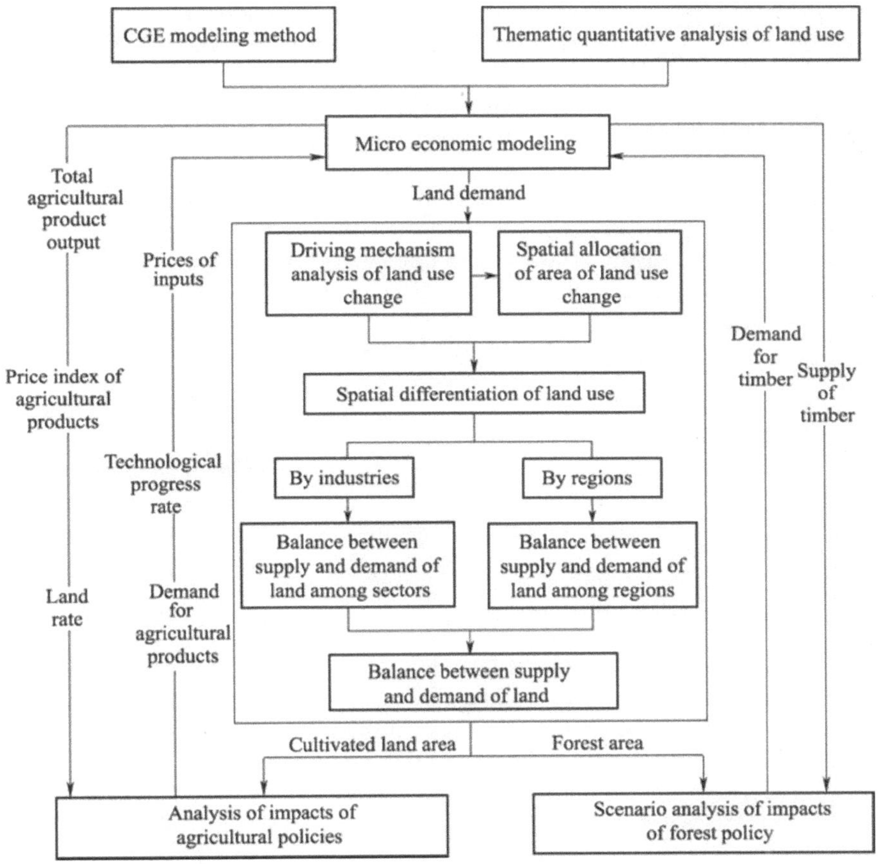

Fig. 6.1 Simulation framework of structural changes in land use in Jiangxi Province based on the CGELUC model.

The quantitative thematic analysis of land use is used to simulate the expansion of land such as urban, infrastructure, and tourism land, given a certain direction. Macroscopic econometric modeling is used to construct models by dividing the national economy into different compartments based on different research purposes, where the economic behavior in all sectors is determined by the objective function of benefit maximization. The spatial variation in land use allocates the land area of each sector onto a 1×1km grid and reintegrates the area of cultivated land and forestry, using them as input variables in the analysis of the impacts of regional agricultural policy and the scenario analysis of regional forestry policy.

The analysis of the impacts of agricultural policy in Jiangxi Province is mainly used to simulate agricultural production under the constraints of agricultural policy impact factors in Jiangxi Province. The scenario analysis of forestry policy in Jiangxi Province is used to simulate and calculate the supply of forest products in Jiangxi Province under forestry policy constraints, i.e., the percentage difference between timber demand and cut timber volumes.

The CGELUC model restrains the behavior of economic agents in Jiangxi Province with the objective function of benefit maximization in the macroscopic econometric modeling. The model calculates a new balance with a series of new parameters generating from the analysis of impacts of agricultural policy and the scenario analysis of forestry policy of Jiangxi Province, and then systematically analyzes the impacts of the implementation of agricultural and forestry policies on agricultural production in Jiangxi Province.

6.2.3 Scenario Design

Five scenarios, baseline, economic priority, environment protection, biofuel development and agricultural subsidy, were developed in this study to simulate the structure changes in land uses in Jiangxi Province under various policies.

6.2.3.1 Design of the Baseline Scenario and the Economic Priority Scenario

The baseline scenario assumes that the change in area of various land use types maintains the current trends and rate. The area ratios among cultivated land, forestry, grasslands, water areas, built-up areas and unused land are predicted on this basis (Priess et al., 2007; Cramb et al., 2009). The economic priority scenario focuses on policies for future industrial structure adjustment and technological change that will promote rapid population growth and economic development. This scenario assumes that the standard deviations of the birth rate and GDP growth rate in Jiangxi Province will double and the mortality rate will be consistent with that of the baseline scenario.

6.2.3.2 Scenario Designs for Other Policies

Scenarios under different policies are also modeled. These scenarios include: predicting the impacts on environmental protection with the return of cultivated land to forestry; biofuel development; and the implementation of appropriate agricultural subsidy strategies on the structural change in land use in Jiangxi Province from the perspectives of environmental protection, biofuel development and agricultural subsidies (Pfaff and Sanchez-Azofeifa, 2004).

The environmental protection scenario considers the impacts of returning cultivated land based on slope classification and subsidy policies for returning cultivated land on land use change. The slope information in 1 km grid land use types was extracted from the data of Jiangxi Province in 1:250 000 topographic maps, and the slope was divided into six grades: 0°, 0°–3°, 3°–8°, 8°–15°, 15°–25°, and > 25°. Land use conversion affects the areas of cultivated land, forestry and grassland, and leads to an increase or a decrease in the area of different land use types, but the final sum of the areas of these land use types must be equal to the total land area of Jiangxi Province. The national subsidy for returning cultivated land is 2 250 kg raw grain and a 300 yuan living allowance for each hectare per year in the southern provinces. The raw grain subsidy has been converted into cash based on the food price in Jiangxi Province to make calculations easier in this chapter (Table 6.1). The subsidy for returning cultivated land is set at 2 589 yuan/ha in the environmental protection scenario based on a trend analysis of food price change during the implementation process of the subsidy policy described in this research.

The biofuel development scenario mainly considers the influence of the biofuel development programs and the biofuel development subsidy on the spatiotemporal pattern of land use. The main influencing factors considered in this scenario include the subsidy for production of crops and timber, average per capita car ownership, agricultural research investment and agricultural investment (Table 6.2). The biofuel subsidy directly contributes to the increased growth of fuel crops and timber, and the 2010 subsidy for fuel production crops and timber is 447 yuan/ha in this scenario. With the improved living standard of the Chinese people, cars have gradually become popular, and the gradual increase of average per capita car ownership has also led to increased energy demands. However, non-renewable oil, natural gas and other natural energy resources are limited, and biofuel is expected to be the main energy source in the future. Changes in the average per capita car ownership are expected to affect the development of biofuel. The average per capita car ownership is set to 37.7 per 1 000 people in 2010 based on the development rate of average per capita car ownership. Biofuel technology is not yet mature, and investment in agricultural research represents the investment in

Table 6.2 Policy variables included in the biofuel development scenario for land use changes in Jiangxi Province

Policy variable	Year	Amount
Subsidy for production of fuel crops and timber (yuan/ha)	2010	447
	2015	598.5
	2020	801
Agricultural investment (100 million yuan)	2010	411.6
	2015	604.8
	2020	888.6

the development of biofuel technology, and the amount of investment determines the rate of development of biofuel technology to some extent. Agricultural investment affects biofuel technology development and also affects the development of fuel production crops and timber.

The agricultural subsidy scenario considers the impacts of national agricultural subsidies and other subsidies related to agriculture for land use change in Jiangxi Province. The main impact factors considered under this scenario are the agricultural subsidy and grain price (Table 6.3). With economic development, agricultural costs increase and the grain price falls, farmers' enthusiasm for growing crops declines rapidly, many farmers get conventional jobs, and most of the cultivated land may turn into unused land. The agricultural subsidy encourages farmers to continue growing crops and stabilizes agricultural development in Jiangxi Province, guaranteeing the grain supply in Jiangxi Province. The subsidy is estimated to be 417.45 yuan/ha in 2010 in the agricultural subsidy scenario based on the current economic development speed. The grain price is also an important factor affecting the change in area of cultivated land, as the grain price directly determines the farmers' income.

Table 6.3 Policy variables included in the agricultural subsidy scenario for the land use changes in Jiangxi Province

Policy variable	Year	Amount
Agricultural subsidy (yuan/ha)	2010	27.83
	2015	37.40
	2020	50.41
Grain price (yuan/kg)	2010	1.73
	2015	2.21
	2020	2.82

6.3 Analysis of Simulation Results of Land Use Structure in Jiangxi Province

Using the CGELUC model, we estimated the area changes in land uses in Jiangxi Province during 2010–2020 under different scenarios, which may help to explore the rules and characteristics of the structural changes in land uses affected by the different policies.

6.3.1 Land Use Change Based on Different Scenarios

The areas of the different land use types in Jiangxi Province from 2010 to 2020 are predicted, and rules and features of land use change in different scenarios are explored based on the driving mechanism analysis module of spatial heterogeneity of land use change in the CGELUC model.

6.3.1.1 Analysis of the Baseline Scenario

There is evident heterogeneity in the land use change in Jiangxi Province under the baseline scenario. The amount of cultivated land reduces each year, and the model prediction indicates that cultivated land will decrease by 278 400 ha during 2010–2020, with an annual average decrease of 27 843 ha, an annual growth rate of –0.94%. The proportion of cultivated land area is also gradually decreasing from 18% of the total land area in 2010 to 17% in 2015 and 16% in 2020. The forestry area shows a substantially increasing trend, with increases of 136 480 and 138 760 ha from 2010 to 2015 and 2015 to 2020, respectively, with an annual growth rate of 0.263%. The proportion of forestry area will increase from 62% in 2010 to 64% in 2020. By contrast, the changes in the grassland area will not be obvious. The grassland in Jiangxi Province will experience an annual average reduction of 0.10% from 2010 to 2015. The grassland will reduce by 400 ha annually on average from 2010 to 2015, and by 390 ha per year from 2015 to 2020. Predictions indicate that the water area change is minimal, decreasing by 1 180 ha from 2010 to 2015, and 1140 ha from 2015 to 2020, with an annual average rate of decrease of 0.024%. The built-up area, however, will increase each year, but the growth rate varies from 2010 to 2015, it will increase by 49 180 ha, and the increase will be 49 070 ha from 2015 to 2020, with an annual average increase rate of 1.30%. As the proportion of the built-up area in Jiangxi Province is not large, this remains at around 5% from 2010 to 2020 (Fig. 6.2).

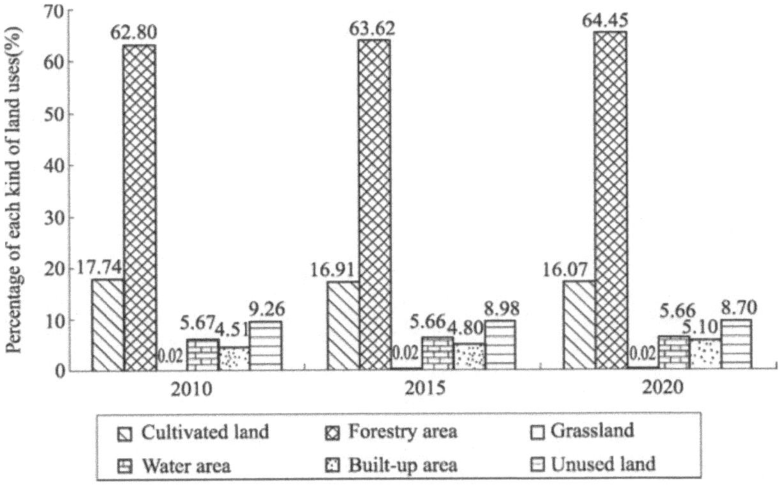

Fig. 6.2 Land use structure in the baseline scenario in Jiangxi Province in 2010, 2015 and 2020.

6.3.1.2 Analysis of the Environmental Protection Scenario

Under the environmental protection scenario, the land use change in Jiangxi Province varies significantly (Yang et al., 2009). The area of cultivated land decreases each year, with predictions indicating a reduction of 273 017 ha from 2010 to 2020, with an annual average reduction of 27 300 ha. The annual reduction rate of 0.92% means that the cultivated land area will reduce gradually, reducing by 132 650 ha from 2010 to 2015, and 140 370 ha from 2015 to 2020. Cultivated land in Jiangxi Province will account for 18% of the total land area in 2010 and 17% and 16% in 2015 and 2020, respectively. By contrast, the forestry area shows a substantial increase; predictions indicate that the forestry area in Jiangxi Province will increase by 138 620 and 136 670 ha from 2010 to 2015 and 2015 to 2020, respectively, with an annual average growth rate of 0.263%. The proportion of forestry area in Jiangxi Province will increase each year, from 62% in 2010 to 64% in 2020. However, the changing trend in grassland is less evident with an annual average decrease rate of 0.39%. Predictions indicate that the water area will reduce by 1 180 ha from 2010 to 2015 and 1 090 ha from 2015 to 2020, with an annual average decrease rate of 0.24%. The built-up area will increase each year, but the growth rate varies from 2010 to 2015, it will increase by 49 680 ha, and it will increase by 45 950 ha from 2015 to 2020, with an annual average increase rate of 1.27% (Fig. 6.3).

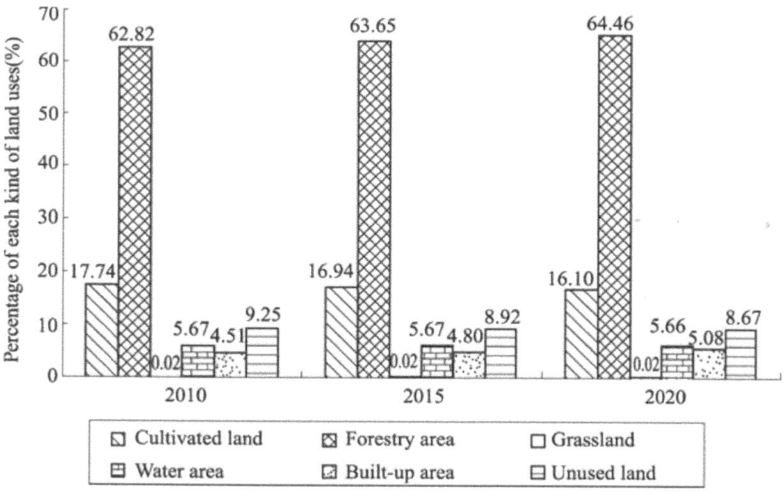

Fig. 6.3 Land use structure under the environmental protection scenario in Jiangxi Province in 2010, 2015 and 2020.

6.3.1.3 Analysis of the Biofuel Development Scenario

In the biofuel development scenario, the cultivated land in Jiangxi Province reduces each year, and predictions indicate that cultivated land will reduce by 263 016 ha from 2010 to 2020, with an annual average reduction of 26 300 ha and an annual reduction rate of 0.888%. The proportion of cultivated land will gradually reduce from 18% in 2010 to 16% in 2020. The forestry area shows substantial growth; predictions indicate that from 2010 to 2015 and 2015 to 2020, the forestry area in Jiangxi Province will increase by 238 620 ha and 179 670 ha, respectively, with an annual average growth rate of 0.399%. The proportion of land in forestry in Jiangxi Province will increase from 62% in 2010, to 64% in 2015 and 65% in 2020. The changing trend in grassland is less obvious. The grassland in Jiangxi Province will decrease with an annual average rate of 0.07% from 2010 to 2020. The grassland area will decrease by 19 ha from 2010 to 2015, and 19.2 ha from 2015 to 2020. Predictions also indicate that the water area will reduce by 3 095 ha from 2010 to 2015 and a further 2 201 ha from 2015 to 2020. However, the built-up area will increase each year, but the growth rate varies, the built-up area will increase by 50 685 ha from 2010 to 2015 and by 47 945 ha from 2015 to 2020, with an annual average rate of increase of 1.31% (Fig. 6.4).

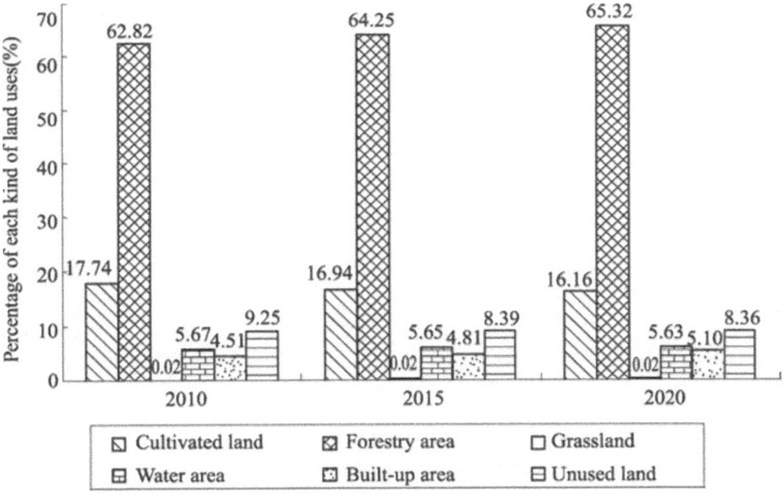

Fig. 6.4 Land use structure under the biofuel development scenario in Jiangxi Province in 2010, 2015 and 2020.

6.3.1.4 Agricultural Subsidy Scenario

Under the agricultural subsidy scenario, the cultivated land in Jiangxi Province still reduces each year, and predictions indicate that the cultivated land area will reduce by180 017 ha from 2010 to 2020, with an annual average reduction of 18 001 ha and an annual decrease rate of 0.608%. The proportion of cultivated land in Jiangxi Province is predicted to reduce gradually from 18% in 2010 to 17% in 2020. Predictions also indicate that the forestry area will increase by 92 672 ha and18 730 ha from 2010 to 2015 and 2015 to 2020 respectively, with an annual average growth rate of 0.179%. The proportion of forestry in Jiangxi Province will increase from 62% in 2010 to 63% in 2020. Changes in grassland are not apparent. Predictions indicate that the water area will reduce by 1 201 ha from 2010 to 2015 and 229 ha from 2015 to 2020, with an annual average rate of decrease of 0.024%. The built-up area will increase each year, but the growth rate gradually decreases, it will increase by 24 945 ha from 2010 to 2015 and 7 463 ha from 2015 to 2020, with an annual average rate of increase of 0.993% (Fig. 6.5).

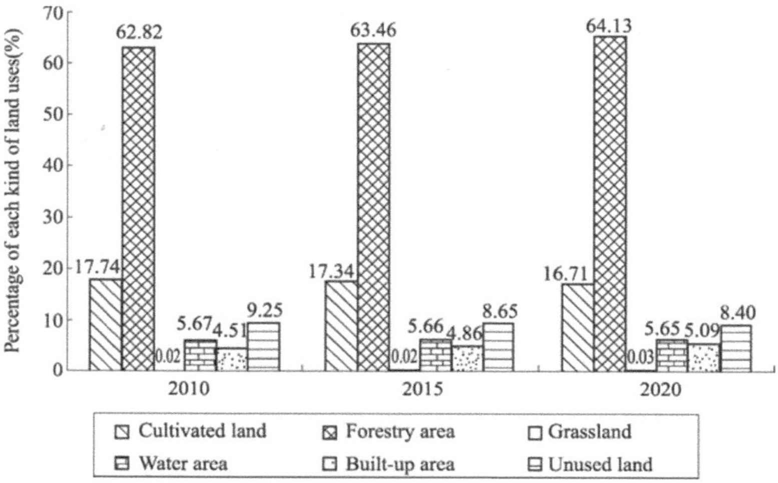

Fig. 6.5 Land use structure under the agricultural subsidy scenario in Jiangxi Province in 2010, 2015 and 2020.

6.3.1.5 Economic Priority Scenario

Under the economic priority scenario, the land use change in Jiangxi Province varies significantly. The cultivated land area decreases each year in this scenario. Predictions indicate that the cultivated land will reduce by 334 920 ha from 2010 to 2020, with an annual average reduction of 33 494 ha, and an annual rate of reduction of 1.131%. The proportion of cultivated land will gradually decline from 18% of the total land area in 2010 to 17% in 2015 and to 16% in 2020. The forestry area shows a slight growth trend; predictions indicate that the forestry area will increase by 122 640 ha and 92 640 ha from 2010 to 2015 and 2015 to 2020 respectively, with an annual average growth rate of 0.205%. The proportion of forestry area in Jiangxi Province will increase from 62% in 2010 to 64% in 2020. By contrast, the change in grassland will be slower, decreasing with an annual average rate of reduction of 0.121% from 2010 to 2020. The grassland will reduce by 126 ha from 2010 to 2015 and 120 ha from 2015 to 2020. Predictions indicate that water area will change proportionally to a lesser extent than the other land use areas.

The water area will decrease by 3 162 ha from 2010 to 2015, and 1 564 ha from 2015 to 2020, with an annual average rate of decrease of 0.049%. The built-up area will increase each year, and its growth rate will also increase each year: the annual average rate of increase in the built-up area will be 1.602% from 2010 to 2015 and 2.062% from 2015 to 2020. The built-up area is predicted to increase by 62 899 ha from 2010 to 2015 and by 89 058 ha from 2015 to 2020, with an annual average rate of increase of 1.997%. As the proportion of the built-up area in Jiangxi Province is not large, this will remain at around 5% from 2010 to 2020. The variation in unused land is significant; the proportion of the unused land area is 9% between 2010 and 2015, but by 2020, it will decrease to 8% (Fig. 6.6).

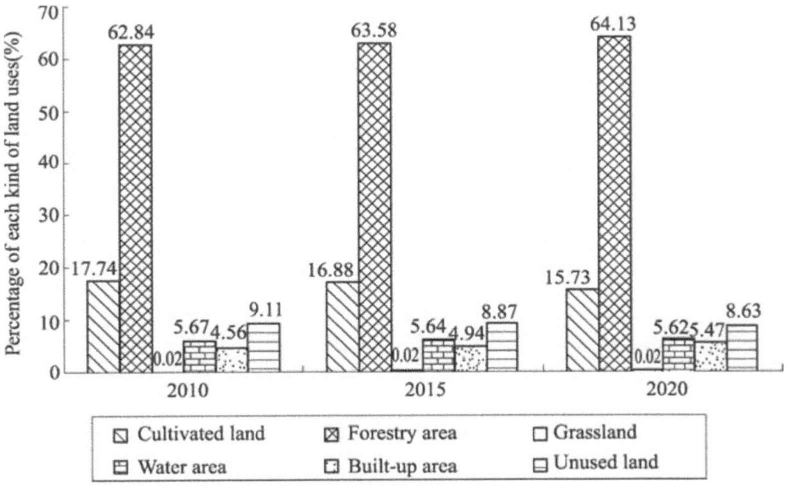

Fig. 6.6 Land use structure under the economic priority scenario in Jiangxi Province in 2010, 2015 and 2020.

6.3.2 Comparative Analysis of Land Use Structure under Different Scenarios

The predictions of land use change based on the CGELUC model reflect the rules and features of the change in various land types under different scenarios (Fig. 6.7). The cultivated land area in Jiangxi Province shows declining tendency with the results of all five scenarios, but the decrease in cultivated land is slowest under the agricultural subsidy scenario and the fastest under the economic priority scenario. Unlike the estimates of the baseline scenario, the environmental protection and biofuel development scenarios have no obvious impacts on the change in cultivated land in Jiangxi Province.

The forestry area in Jiangxi Province shows an increasing tendency with

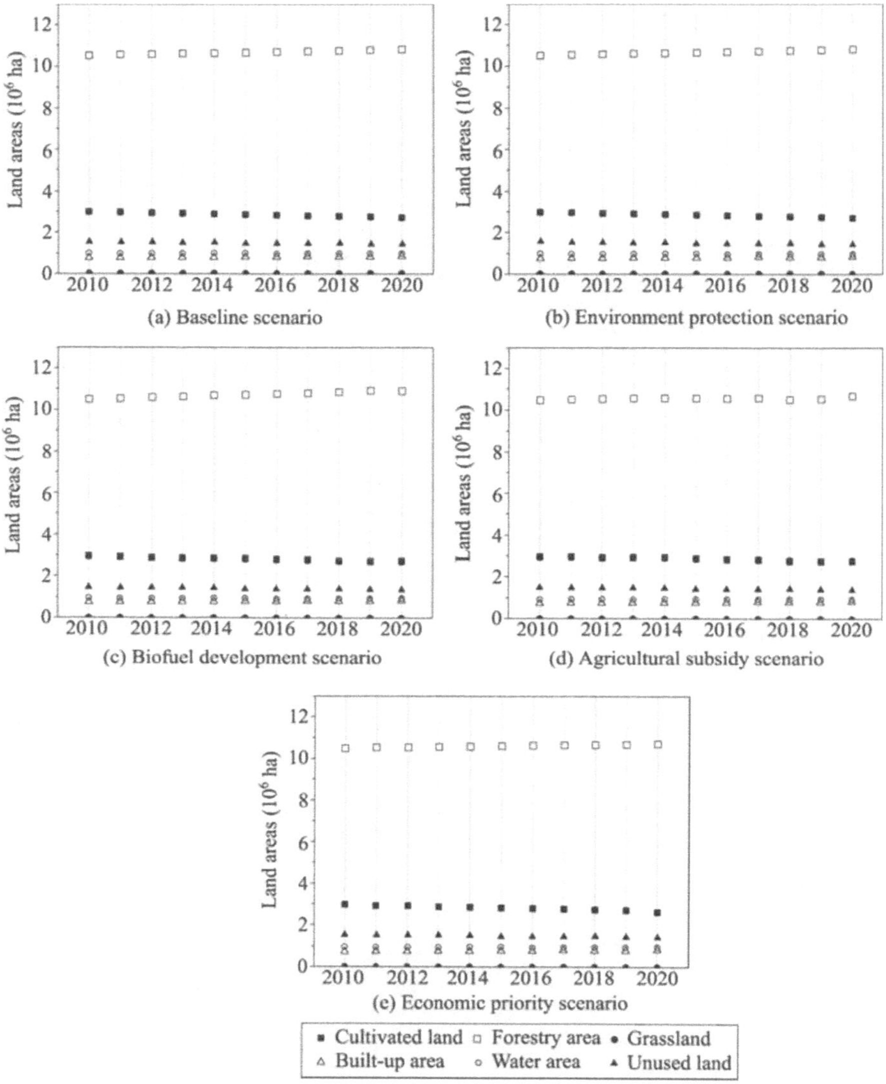

Fig. 6.7 Area change in cultivated land in Jiangxi Province from 2010 to 2020 under various scenarios.

the results of all five scenarios, and its rate of increase is highest under the biofuel development scenario and lowest under the agricultural subsidy scenario. This may be because biofuel development planning and biofuel subsidies can directly promote the growth of fuel crops, while agricultural subsidies play negative roles in promoting the conversion from cultivated land to forests (Fig. 6.7). Comparatively, the forestry area expansion in Jiangxi Province under the baseline and environmental protection scenarios is more significant than that under economic priority scenario.

The changes in grassland in Jiangxi Province are not consistent under agricultural subsidy scenario and biofuel development scenario (Fig. 6.7). Take biofuel development scenario as an instance, while experiencing a slight decline in the period of 2010–2014, the grassland area in Jiangxi Province expands rapidly during 2015–2020, which may be related to a lagged effect of policy implementation. Overall, the agricultural subsidy policy, biofuel development planning and biofuel subsidies have positive effects on the expansion of grassland in Jiangxi Province. However, the baseline, environmental protection and economic priority scenarios have no overall impacts on the grassland in Jiangxi Province. Because Jiangxi Province lies on the middle and lower reaches of Yangtze River, in southeastern China, the proportion of grassland in the total land area is relatively small, so the influence of the five different scenarios on the grassland in is less significant than for other land types.

The water area of Jiangxi Province shows a declining tendency in the results of all five scenarios (Fig. 6.7). The rate of decline is relatively low under the baseline and environmental protection scenarios and is highest under the economic priority scenario. The biofuel development and agricultural subsidies scenarios both influence the decrease in water area in Jiangxi Province.

The built-up area in Jiangxi Province shows an increasing tendency in the results of all five scenarios (Fig. 6.7). The rate of increase is fastest under the economic priority scenario, while the other four scenarios do not have significantly different impacts on the built-up area in Jiangxi Province.

In the results of all five scenarios, the unused land in Jiangxi Province shows a declining tendency (Fig. 6.7). The rate of decline is highest under the biofuel development scenario, and the policy of agricultural subsidies also has significant impacts on unused land in Jiangxi Province. The baseline, environmental protection and economic priority scenarios also cause a decrease in the unused land in Jiangxi Province. Irrespective of the scenario simulation, the change in unused land area is not significant, and perhaps related to the fact that the proportion of unused land in the total land area in Jiangxi Province is not large.

By comparing the simulation results for land use change between the different scenarios, we can determine the competition and succession laws for various land use types under different scenarios and at different temporal scales. By integrating the simulation results based on scenario design, we find that cultivated land, water area and unused land in Jiangxi Province all show declining trends in the simulation results for all different scenarios. The rate of decline for cultivated land is lowest under the agricultural subsidy scenario and highest under the economic priority scenario; the decrease in water area is comparatively slow under the baseline and environmental protection scenarios and the fastest under the economic priority scenario; the unused land decreases fastest under the biofuel development scenario and agricultural subsidies also have an obvious impact on unused land in Jiangxi

Province.

The simulation results for different scenarios can provide policy-makers with a reference for understanding how land use planning affects land use types. About 97% of the land in Jiangxi Province is part of the Poyang Lake watershed, which is a world-famous wetland and ecological nature reserve. Therefore, this research is also of global significance for ecological and environmental protection.

6.4 Summary

Simulations and scenario based predictions of the structural change in land use in Jiangxi Province using the CGELUC model were conducted, and are discussed in this chapter. Changing trends in land use structure were obtained for a baseline scenario, environmental protection scenario, biofuel development scenario, agricultural subsidies scenario and economic priority scenario from 2010 to 2020. The succession laws and competition among various land use types in Jiangxi Province over the next 10 years are also illustrated.

The simulation results show that cultivated land in Jiangxi Province presents a decreasing trend and forestry area an increasing trend in all five scenarios; the grassland has a slight increase in the economic priority scenario, and it does not change significantly in the other four scenarios; the water area presents declines slightly in all five scenarios; while the built-up area presents increases in all five scenarios; the unused land area does not change significantly in any scenarios except the biofuel development and economic priority scenarios in which it slightly decreases.

References

Brooke A, Drud A, Meeraus A.1985. Modeling systems and nonlinear programming in a research environment. In Ragavan R, Rohde S M (Eds), Computers in Engineering, Vol. Ⅲ. ACME, 1985.

Cramb R A, Colfer C J P, Dressler W, Laungaramsri P, Trung L Q, Mulyoutami E, Peluso N L, Wadley R L. 2009. Swidden transformations and rural livelihoods in Southeast Asia. Human Ecology, 37(3): 323–346.

Dawn C Parker, Hessl A, Davis S C. 2008. Complexity, land-use modeling, and the human dimension: Fundamental challenges for mapping unknown outcome spaces. Geoforum, 39(2): 789–804.

Fontaine C M and Rounsevell M D A. 2009. An agent-based approach to model future residential pressure on a regional landscape. Landscape Ecology, 24(9): 1237–1254.

Haberl H, Batterbury S, Moran E. 2001. Using and shaping the land: A long-term perspective. Land Use Policy, 18(1): 1–8.

Haberl H, Erb K H, Krausmann F, Adensam H, Schulz N B. 2003. Land-use change and socio-economic metabolism in Austria — Part II: Land-use scenarios for 2020. Land Use Policy, 20(1):21–39.

Kerr S, Liu S G, Pfaff A S P, Hughes R F. 2003. Carbon dynamics and land-use choices: Building a regional-scale multidisciplinary model. Journal of Environmental Management, 69(1): 25–37.

Krausmann F, Haberl H, Schulz N B, Erb K H, Darge E, Gaube V. 2003. Land-use change and socio-economic metabolism in Austria — Part I: Driving forces of land-use change: 1950—1995. Land Use Policy, 20(1): 1–20.

Liu J Y, Deng X Z, Liu M L, Zhang S W. 2002. Study on the spatial patterns of land-use change and analyses of driving forces in Northeastern China during 1990—2000. Chinese Geographical Science, 12(4): 299–308.

Pfaff A S P and Sanchez-Azofeifa G A. 2004. Deforestation pressure and biological reserve planning: A conceptual approach and an illustrative application for Costa Rica. Resource and Energy Economics, 26(2): 237–254.

Polhill J G. 2009. Agent-based modeling of socio-economic processes related to the environment: Example of land-use change. Uncertainties in Environmental Modelling and Consequences for Policy Making: 61–76.

Priess J A, Mimler M, Klein A M, Schwarze S, Tscharntke T, Steffan-Dewenter I. 2007. Linking deforestation scenarios to pollination services and economic returns in coffee agroforestry systems. Ecological Applications, 17(2): 407–417.

Greenberg A, Nielsen T L, Rasmussen K. 1998. Field expansion and reallocation in the Sahel—Land use pattern dynamics in a fluctuating biophysical and socio-economic environment. Global Environmental Change, 8(4): 309–327.

Seto K C, Kaufmann R K, Woodcock C E. 2000. Landsat reveals China's farmland reserves, but they're vanishing fast. Nature, 406: 121.

Seto K C and Kaufmann R K. 2003. Modeling the drivers of urban land use change in the Pearl River Delta, China: Integrating remote sensing with socio-economic data. Land Economics, 79: 106–121.

Stevens D and Dragicevic S. 2007. A GIS-based irregular cellular automata model of land-use change. Environment and Planning B—Planning and Design, 34(4): 708–724.

Verburg P H, Soepboer W, Veldkamp A, Limpiada R, Espaldon V, Mastura S S A. 2002. Modeling the spatial dynamics of regional land use: The CLUE-S model. Environmental Management, 30(3): 391–405.

Weinstoerffer J and Girardin P. 2000. Assessment of the contribution of land use pattern and intensity to landscape quality: Use of a landscape indicator. Ecological Modelling, 130(1–3): 95–109.

Yang J, Huang J K, Qiu H G, Rozelle S, Sombilla M A. 2009. Biofuels and the Greater Mekong Subregion: Assessing the impact on prices, production and trade. Applied Energy, 86: S37–S46.

Yue T X, Fan Z M, Liu J Y. 2005. Changes of major terrestrial ecosystems in China since 1960. Global and Planetary Change, 48(4): 287–302.

Chapter 7 Modeling the Dynamics of the Land System in an Agriculture-Pasture Transition Zone in China

Simulations of land system dynamics provide significant reference information for land use planning and land resource optimization management decision-making. Land system dynamics are reflected by changes in patterns of the land uses influenced by various driving factors (Heilig, 1997; Li, 1999; Lambin et al., 2001, 2003; Haberl et al., 2004; Burgi et al., 2004; Aguiar et al., 2007; Turner II et al., 2007). The Taips League, an area which is typical of the agriculture-pasture transitional zone, is used as a case study area in this chapter to analyze the spatial dependency relationships between land use patterns and driving factors. These relationships are based on a comprehensive analysis of the natural controlling factors, diverse climatic factors and socioeconomic factors which influence changes in the land use pattern, and are used to simulate the spatial patterns of the future land uses(de Koning et al., 1999; Verburg et al., 2004; Yue et al., 2005; Deng et al., 2008).

7.1 Taips League Background

The Taips League is 85 km from east to west and 65.5 km from north to south, covering an area of 3 414.7 km^2, of which agricultural zones, pastoral regions and urban areas account for 2 557.7, 850 and 7.04 km^2, respectively (TLAEB, 2000).

7.1.1 Location

The Taips League is located in the extreme south of the Xilin Gol League, Inner Mongolia, between 114°51′–115°49′ E and 41°35′–42°10′ N. The Taips League borders the Zhengxiangbai Banner to the northwest and the Zhengxianglan Banner in the northeast, Guyuan County, Hebei Province to the southeast and Kangbao County, Hebei Province to the west.

7.1.2 Climate

The Taips League is located in a mid-latitude inland area and climate is controlled throughout the year by the westerly wind circulation. The monsoon circulation is influenced by wind from the land, by the winter monsoon for long periods and by the summer monsoon for short periods. During winter and spring, there are frequent cold air flows and cold snaps due to the location at the edge of the Siberian-Mongolian high pressure system in winter. During summer, the Taips League experiences plentiful rain and warmth due to the monsoon. The Taips League is characterized by a sub-temperate continental climate due to the control of the polar continental air mass and the influences of solar radiation and atmospheric circulation.

7.1.2.1 Sunshine Hours

The Taips League is rich in solar radiation and sunshine with many sunny days. Since the 1970s, the annual sunshine hours have generally fluctuated between 2 200 and 2 600 hours, with an average of 2 450 hours per year (Fig. 7.1), of which typically 1 090 sunshine hours occur between May and August. During this period, the average number of annual sunshine hours has gradually increased. This is very beneficial for plant growth because of its annual average percentage of sunshine as high as 60–70%, a total solar radiation of 134–138 kcal/cm^2 and a photosynthetic active radiation of 66–73 kcal/cm^2.

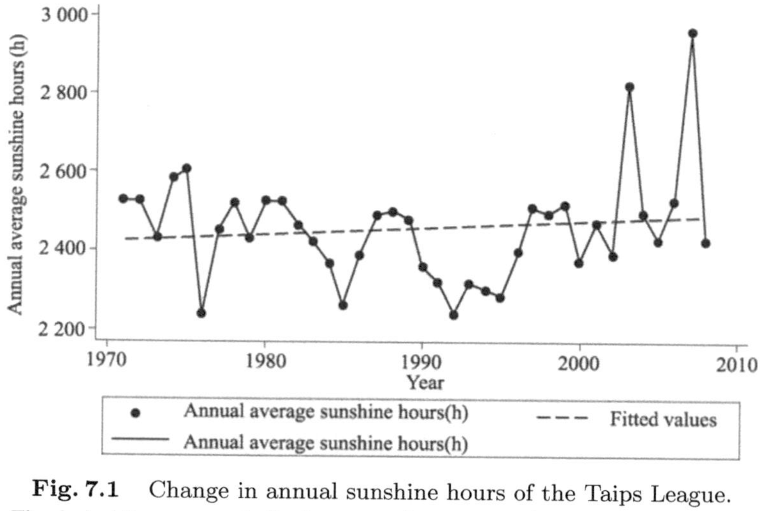

Fig. 7.1 Change in annual sunshine hours of the Taips League.
The dashed line represents the 5-year moving average of annual sunshine hours.

7.1.2.2 Temperature

The annual average temperature of the Taips League between 1971 and 2008 was 1.6℃, with a slightly increasing trend (Fig. 7.2). The average minimum temperature was –17.6℃ in January, with an extreme of –35.7℃ (Dec 1971), and the average maximum temperature was 17.8℃ in July, with an extreme of 33.3℃ (July 1987). The annual average daily temperature range for the period was 13.1℃. Typically, the frost period starts in mid-September and ends in mid-May of the following year.

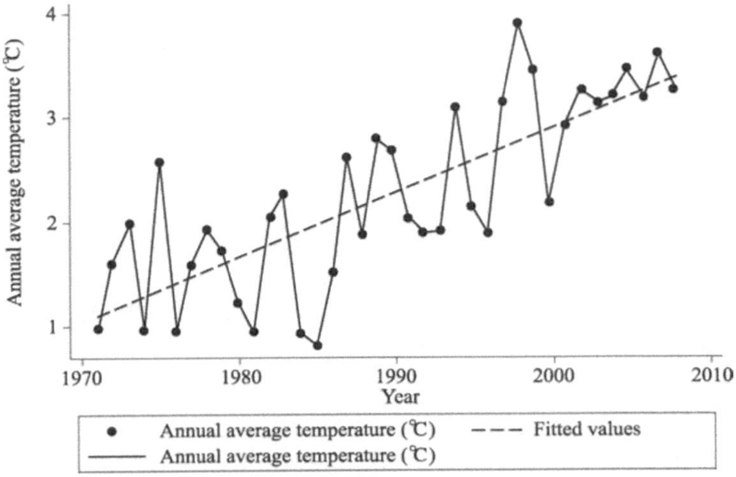

Fig. 7.2 Annual change in average temperature in the Taips League. The dashed line shows the 5-year moving average of the annual average temperature.

7.1.2.3 Precipitation and Evaporation

The annual average precipitation in the Taips League is 407 mm, with a maximum of 625 mm and a minimum of 240 mm. Due to the monsoon climate, seasonal precipitation clearly fluctuates throughout the year, with 65% of the total annual precipitation occurring in summer, 18% in autumn, 13% in spring and 4% in winter. The annual precipitation has also varied; the precipitation was high in the 1970s, and then decreased slightly in the 1980s (Fig. 7.3). The monthly precipitation can also vary dramatically, the maximum and minimum precipitations in January were 12.3 mm and 0.8 mm, respectively, and the maximum and minimum precipitations in July were 247.2 mm and 32.7 mm, respectively.

The annual average humidity in the Taips League is below 61%. The annual average evaporation was 1 900.6 mm, with a maximum of 2 138.8 mm (1973) and a minimum of 1 681.7 mm (1967). Droughts often occur in spring, autumn and winter in the Taips League as the annual average evaporation is about five times the annual average precipitation.

7.1.2.4 Wind

The prevailing winds in the Taips League are northwest in winter and southerly

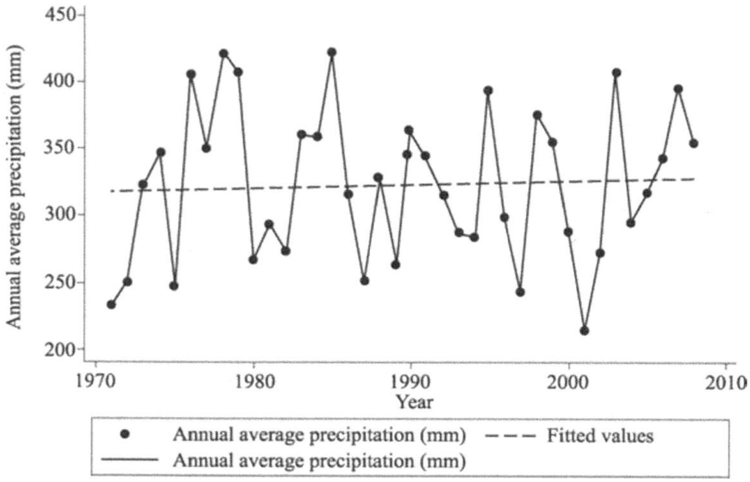

Fig. 7.3 Annual fluctuation of average precipitation in the Taips League. The dashed line represents the 5-year moving annual average precipitation.

in summer with an annual average wind speed of 4 m/s, and a maximum average wind speed of 5.3 m/s in April. Each year there are an average of 76 days of gale force winds, with an average of 35 days in spring and just 3 days in July and August. The annual effective wind power density is 150–200 W/m^2. According to long-term records, the annual wind speed has decreased year by year in the Taips League (Fig. 7.4).

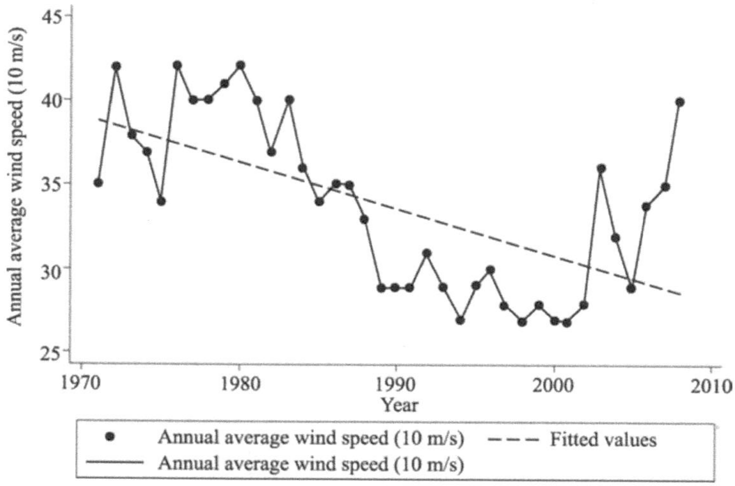

Fig. 7.4 Annual fluctuation of average wind speed in the Taips League. The dashed line represents the 5-year annual moving average wind speed.

7.1.3 Terrain and Landform

The Taips League is located in the eastern part of the Yinshan Mountains, in the Chahar hilly area, with a descending slope from northeast to southwest forming a beach-hill-mountain terrain. The altitude is generally 1 300 and 1 400 m above sea level, with a maximum elevation of 1 802 m and a minimum elevation of 1 325 m (Fig. 7.5).

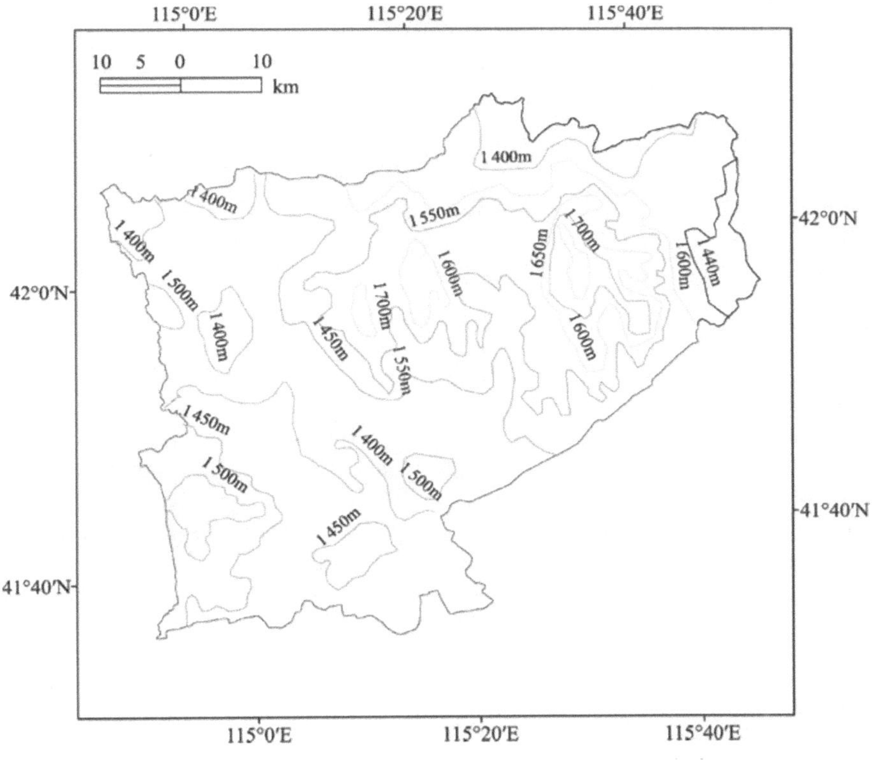

Fig. 7.5 Spatial heterogeneity of altitude in the Taips League.

Various composite tectonic structures are found in the Taips League, leading to a variety of landforms, including low mountains, hilly areas, sloping hummock, valley lowlands, intervals, valley plains, low hills and ridges.

7.1.3.1 Low Mountains

The low mountainous areas are located in the northwest and northeast of the Taips League, around Houfangzi Village of Touzhijian Town, covering a total area of 145 km^2. These perfectly rounded hills are generally between 1 500 and 1 800 m above sea level with wavy ridge lines and linear or low arched hillsides, with slopes ranging from 10° to 15°. The valleys in the range are underdeveloped, with relative altitude differences of 100–200 m, and are groundwater recharge areas in the Taips League.

7.1.3.2 Hilly Areas

The hilly areas are mainly located from around Chedaogou Village of Touzhijian Town, farms of Wanshoutan Town, Dongxiangzi towns, the western parts of Hongqi Town, Xingfu Town, and the northeastern part of Luotuoshan Town, covering a total area of 858 km^2. The hilly areas have an altitude between 1 400 m and 1 500 m with relative differences less than 100 m. The landform is generally characterized by dome-shaped hills with slightly concave slopes between 3° and 10°. Valleys in this area are underdeveloped.

7.1.3.3 Sloping Hummocks

The sloping hummocks are located on the piedmont of the low mountains, covering a total area of 253km^2. As a groundwater runoff area, the landform is undulating, and tilted against the low mountains with a gradient less than 5°. The altitude differences of the hummocks are less than 15 m.

7.1.3.4 Valley Lowlands

The valley lowlands are distributed in the middle part of the Taips League, around Shagou, Chengjiao and Mafangzi towns, covering a total area of 580 km^2. The valley lowlands are covered by very thick sedimentary layers, reaching 100 m in some areas, on which there are some recent riverbeds with widths of 5–10 m. The rivers are characterized by intermittent small streams and incomplete first-order terraces, which are 0.5–1.0 m above the riverbed. Their flat surfaces tilt slightly toward the riverbed, with inclinations of less than 5°. The valley lowlands are the groundwater runoff areas in the lower mountain hills.

7.1.3.5 Basins Among Hills

The basins among hills are located around the Wumianjiang, Hongqi, Wanshoutan, Hongshanzi towns and Gongbaolage Sumu, covering a total area of 729 km^2. These regions are characterized with thin sedimentary layers, and open bedrock around in an east-west direction in Ulan Nur. Also, the basins among the hills are groundwater flow and discharge zones. Their flat land surfaces extend in northeast-southwest direction, with some recently formed lakes scattered around.

7.1.3.6 Valley Plains

The valley plains are mainly located on the western bank of the Shandian River in the eastern part of the Taips League, covering a total area of 181km^2. The plains are flat and tilt slightly toward the riverbed. There are some granodiorite erosion remnant mounds on the valley plains, which are areas of groundwater runoff.

7.1.3.7 Low Hills

The low hills are located in the eastern part of the Taips League with spire-shaped peaks and steeply straight hillsides. The slopes of the low hills exceed 15° and the altitude difference is greater than 200 m. These areas are also groundwater recharge areas.

7.1.3.8 Ridges

The ridges are mainly located in the southeast part of the Taips League, covering a total area of 588 km^2, and are groundwater recharge areas. They generally have perfectly round-shaped mound tops and some undulation of the ridge surface. The slopes of the ridges are generally straight or convex, with slopes of 10°–20°. The altitude differences of the ridges are less than 200 m, typically 80–150 m, and the ridge lines generally extend in north-south and north-east directions.

7.1.4 Soil

Soil is the underlying factor of land use. Soils have many functions, but not all soils equally influence land uses. Soil types and soil properties are two main determinants of regional land use pattern.

7.1.4.1 Soil Types

There are three main soil types in the Taips League: light chernozem soil, chestnut soil and meadow soil.

There are four subclasses of the light chernozem soil: the leaching light chernozem subclass, the light chernozem subclass, the carbonate light chernozem subclass and the regosol light chernozem subclass, which are found in the upper parts of the vertical belts in the east and northeast low mountains, in the lower parts of the vertical belts in the east, and in the upper and tops of the gentle slopes between the hills, respectively.

The chestnut soil also includes four subclasses: dark chestnut soil, typical dark chestnut soil, meadow chestnut soil and regosol chestnut soil, which are located in the east low mountains, in the west and northwest hills, valleys and sloping hummocks, and the upper and top of the hillsides and hills, respectively.

The meadow soil includes gray meadow soil which is scattered in the alluvial valley area among the mounds, dark meadow soil found in the lower beaches. The salinized meadow soil is located at the bottomland of the lakes and alkalized meadow soil which is found in the sink areas in the southern and western areas.

7.1.4.2 Soil Properties

The soil texture in the Taips League is relatively coarse and mainly consists of sandy loam. The light chernozem soil is mainly loam and light loam, while there is an alternation between sandy loam and clay in the chestnut soil. The light chernozem soil is completely or partly granular. The chestnut soil is generally granular and clumpy, while the meadow soil is mainly granular.

Soil nutrients vary greatly due to the complex terrain, various soil parent materials, farming practices and fertilizer input levels.

In the eastern and northern areas, 76.86% of the hilly chernozem soil has a soil organic matter (SOM) content of more than 3%, while a further 20.68% having a SOM of 2–3% and the remaining 3.46% has only 1–2% SOM. The total nitrogen is more than 0.15% and the readily available potassium is more than 500ppm in all hilly chernozem soil. The phosphorus content is very low, and soil with phosphorus less than 5ppm accounts for 82.76% of the hilly chernozem soil.

In the middle hills, the area of dark chestnut soil with soil organic contents of more than 3%, 2–3%, and less than 2% accounts for 38.86%, 46.46% and 14.68% of the area respectively. The areas with soil total nitrogen contents of more than 0.15%, 0.10–0.15% and less than 0.10% account for 55.06%, 36.44% and 8.5% of the area, respectively. Approximately 87.65% of the area has phosphorus content between 10 and 20 ppm.

The western hills, the typical chestnut soil zone, suffer from serious wind erosion and desertification, and the content of the soil organic matter and nutrients is lower than that for the chernozem soil and dark chestnut soil.

The eastern and southern valley lowlands are comprised of meadow soil and saline zones, where the soil organic matter and nutrient contents are higher. Meadow soil areas with SOM of more than 3%, 2–3% and less than 2% account for 68.42%, 21.05%, 10.53%, respectively, of the meadow soil areas. In this area, the soil total nitrogen content is similar to the chernozem soil, but the readily available phosphorus content is lower than that for the chernozem soil.

7.1.5 Hydrology

There are 48 nurs (lakes) in the Taips League, most of which are seasonal lakes, covering a total area of 38 km^2, with a water storage capacity of 1.739 million km^3. The catchments include the Wulan Nur-Guancaishan Nur Basin and the Qilama Nur Basin. There are several perpetual nurs in the Wulan Nur-Guancaishan Nur Basin located along an undulating landform in the middle and southwest of the Taips League. The Qilama Nur Basin is located in the northwest of the Taips League, with the major axis in the northeast-southwest direction. Due to the topographic relief, there are also several seasonal lakes scattered around.

7.1.6 Vegetation

Natural vegetation is distributed over the low hills and hilly areas as well as in valley lowlands mainly around gentle slope hills and low mountains with altitudes above 1 500 m. The main species are members of the grass family, with *leymus* and *Belga Stipa grandis* as the main species on the lower parts of the gentle slopes, followed by *Cleistogenes squarrosa* and *Carex* spp. The forest resources include timber forests, agricultural protection forests, economic forests, the trees around forest networks, herd protection forests and firewood forests.

7.1.7 Natural Disasters

Natural disasters such as droughts, snowstorms and black disasters (disasters of long periods without snow), storms and hail occur frequently and have an extensive influence on the Taips League. Livestock breeding and crop farming are badly affected by the cold snaps, which mainly occur during April, May, October and November. Frost in the Taips League can be divided into two classes: autumn frosts (early frosts) which occur when many crops are forming grain and fruit almost ripe, and spring frosts (late frosts) which occur during the seedling stage of most spring crops. Both early and late frosts have significant impacts on the growth and yield of crops.

7.2 Simulation of Land Use Pattern Changes in the Taips League

The land use pattern changes in the Taips League were carried out using the DLS model and a systematic data preparation procedure. This section quantitatively presents the relationships between the spatial pattern of land uses and the driving factors.

7.2.1 Data Preparation

To improve the spatial accuracy of simulation results, the spline interpolation algorithm was employed to convert the natural background data and socioeconomic data into a 250×250 m scale (Zhuang et al., 2002; Gao and Deng, 2002; Deng et al., 2008).

As described previously, there are many factors that influence land system dynamics (Greenberg, 1994; Verburg et al., 2002; Seto and Fragkias, 2005; Ge et al., 2008), including geographical conditions, climatic factors, proximity conditions, and socioeconomic development. All these factors (Table 7.1) were employed in the simulation of land system dynamics in the Taips League in this study.

Table 7.1 Variables used in simulating land system dynamics in the Taips League

Influencing factors	Detailed explanation
Geographical variables	
Terrain	0: Mound 1: Plain 2: Platform 3: Plateau
Soil pH value	Increasing values relate to lower soil acidity
Soil depth	Depth of the surface soil (cm)
Average altitude	Average altitude of each 1 km^2 grid (m^2)
Slope	Slope variables derived from 1:250 000 DEM (0.01degree)
Climatic variables	
Temperature	Mean annual air temperature (0.1℃)
$\geqslant 0°C$ Accumulated temperature	Accumulated temperature of days with an average daily temperature above 0℃ (0.1℃)
$\geqslant 10°C$ Accumulated temperature	Accumulated temperature of days with an average daily temperature above 10℃ (0.1℃)
Percentage of sunshine	Percentage of sunshine (%)
Proximity variables	
Distance to the provincial capital	Distance from the center of the county town to the provincial capital (km)
Distance to the nearest highway	Distance from the center of the county town to the nearest highway (km)
Distance to the nearest provincial highway	Distance from the center of the county town to the nearest provincial highway (km)
Socioeconomic variables	
Population density	Spatial population density (persons/km^2)
Urbanization level	Proportion of the non-agricultural population to the total population in each county (%)
Agriculture infrastructure investment	Proportion of agriculture infrastructure investment to total investment (%)
GDP	Spatial GDP density (10^4 yuan/km^2)

7.2.1.1 Preparation of Geographical Data

The landform data for the Taips League was derived from the 1:250 000 topographic map of the Inner Mongolia Autonomous Region. The soil erosion data were acquired from the Chinese soil erosion intensity database produced by the Data Center for Resources and Environmental Sciences, Chinese Academy of Sciences (RESDC) by interpreting remote sensing data. The original landform data and soil erosion data were stored in a vector format and then converted into a 250×250 m raster format after being clipped to the Taips League boundary (Liu et al., 2002; Deng et al., 2006).

It was necessary to convert the 250×250 m raster format sequence data to multilayer binary raster data to represent the spatial distribution of the landforms. The data conversion was carried out in the Workstation module in the ArcGIS software environment, with the following aml program:

```
/*bnd: Taips League boundary file, recorded in 250×250 meters raster format. */
/*landform: landform type, represented in 250×250 meters raster format. */
/*mountain: binary mountain 250×250 meters raster data after conversion. */
/*hill: binary mound 250×250 meters raster data after conversion. */
/*plain: binary plain 250×250 meters raster data after conversion. */
/*platean: binary plateau 250×250 meters raster data after conversion. */
grid
setwindow bnd
setmask bnd
docell
  if(landform == 1)
    mountain = 1
  else
    mountain = 0
end
docell
  if(landform == 2)
    hill = 1
  else
    hill = 0
end
docell
  if(landform == 3)
    plain = 1
  else
    plain = 0
end
docell
  if(landform == 4)
    platean = 1
  else
    platean = 0
end
quit
```

Finally, a spatial distribution map of the main landforms was produced (Fig. 7.6).

The soil erosion intensity data were converted to corresponding sequence variables (Fig. 7.8), using the Arc module in the ArcGIS software environment, mainly using the "reclassify" command, with the following program:

```
/* bnd: Taips League boundary file, recorded in 250×250 meters raster format.*/
/* soile: 250×250 meters raster soil erosion intensity data of Taips League.*/
/* soilecls: reclassified 250×250 meters raster soil erosion intensity data of Taips League.
```

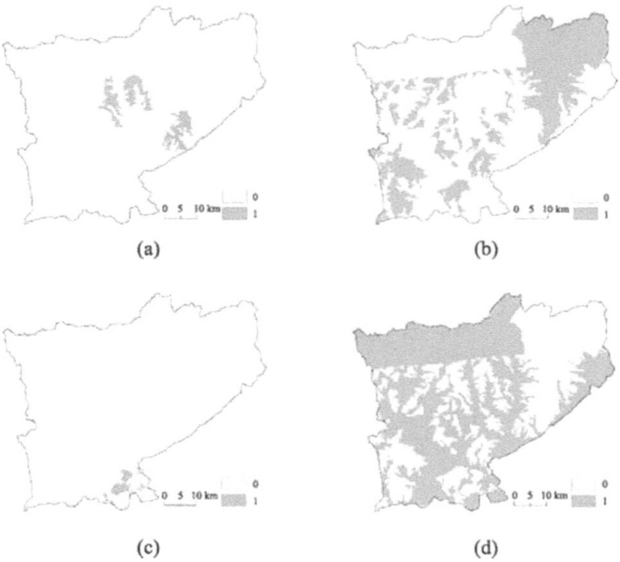

Fig. 7.6 Binary variables of landforms of the Taips League.
(a), (b), (c) and (d) represent mountains, mounds, plains and plateau, respectively.

```
*/
grid
setmask bnd
setwindow bnd
docell
   if (soile == 11 or soile == 21 or soile == 31 or soile == 12 or soile == 22 or
      soile == 32)
   soilecls = 1
   if (soile == 13 or soile == 23 or soile == 33)
   soilecls = 2
   if (soile == 14 or soile == 24 or soile == 34)
   soilecls = 3
   if (soile == 15 or soile == 25 or soile == 35 or soile == 16 or
   soile == 26 or soile == 36)
   soilecls = 4
end
quit
```

Finally, a soil erosion intensity spatial heterogeneity map was produced (Fig. 7.7).

The slope and aspect data were derived from the 1:250 000 contour data by the following steps: clip the 50×50 m DEM data for the Taips League in the ArcGIS software environment; use the "SLOPE" and "ASPECT" commands to generate slope and aspect GRIDs; spatially interpolate the grids

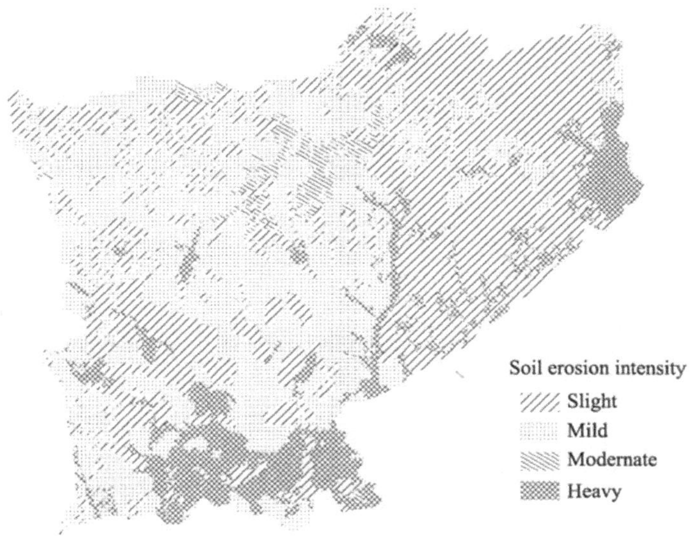

Fig. 7.7 Spatial heterogeneity map of soil erosion intensity in the Taips League.

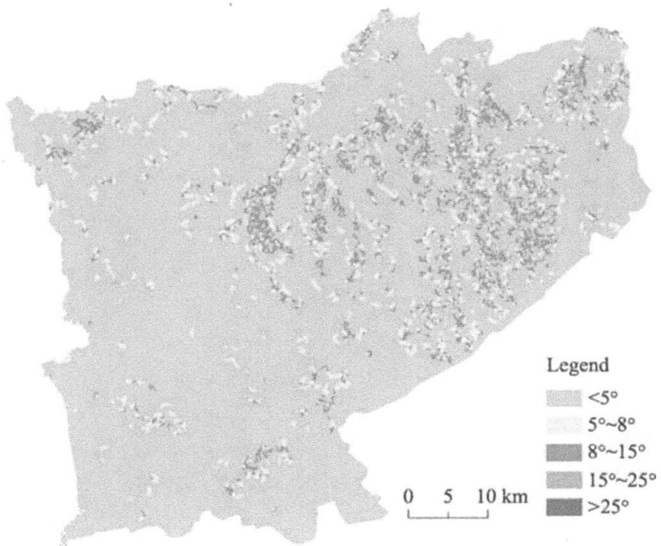

Fig. 7.8 Slope spatial heterogeneity map of the Taips League.

at 250×250 m scales. The slope data produced by this method is continuous and can be directly imported into the model. The aspect data are categorical variables, and needs to be converted using the re-mapping table (Table 7.2), encoding flat land as "0", and other aspects into sequence variables representing true aspect information based on Table 7.2. Fig. 7.9 is the spatial aspect heterogeneity map for the Taips League based on the reclassification mapping table (Zhan et al., 2007).

Table 7.2 Remapping the terrain aspect of the Taips League

Aspect	North slope	North-east slope	East slope	Southeast slope	South slope	South-west slope	West slope	Northwest slope
Code	1	2	3	4	5	6	7	8
Range (°)	0–22.5 337.5–360	22.5–67.5	67.5–112.5	112.5–157.5	157.5–202.5	202.5–247.5	247.5–292.5	292.5–337.5

Note: North is defined as "0" degree and the aspect range is then calibrated in a clockwise manner.

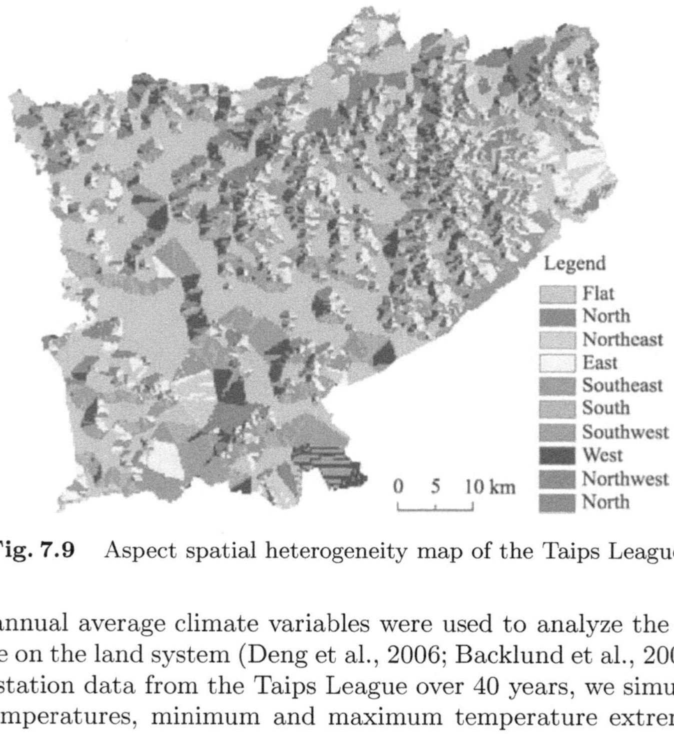

Fig. 7.9 Aspect spatial heterogeneity map of the Taips League.

The annual average climate variables were used to analyze the influence of climate on the land system (Deng et al., 2006; Backlund et al., 2008). From weather station data from the Taips League over 40 years, we simulated the yearly temperatures, minimum and maximum temperature extremes, sunshine percentages and annual average precipitation in the Taips League from 2000 to 2020 by comprehensively analyzing the conventional meteorological indicators and using the state space modeling process described in this section. The state-space model is used to predict multiple time series variables, and is suited for the prediction of several time series with dynamic interactions through the modeling process of the state space model. Given the spatial correlation of interannual change variables, this model is most appropriate for the simulation of climatic variables. The model is defined by the following state transition equation:

$$z_{t+1} = Fz_t + Ge_{t+1} \tag{7.1}$$

where the coefficient matrix $F_{s \times s}$ is called the transition matrix, and determines the dynamic properties of the model; the coefficient matrix $G_{s \times r}$, which is the input matrix, determines the variance structure of the transition equation, the first r lines and r rows of which are configured into an $r \times r$ matrix to identify the model. The r-dimensional input and normally distributed vector e_t is an independent random vector column, with an average value of 0 and a variance matrix $\sum_{ee}$. The random error e_t is sometimes called a new information vector or vibration vector.

In addition to the state transition equation, the state space model usually contains a measurement equation or observation equation, in which the observation value x_t is a function of the state vector z_t. However, since the observation value x_t is always included in the state vector z_t, the measurement equation only represents the first r components selected in this case. The measurement equation used in the model is as follows:

$$x_t = [I_r 0] z_t \tag{7.2}$$

where I_r is an $r \times r$ identical matrix and extracting x_t from z_t in the modeling process is independent of the measurement equation in the state space model. x_t is an r-dimensional observation vector; z_t is an s-dimensional state vector, of which the first r component is x_t, and the last s-r components denote the predicted x_t under certain conditions.

Based on the annual average climate variables calculated by the state space model, the Kriging spatial interpolation algorithm was used to determine the spatial approximations, and calculate the value of the variables on each grid, which were then imported into the model as parameters.

7.2.1.2 Disaggregating Socioeconomic Variables

The socioeconomic variables simulated by CGELUC model were disaggregated to a 250×250 m scale. For example, the total population variable is the output of CGELUC model, so the corresponding population represents the population for each year under each scenario. The spatially disaggregated population for different years can precisely reflect the spatial distribution of the population (CIESIN, 2005).

With the 1:250 000 topographic maps, the coordinates for the centers of county government offices in the Taips League were selected, and the distances from each 250×250 m pixel to the county government office were calculated. With the corrected Taips League Landsat TM/ETM image from the mid-1990s, the major traffic routes and main water systems including lakes and rivers were sketched in the ArcMap module of ArcGIS. The traffic data were reclassified as national highways, provincial roads and county roads with reference to the basic 1:250 000 geographic information data in the Workstation module of ArcGIS. Then the distances from each 250× 250 m grid to the linear objects were calculated, and were then imported into the model as parameters (Fig 7.10) (Deng et al., 2008). Other socioeconomic variables were similarly disaggregated to form the socioeconomic grid data layer.

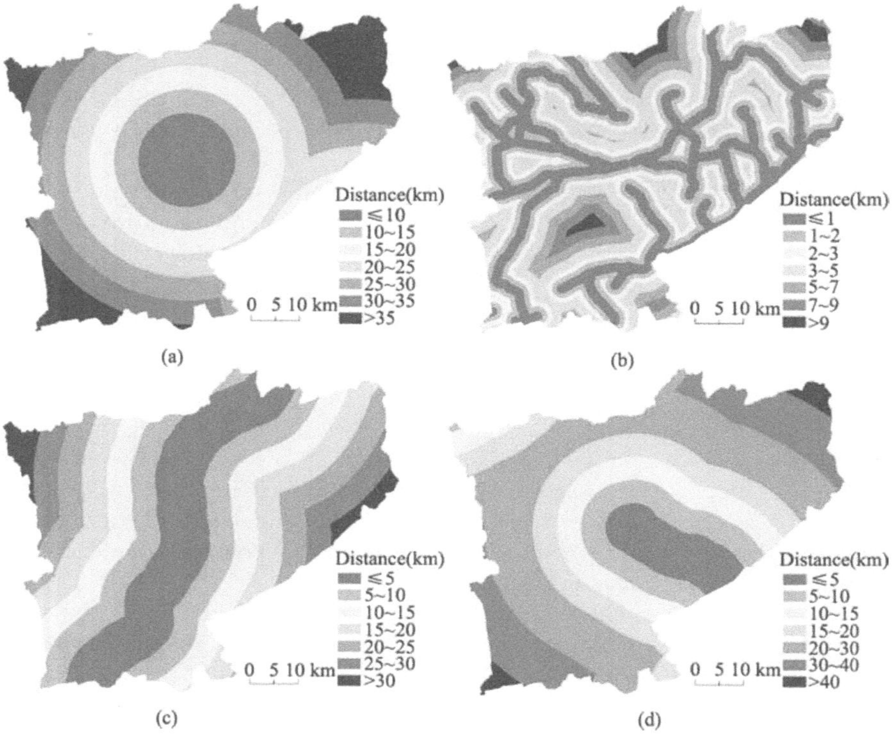

Fig. 7.10 Distance load on the 500×500 m grids of the Taips League.
(a), (b), (c), (d) are the distances to the centers of the county government office, nearest national highway, nearest provincial road and nearest county road, respectively.

After the data processing described above, the driving factors including geographical, climate, socioeconomic, and policy and management variables related to the land system dynamics were integrated into a factor set and formed a number of grid data layers. The driving factors were then used to generate a grid stack in the Grid module in the ArcGIS software environment.

7.2.1.3 Reclassification of Land Use Types

The original land use map of the Taips League was derived from the Landsat Thematic Mapper images and land use types were then reclassified and expressed in a special representation scheme. In the new land use scheme, the land use type is represented by binary values of 1 or 0 for each 250 ×

250 m grid cell to show the existence or nonexistence of that type of land use. The dependent variables for the spatial regression between land use and the influencing factors in the Taips League are listed in Table 7.3.

Table 7.3 Reclassification of land use types

Code	Land use	Description
0	Cultivated land	Original data include both paddy and non-irrigated uplands.
1	Forestry	Natural or planted forests with canopy covers greater than 30%; land covered by trees less than 2 m high, with a canopy cover greater than 40%; land covered by trees with canopy cover between 10 and 30% and used for tea-gardens, orchards and nurseries.
2	Grassland	Lands covered by herbaceous plants with coverage greater than 5% and mixed rangeland with the coverage of shrub canopies less than 10%.
3	Water areas	Land covered by natural water bodies or land with facilities for irrigation and water preservation, including rivers, canals, lakes, permanent glaciers, beaches and shorelines, and bottomland.
4	Built-up areas	Land used for urban and rural settlements, industry and transportation.
5	Unused land	All other land.

The process used to convert these data on these six land use types from grid data into binary variables was mainly completed in the Workstation module of the ArcGIS software environment with the following program:

```
/*bnd: Taips League boundary file, recorded in 250×250 meters raster format. */
/*ld1988: 250×250 meter land use structure raster data of Taips League in 1988
/*ld1: 250×250 meter binary raster data of cultivated land after conversion
/*ld2: 250×250 meter binary raster data of forestry area after conversion
/*ld3: 250×250 meter binary raster data of grassland after conversion
/*ld4: 250×250 meter binary raster data of water area after conversion
/*ld5: 250×250 meter binary raster data of built-up area after conversion
/*ld6: 250×250 meter binary raster data of unused land after conversion
grid
setmask bnd
setwindow bnd
    docell
      if(ld1988 == 1)
        ld1 = 1
      else
        ld1 = 0
      if(ld1988 == 2)
        ld2 = 1
      else
        ld2 = 0
```

```
        if(ld1988 == 3)
            ld3 = 1
        else
            ld3 = 0
        if(ld1988 == 4)
            ld4 = 1
        else
            ld4 = 0
        if(ld1988 == 5)
            ld5 = 1
        else
            ld5 = 0
        if(ld1988 == 6)
            ld6 = 1
        else
            ld6 = 0
    end
quit
```

It was necessary to study the land use structure of the Taips League in 1988 and encode the land use types with 0, 1, 2, 3, 4 and 5 corresponding to cultivated land, forestry area, grassland, water area, built-up area and unused land, respectively (Table 7.4).

Table 7.4 Land use structure of the Taips League in 1988

Code	Land use type	Area (ha)	Proportion (%)
0	Cultivated land	149 677.80	43.19
1	Forestry area	2 044.61	0.59
2	Grassland	166 729.26	48.11
3	Water area	4 634.86	1.34
4	Built-up area	10 922.40	3.15
5	Unused land	12 544.79	3.62

Similarly, a grid map of land use structure in the Taips League in 1995 (Fig. 7.11) can be represented by the same six binary variables to represent land use types on a 250 m scale (Fig. 7.12).

7.2.2 Analysis of Driving Forces

The analysis of land system dynamics within the framework of the DLS model aims to estimate the statistical relationship between land use pattern successions and driving factors, which theoretically provides the response function for each land use type. All the driving factors are endowed with corresponding weights according to certain principles which can be assumed not to change during a short period, while the driving factors vary with time. After formu-

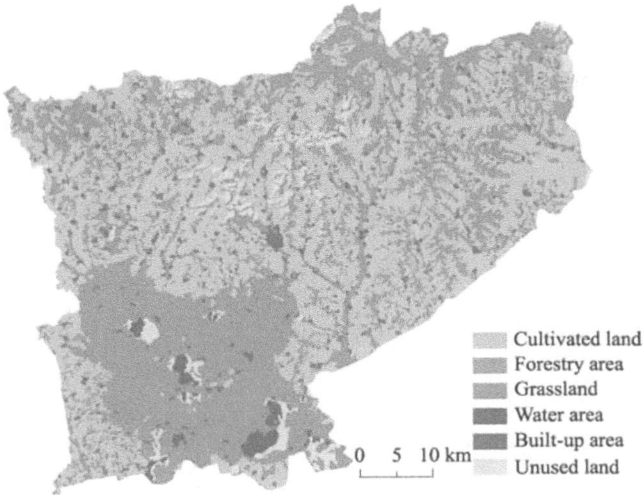

Fig. 7.11 Land use structure raster map of the Taips League in 1995.

lation of the response function, discrepancies between the simulated land use type distribution and the actual land use type distribution in the forecast years can be attributed to changes in parameter values for driving factors such as population growth and climate change and competition among dif-

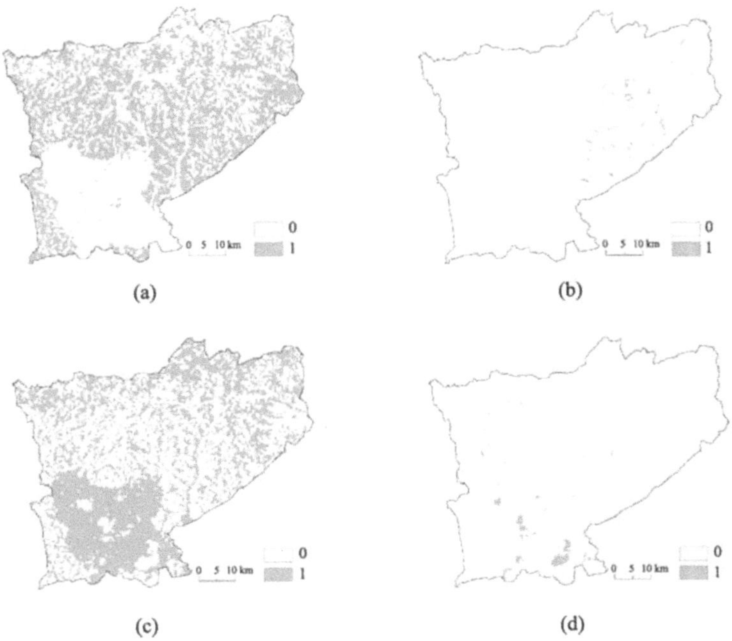

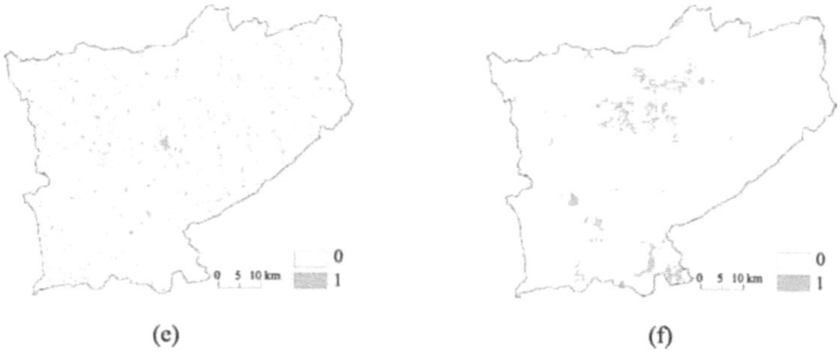

Fig. 7.12 Binary presentation of land use types in the Taips League in 1995. (a), (b), (c), (d), (e) and (f) represent cultivated land, forestry area, grassland, water area, built-up area and unused land, respectively.

ferent land use types; constraints imposed by local conditions and trends (Deng et al., 2002).

An analysis of the land system dynamics in the Taips League was carried out at a 250×250 m scale. Based on the ELMLUP model embedded in DLS, the relationships between binary land use types and spatially disaggregated driving factors were estimated.

Collinearity among the explanatory variables may induce bias in the ELMLUP regression function. Therefore, the collinearity was diagnosed before carrying out the regression analysis. There are many collinearity diagnosis methods, but in this section, the variance inflation factor was chosen to measure the collinearity. The results (Table 7.5) indicate that there is minor collinearity.

Table 7.5 Collinearity diagnosis of ELMLUP parameters in the Taips League

Variables	VIF	1/VIF
Distance to the provincial capital	3.91	0.256
Sunshine hours	3.87	0.258
Distance to water area	3.85	0.260
Distance to the port city	3.84	0.260
Annual precipitation	3.80	0.263
Landform: plain	3.78	0.265
Landform: mound	3.78	0.265
Annual temperature	3.75	0.267
Population density	3.37	0.297
GDP	3.22	0.311
Soil erosion intensity: moderate	3.09	0.324
Soil erosion intensity: slight	3.04	0.329
$\geqslant$ 10°C accumulated temperature	2.95	0.339
Aspect: southwest slope	2.79	0.358
Aspect: east slope	2.78	0.360

Continued

Variables	VIF	1/VIF
Aspect: southeast slope	2.61	0.383
Elevation	2.58	0.387
Aspect: northeast slope	2.52	0.396
Aspect: west slope	2.46	0.407
Aspect: south slope	2.38	0.420
Aspect: southwest slope	2.32	0.432
Aspect: north slope	2.31	0.434
Disaster damage area ratio	1.75	0.572
Distance to the main road	1.56	0.641
Soil erosion intensity: heavy	1.48	0.677
Landform: plateau	1.46	0.684
Soil potassium content	1.44	0.695
Multiple crop index	1.30	0.767
Slope	1.20	0.832
Proportion of secondary industry	1.01	0.985
Mean VIF	2.67	

VIF: variance inflation factor; 1/VIF is tolerability.

Singular values and their impact on the estimation results were also evaluated. The diagnosis result showed that there were three singular values in the cultivated land dynamic analysis model dataset (Fig. 7.13).

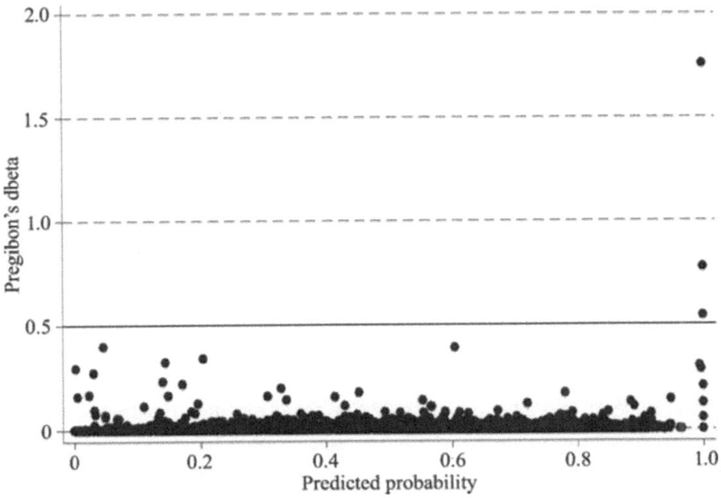

Fig. 7.13 Singular value judgment of the cropland distribution samples. Criterion for a singular value is db>0.500.

A 2×2 crosstab was used to indicate differences in the prediction accuracy with or without singular value processing. The crosstab analysis indicated that the prediction accuracy can be improved by singular value processing. Without singular value processing, the prediction accuracy is 73.5% when the cultivated land is 0 and 77.9% when the cultivated land is 1, with an overall accuracy of 75.7% (Table 7.6).

Table 7.6 Crosstab prior to handling singular values in the samples

		Predicted value		
		Farmland		Accuracy
Observation		0	1	
Farmland	0	4 917	1 776	73.5
	1	1 526	5 391	77.9
Overall				75.7

Note: Cutoff value is 0.500.

With singular value processing, the prediction accuracy is 73.5% when the cultivated land is 0 and 78.2% when the cultivated land is 1, with an overall accuracy of 75.9% (Table 7.7).

Table 7.7 Crosstab after handling of singular values in the samples

		Predicted value		
		Farmland		Accuracy
Observation		0	1	
Farmland	0	4 937	1 776	73.5
	1	1 506	5 388	78.2
Overall				75.9

Note: Cutoff value is 0.500.

The fitted results can be evaluated by drawing a receiver operating characteristic (ROC) curve (Hanley and McNeil, 1982). The larger the area under the ROC curve is, the better the model will simulate the actual conditions. Fig. 7.14 indicates that the area under the ROC curve is 0.839 before and 0.840 after singular values processing, with the accuracy increasing by 0.001. As the gradual significance probability value was 0.000, the null hypothesis was rejected. Thus, we can conclude that the relationship between the cultivated land area and driving factors estimated based on ELMLUP is of high reliability.

By comparing the estimation results before and after singular value processing, we found that the model accuracy could be improved by eliminating the singular values. Therefore, the singular values in the datasets of the other five land use type dynamic analysis models were eliminated which improved the simulation accuracy. These results indicated that the estimated results of the relationship between land use types and driving factors were reliable.

The relationships between the driving factors and different land use types are shown in Table 7.8. It can be seen that the impact of plateau on cultivated

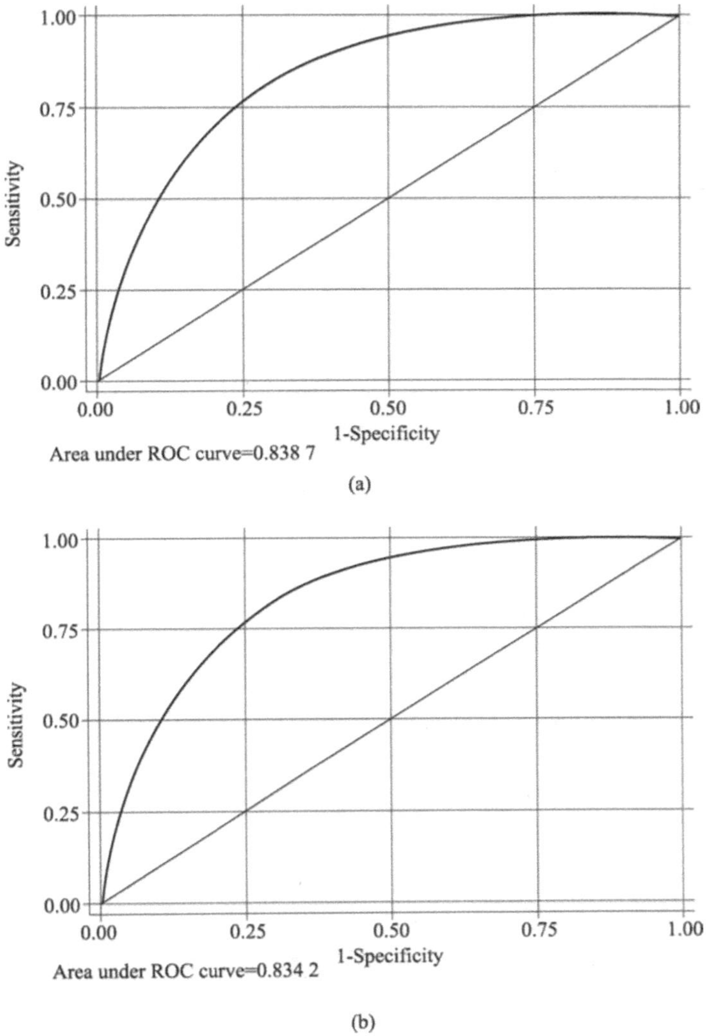

Fig. 7.14 ROC curve of the land distribution effect based on the ELMLUP simulation.

(a) Before eliminating the singular value; (b) After eliminating the singular value.

land and grassland is more prominent than the impact of mountains, with a cultivated land frequency of 0.726 and a grassland frequency of 1.119. The impact of hills on grassland is more prominent than the impact of mountains, with a value of 1.319.

The impact of plains on built-up areas (1.791) is more prominent than the impact of mountains; the impact on forestry areas is less (0.521). The frequency of forestry areas, grassland and unused land all increase with increasing elevation, averaging 0.28%, 0.56% and 1.58% per elevation unit, respectively. By contrast, the frequency of cultivated land, water areas and built-up areas decreases with decreasing elevation; steeper slopes are less suited for cultivated land. The regions with steep slopes are mainly covered with forestry and grassland and the frequencies of grassland and unused land are 2.74% and 7.36% per elevation unit on average.

Table 7.8 Relationships between the frequency of each land use type and the driving factors

	Cultivated land	Forestry	Grass-land	Water areas	Built-up areas	Unused land
Landform: hill	-	-	1.319	-	-	-
Landform: plateau	0.726	-	1.119	-	-	-
Landform: plain	-	0.521	-	-	1.791	-
Elevation	0.996	1.006	1.003	0.953	0.998	1.016
Aspect	0.996	-	1.027	-	0.834	1.074
Aspect: north slope	-	-	-	-	-	0.286
Aspect: northeast slope	0.835	-	0.750	-	-	-
Aspect: east slope	0.842	-	0.840	-	-	1.006
Aspect: southeast slope	0.921	-	-	-	1.546	1.003
Aspect: south slope	-	-	1.159	0.403	-	1.001
Aspect: southwest slope	0.925	-	-	-	-	1.005
Aspect: west slope	0.881	-	-	0.724	-	1.003
Aspect: northwest slope	0.876	4.625	0.832	-	-	1.162
Soil erosion intensity: slight	0.967	-	0.924	0.871	-	1.500
Soil erosion intensity: moderate	0.941	-	0.853	0.928	-	1.581
Soil erosion intensity: heavy	0.904		0.832	-	-	-
Soil potassium content	-	-	-	-	-	1.135
Annual average temperature	1.199	1.228	1.322	-	0.426	1.180
⩾ 10°C accumulated temperature	1.003	1.005	-	-	-	0.981
Sunshine hours	0.901	0.869	1.061	-	0.954	1.074
Annual precipitation	-	-	1.028	0.872	-	0.771
Distance to the provincial capital	-0.944	0.932	1.019	-	-0.973	1.138
Distance to the port city	0.983	0.854	-	-	-	0.939
Distance to the road	1.018	1.116	0.968	1.069	-	1.117
Distance to the water area	1.056	1.108	-	0.834	-	0.890
Population density	1.028	1.002	0.962	1.010	-	0.967
GDP	0.936	-	1.086	0.952	1.026	0.744
Proportion of secondary industry	-	-	-		-	-
Multiple crop index	-	-	-	0.627	-	-
Disaster loss rate	1.031	-	0.978	0.891	-	-

The impacts of aspect on both cultivated land and unused land are prominent. Unlike on flat land, the frequency of cultivated land is less than 1 on sloping land, while frequency of unused land is more than 1. Flat land is more favorable for the expansion of cultivated land, while unused land is more common in sloping areas (Verburg et al., 1999; Seto et al., 2000; Lambin et al., 2001; Rudel et al., 2005; Marlon et al., 2008). Soil erosion intensity is another important factor that hinders the expansion of cultivated land. The frequencies of cultivated land in areas with slight, moderate and heavy erosion are 0.967, 0.941 and 0.904, respectively.

Climate is the main driving factor for plant growth. The frequencies of cultivated land, forestry area, grassland and unused land increase by 19.87%, 22.83%, 32.24% and 17.98% per unit of annual average temperature, respectively. The impact of sunshine hours on land use types is generally consistent with the annual average temperature, but with a much lower incidence. The frequencies of grassland and unused land increase by 6.05% and 7.4% per sunshine hour, respectively, on average. Increases in the ⩾10℃ accumulated temperature enhance the frequency of cultivated land and forestry areas and decrease the frequency of unused land. As the ⩾10℃ accumulated temperature increases by one unit, the frequencies of cultivated land and forestry areas increase by 0.28% and 0.46% on average, respectively. As the precipitation increases by one unit, the grassland frequency increases by 2.75% and the frequency of unused land decreases by 77.10% on average.

As the provincial capital is usually located on the plains near large areas of cultivated land and built-up areas, the frequencies of cultivated land and built-up areas generally decrease with increasing distance to the provincial capital, while the frequencies of unused land and grassland increase with increasing distance. The impacts of natural disasters are generally related to cultivated land, so losses from disasters are usually very serious in areas with a high cultivated land frequency (Pontius et al., 2007). The GDP has a positive impact on the frequencies of grassland and built-up areas, with the built-up area frequency increasing by 2.56% on average with a one-unit increase in GDP.

7.2.3 Scenario Design

Based on the agricultural activities and land use patterns in the Taips League, three scenarios were designed for this research by regulating the population density, GDP and the rate of change in the proportion of secondary industry: a baseline scenario, an economic priority scenario, and an environmental protection scenario (Deng et al., 2008).

7.2.3.1 Baseline Scenario

The baseline scenario was designed in accordance with the historical statistics in the Taips League, which reflect the land system dynamics resulting from following the historical development trend. The population density is assigned its 5-year moving average value; the GDP and rate of change in the proportion of secondary industry change are based on the historical average rate of change; the proportion of secondary industry was obtained from the quotient of the secondary industry production value and GDP.

7.2.3.2 Economic Priority Scenario

The economic priority scenario for land use change was designed because the economic development is at a relatively low level in the Taips League, the grain and livestock markets are yet to be exploited and the production scale is yet to be expanded. Under the economic priority scenario: the population density is assigned its 5-year moving average value; the standard deviations of the rate of change in GDP and the proportion of secondary industry are twice as high as in the historical period; and the change in the proportion of secondary industry is obtained from the quotient of the secondary industry output value and GDP.

7.2.3.3 Environmental Protection Scenario

The environmental protection scenario was designed because of the grassland degradation and cultivated land desertification occurring in the Taips League. The rate of increase in the population density is one standard deviation lower than in the historical period, and the rates of change in both the GDP and the proportion of secondary industry are also one standard deviation lower than in the historical period. The proportion of secondary industry change is

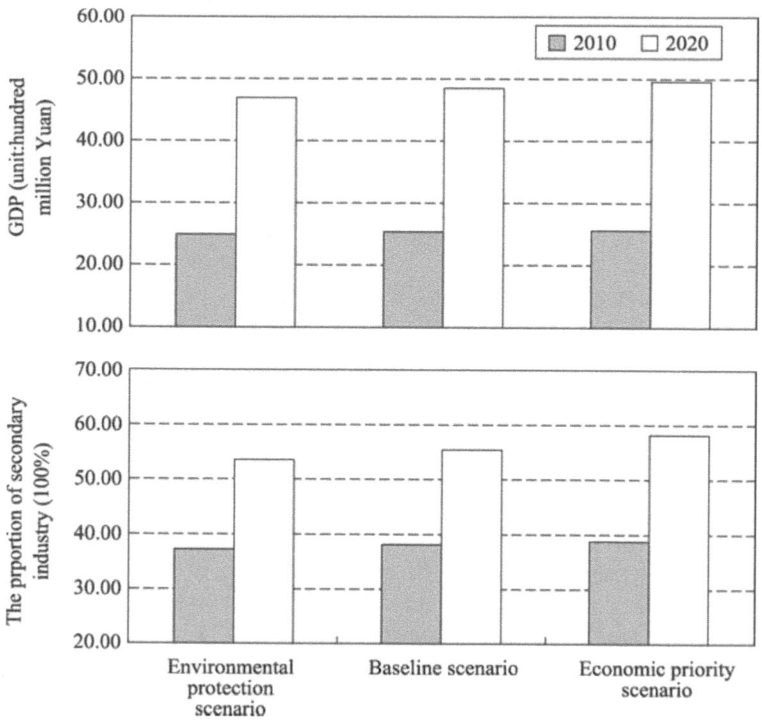

Fig. 7.15 Scenario design of the Taips League.

obtained from the quotient of the secondary industry output value and GDP (Fig 7.15).

7.2.4 Conversion Rules

Defining the conversion rules at the pixel level can significantly improve the accuracy of the land system dynamics simulation (Veldkamp and Lambin, 2001; Verburg et al., 2004; Pontius et al., 2007). Two conversion rules were mainly used and combined in simulating the temporal-spatial dynamics of land use succession patterns in the Taips League: (i) the conversion probability rule, which is used to define the probability of conversion from one land use type to another land use type; and (ii) the conversion protection rule, which is used to define the grids that are under protection so that no land use type conversions will take place within those grids. The land use conversion rules in the Taips League quantitatively represented the difficulty level of conversions among different land use types based on the features of the land system dynamics, through the frequency statistics and with reference to related information from the questionnaires (Table 7.9).

Table 7.9 Land use conversion rules in the Taips League

Land use type	Cultivated land	Forestry area	Grassland	Water area	Built-up area	Unused land
Conversion rule	0.6	0.8	0.5	0.9	1.0	0.4

In defining the conversion rules, numbers from "0" to "1" represent the difficulty level of the conversion, with "1" assigned to a land use type that is so difficult to convert that it will not be converted into other land use types in the simulation period. Conversely, a difficulty level of "0" indicates that the land use is easily converted to other land use types. The numbers between "0" and "1" indicate that a particular land use type can be converted into other land use types with larger numbers indicating a more difficult conversion.

7.2.5 Simulation Results

The land use patterns from 2000 and 2020 were simulated with the DLS software and the process and rules of the land system dynamics were analyzed (Fig. 7.16).

We determined the competition among different land use types and the spatial distribution land use type succession rules under the influence of various driving factors by comparing the land use pattern succession dynamics in the Taips League under the three scenarios — baseline, economic development and environmental protection.

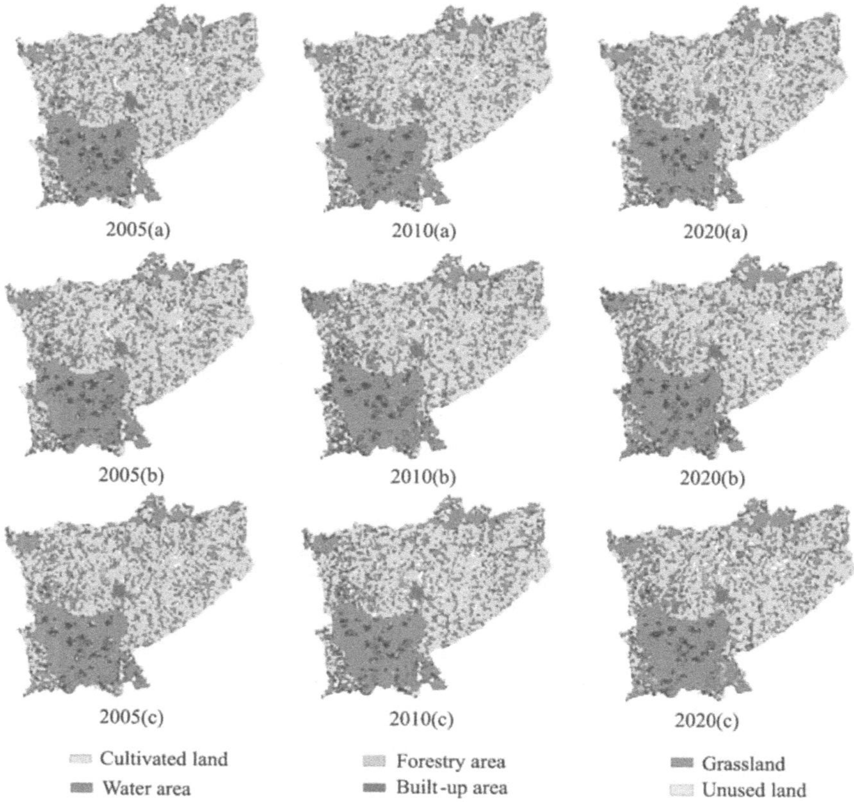

Fig. 7.16 Changing patterns of land system of the Taips League under the (a) baseline, (b) environment protection, and (c) economic priority scenarios.

Under the baseline scenario, there is some change in the size of all the land use types in the same general area as their original location over time. By 2020, most of the unused land in the middle and northern parts of the Taips League had been exploited, with only the heavily eroded and difficult to exploit unused land left. The forestry area had expanded significantly mainly into the unused land regions to the northwest and northeast of the Taips League county town. The grassland remained in balance generally, without evident changes in distribution. There was some expansion of the built-up area, as the original town or residential centers expanded into the surrounding area, but there was no continuous expansion on a large scale by 2020. The water area in the Taips League is very small, mainly focused on the nurs (lakes) in the middle and southern parts, and this area was mainly influenced by the annual precipitation change. The simulation results for 2000–2020 indicate that the water area will not change dramatically, but the unused land will shrink substantially. In many areas, cultivated land expanded into unused land already neighboring other areas of cultivated land.

The forestry area increased dramatically under the environmental protection scenario, compared with the baseline scenario. During the simulation period, a considerable forestry area gradually appears to the northwest and northeast of the county town. In addition to, the decrease in the forestry area, the grassland was controlled at a reasonable level, without centralized and continuous disappearance.

Under the economic priority scenario the prominent feature of the land use pattern succession was the dramatic decrease in the unused land. The unused land to the northwest and northeast of the county town was almost all converted into cultivated land, grassland or forestry. Although there was some increase in forestry, this was very limited, and the increase occurred mainly in the northwest and northeast of the county town, not through the eastern part of the Taips League, as predicted by the environmental protection scenario.

The spatiotemporal process of land system dynamics and land use pattern succession in the Taips League under the three scenarios can provide important decision-making reference points for determining land use plans and even sustainable development strategies. First, given the predicted results of the land system dynamics under the three scenarios, and based on the grassland degradation and land desertification in the Taips League, it is suggested that the local government should develop a reasonable plan for land resource exploitation, industrial structure adjustment, population control, economic development, and sustainable development. Second, the prediction results of the three scenarios indicate that the area of unused land to the northeast and northwest of the county town is sensitive to land use change during 2000–2020. The land use patterns resulting from competition among different land use types in this region vary greatly under different scenarios, reminding us that more attention should be given to land system dynamics in this region. Unreasonable land use conversion should be strictly prohibited and the sustainable use of land resources should be encouraged (Liu et al., 2003).

7.3 Summary

The dynamic simulation and scenario analysis of land use pattern changes in the Taips League were carried out using the DLS model and quantitative analysis in this chapter. As an important traditional agricultural production base in China, the Taips League is experiencing population increases, economic development and accelerated urbanization, and frequent land use pattern succession is a prominent characteristic of the land system dynamics in this area. Using the DLS model, this chapter quantitatively presents the relationships between the distribution of land use types and the driving factors by statistical analysis.

The DLS model verifies the simulation results giving it an unprecedented advantage over traditional methods in the study of regional land use change. The possible land system dynamic trends and spatial characteristics of land use pattern succession under the different scenarios provided by the DLS model will provide decision-making reference points for environmental protection, ecological restoration, land resource management and sustainable development of the economy.

References

Aguiar A P D, Câmara G, Escada M I S. 2007. Spatial statistical analysis of land-use determinants in the Brazilian Amazonia: Exploring intra-regional heterogeneity. Ecological Modelling, 209(2–4): 169–188.

Backlund P, Janetos A C, Schimel D. 2008. The effects of climate change on agriculture, land resources, water resources, and biodiversity. Climate Change Science Program Synthesis and Assessment Product 4.3, Washington, DC.

Burgi M, Hersperger A M, Schneeberger N. 2004. Driving forces of landscape change—Current and new directions. Landscape Ecology, 19: 857–868.

CIESIN (Center for International Earth Science Information Network, Columbia University). 2005. Gridded population of the world version 3 (GPWv3). Palisades, NY: Socioeconomic Data and Applications Center (SEDAC), Columbia University. Available at http://sedac.ciesin.columbia.edu/gpw.

de Koning G H J, Veldkamp A, Fresco L O. 1999. Exploring changes in Ecuadorian land use for food production and their effects on natural resources. Journal of Environmental Management, 57(4): 221–237.

Deng X Z, Liu J Y, Zhuang D F, Zhan J Y, Zhao T. 2002. Modeling the relationship of land use change and some geophysical indicators for the interlock area of farming and pasturing in China. Journal of Geographical Sciences, 12(4): 397-404.

Deng X Z, Huang J K, Rozelle S, Uchida E. 2006. Cultivated land conversion and potential agricultural productivity in China. Land Use Policy, 23(4): 372–384.

Deng X Z, Su H B, Zhan J Y. 2008. Integration of multiple data sources to simulate the Dynamics of Land Systems. Sensors, 8(2): 620–634.

Gao Z Q and Deng X Z. 2002. Analysis on spatial features of LUCC based on dataset of land use and land cover change in China. Chinese Geographical Science, 12(2): 107–113.

Ge Q S, Dai J H, He F N, Pan Y, Wang M M. 2008. Land use changes and their relations with carbon cycles over the past 300a in China. Science in China Series D—Earth Sciences, 51(6): 871–884.

Greenberg A. 1994. Ethologically informed design in reptile research. In: C. Warwick, F.L. Frye, J.B. Murphy (eds). Health and Welfare of Captive Reptiles. London: Chapman and Hall.

Haberl H, Wackernagel M, Wrbka T. 2004. Land use and sustainability indicators. An introduction. Land Use Policy, 21(3): 193–198.

Heilig, G K, 1997. Anthropogenic factors in land-use change in China. Population

and Development Review, 23, 139–168.
Hanley J A and McNeil B J. 1982. The meaning and use of the area under a receiver operating characteristic (ROC) curve. Radiology, 143: 29–36.
Lambin E F, Geist H J, Lepers E. 2003. Dynamics of land-use and land-cover change in tropical regions. Annual Review of Environment and Resources, 28: 205–241.
Lambin E F, Turner B L, Geist H J, Agbola S B, Angelsen A, Bruce J W, Coomes O T, Dirzo R, Fischer G, Folke C, George P S, Homewood K, Imbernon J, Leemans R, Li X, Moran E F, Mortimore M, Ramakrishnan P S, Richards J F, Skanes H, Steffen W, Stone G D, Svedin U, Veldkamp T A, Vogel C, Xu J. 2001. The causes of land-use and land-cover change: Moving beyond the myths. Global Environmental Change, 11(4): 261–269.
Li X B. 1999. Change of arable land area in China during the past 20 years and its policy implications. Journal of Natural Resources, 14(4): 329–333.
Liu J Y, Deng X Z, Liu M L, Zhang S W. 2002. Study on the spatial patterns of land-use change and analyses of driving forces in Northeastern China during 1990—2000. Chinese Geographical Science, 12(4): 299–308.
Liu J Y, Liu M L, Zhuang D F, Zhang Z X, Deng X Z. 2003. Study on spatial pattern of land-use change in China during 1995—2000. Science in China Series D—Earth Sciences, 46(4): 373–384.
Marlon J R, Bartlein P J, Carcaillet C, Gavin D G, Harrison S P, Higuera P E, Joos F, Power M J, Prentice I C. 2008. Climate and human influences on global biomass burning over the past two millennia. Nature Geoscience, 1(10): 697–702.
Pontius Jr R G, Walker R, Yao-Kumah R, Arima E, Aldrich S, Caldas M, Vergara D. 2007. Accuracy assessment for a simulation model of Amazonian deforestation. Annals of the Association of American Geographers, 97(4): 677–695.
Greenberg A. 1994. Land-use dynamics in the Sahelian zone in eastern Niger—Monitoring change in cultivation strategies in drought prone areas. Journal of Arid Environments, 27(2): 179–192.
Rudel T K, Coomes O T, Moran E, Achard F, Angelsen A, Xu J C, Lambin E F. 2005. Forest transitions: Towards a global understanding of land use change. Global Environmental Change Part A, 15(1): 23–31.
Seto K C and Fragkias M. 2005. Quantifying spatiotemporal patterns of urban land-use change in four cities of China with time series landscape metrics. Landscape Ecology, 20(7): 871–888.
Seto K C, Kaufmann R K, Woodcock C E. 2000. Landsat reveals China's farmland reserves, but they're vanishing fast. Nature, 406: 121.
TLAEB (Taips League Annals Editorial Board). 2000. Taips League Annals. Inner Mongolia Culture Press.
Turner B L II, Lambin E F, Greenberg A. 2007. The emergence of land change science for global environmental change and sustainability. Proceedings, National Academy of Sciences of the United States of America, 104(52): 20666–20671.
Veldkamp A and Lambin E F. 2001. Predicting land-use change. Agriculture Ecosystems and Environment, 85: 1–6.
Verburg P H, de Koning G H J, Kok K, Veldkamp A, Bouma J. 1999. A spatial explicit allocation procedure for modelling the pattern of land use change based

upon actual land use. Ecological Modelling, 116(1): 45–61.

Verburg P H, Soepboer W, Veldkamp A, Limpiada R, Espaldon V, Mastura S S. 2002. Modeling the spatial dynamics of regional land use: The CLUE-S model. Environmental Management, 30(3): 391–405.

Verburg P H, Van Eck J R R, de Nijs T C M, Dijst M J, Schot P. 2004. Determinants of land-use change patterns in the Netherlands. Environment and Planning B—Planning and Design, 31(1): 125–150.

Verburg P H, Veldkamp A, Fresco L O. 1999. Simulation of changes in the spatial pattern of land use in China. Applied Geography, 19(3): 211–233.

Verburg P H, Veldkamp A, Willemen L, Overmars K P, Castella J-P. 2004. Landscape level analysis of the spatial and temporal complexity of land-use change. Ecosystems and Land Use Change, 153: 217–230.

Yue T X, Fan Z M, Liu J Y. 2005. Changes of major terrestrial ecosystems in China since 1960. Global and Planetary Change, 48(4): 287–302.

Zhan J Y, Deng X Z, Jiang Q O, Shi N N. 2007. The application of system dynamics and CLUE-S model in land use change dynamic simulation: A case study in Taips County, Inner Mongolia of China. Proceedings of the 2007 Conference on Systems Science, Management Science and System Dynamics: Sustainable Development and Complex Systems, 1–10: 2781–2789.

Zhuang D F, Liu M L, Deng X Z. 2002. Spatialization model of population based on dataset of land use and land cover change in China. Chinese Geographical Sciences, 12(2): 114–119.

Chapter 8 Estimation of the Impacts of Land System Change on Land Productivity in the North China Plain

Land resources are multifunctional natural resources, which are under continuously growing demand due to population growth and socioeconomic development (Lin and Ho, 2003; Veldkamp and Verburg, 2004; Dent et al., 2006). This is particularly apparent in China where the economy is rapidly developing and land resources are undergoing unprecedented change in land use due to pressure from the demand (Ash and Edmonds, 1998; Liu et al., 2004). The structural change and succession patterns in the land system will undoubtedly lead to changes in the suitability and quality of types of land use patterns, and may directly influence land productivity (de Koning et al., 1999; Seto et al., 2000; Deng, 2008a). In discussions about "Who will feed China" and the global food security crisis, the issue of land resource loss has aroused broad concern at all levels of government. Therefore, structural change in the land system and changes in land productivity resulting from land use succession patterns have become one of the focuses of present academic research (Fischer and Sun, 2001; Jonathan et al., 2005; Deng et al., 2006).

The ESLP model can provide an important method for predicting scenarios of future land productivity change (Deng, 2008b; Deng et al. 2009). Combined with other related models, it can analyze trends in land productivity under reasonable hypotheses and provide decision-making information support for land use planning and land resource management.

8.1 Historical Land Productivity in the North China Plain

China is an agricultural country with a large population and little cultivated land. Grain production is an important issue that has always affected the national economy and people's livelihoods (Heilig, 1999; Cai, 2000; Yang and Li, 2000). Zhu (1964) discussed the climatic features of China and its relationship with grain production in 1964, and deduced the crop yield per unit of land under assumed ideal conditions. Many scientists have been devoted to exploring the potential crop productivity in agricultural production in China due to the need for agricultural modernization in the late 1970s (Yu and Zhao, 1982; Tang, 1997). Given the population growth, land decreases and environmental degradation, grain production has become increasingly urgent, and has become an important factor in the sustainable development of agriculture.

To increase grain production and feed the Chinese people, it is necessary to make use of the existing land resources and enhance land productivity, as well as strictly controlling population growth and investigating non-agricultural land (Fischer, et al., 2000; Fischer et al., 2005). The only two approaches for enhancing land productivity are to increase the multiple-crop index and enhance the yield per unit area (Tanrivermis, 2003; Deng et al., 2009). To achieve increased land productivity, several questions should be asked. What is the potential land productivity in China? What is the potential productivity of the main crops? Can these crops meet the needs of the people? Where are the regions with the good light, temperature, water and climate resources that have the biggest potential yield increases? What factors limit the increase in crop yield? Estimations of the climate potential productivity objectively and quantitatively analyze the potential land productivity of specific crops in different climates, soils and types of agricultural techniques (Fischer et al., 2005). The results of the climate potential productivity analysis provide a scientific basis for estimating the population supporting capacity of the land, formulating national or regional agriculture development planning and determining the direction of agricultural investment (Fischer, 1998).

The North China Plain is an important grain production base in China, thus it is imperative for China to estimate its land productivity.

8.1.1 Overview of the North China Plain

The North China Plain is located at 32°–40°30′N and113°–120°30′E, covering two municipalities Beijing and Tianjin, and five provinces Hebei, Shandong, Henan, Anhui and Jiangsu. These areas include 306 counties, with a total area of about 33.4 million ha of which the land area is 21.0 million ha. The North China Plain is the largest plain in China, and has 16.67 million ha of cultivated land and a population of 1 500 million, both of which account for 16% of the total cultivated area and population in the country. There are 58 ha of cultivated land and 520 people per km^2 on average, which is five times the national average.

The North China Plain was once a poor region short of food due to droughts, floods and alkaline soil. However, after 40 years of hard work since the founding of the People's Republic of China in 1949, this plain has been converted from a region short of food into an important grain, cotton and oil production base, reversing the previous situation where grain was shipped from the south to the north in China.

The region is in a warm temperate and sub-humid climate zone, with an annual average temperature of 10–15℃ and annual precipitation of 500–800 mm, which is suitable for the development of rain-fed agriculture and growth of various crops and fruit trees. The terrain is broad and flat with deep soil, and concentrations of cultivated land, which make it favorable for mechanization and irrigation. These advantages have leaded this region to become an important agricultural area and an important commodity base for grain, cotton, meat, soil and vegetables in China. Therefore, this region has begun to play an important role in the agricultural development of China.

The North China Plain has played an increasingly important role in the agricultural development of China in recent years with the area and production of grain crops remaining stable at 8% to 10% of the total in China. Wheat in the North China Plain accounts for 36–40% of the total area of wheat in China and about 40% of the national production. The area of cotton accounts for 32–42% of the national total and the production accounts for 40% of the total. The area and production of maize account for 27–29% and about 30% of the national total, respectively, while the area of soy beans accounts for 18–19.4% of the total and the production of the oil and fruit accounts for about 30% of the national production. Meat production in the North China Plain accounts for 20% of the national meat production. The total production of the main agricultural products in the North China Plain and their proportions of the national total production are listed in Table 8.1. It confirms that the North China Plain plays an important role in China's agricultural production, and is the main region guaranteeing the future food security in China.

Table 8.1 Main agricultural products of the North China Plain compared with national production in 2005

Agricultural product	North China Plain (10^5 metric ton)	National (10^5 metric ton)	North China Plain/ national (%)
Grain	11 060.7	46 946.9	23.60
Cotton	279.2	632.4	44.10
Cooking oil	892.47	3 065.9	29.10
Meat	1 807.2	7 244.8	24.90

8.1.1.1 Constraints on Grain and Agricultural Production

Precipitation in the North China Plain is unevenly distributed and fluctuates dramatically with seasons and years due to the impacts of the Pacific monsoon and migration of the rainy area, which concentrates 60–80% of the annual precipitation between June and October. The seasonal alternation of floods and droughts, both between years and in successive years has historically resulted in extreme instability in the agricultural production of this region. Based on historical records for nearly 500 years, the drought disaster rates in the North China Plain have been 25–30% for droughts, and 32–66% for floods. In other words, there is a major drought every three or four years and a big flood every 1.5–3 years in this plain.

Soil salinization is also very serious in the North China Plain. Currently, there are 2.33 million ha of saline land, about 2.67 million ha of potentially saline land, 266.67 ha of mortar clay land and 166.67 ha of sandy land. There is about 13.33 million ha of land with low and moderate yields, accounting for 70% of the cultivated land in this region due to the impacts of drought, flood and salinization. The low and moderate yields are equivalent to 30% and 66% of land with high yields, respectively. The North China Plain mostly consists of flat to rolling lowlands, so the runoff is uneven, which further aggravates the effects of droughts, floods and soil salinization in this region.

8.1.1.2 Timeline of Technological Breakthroughs in Agricultural Production

The central government has invested substantial amounts of money and transferred technology to the North China Plain since the founding of the People's Republic of China to investigate and implement various projects and fundamentally improve the quality of the cultivated land. These projects include dredging and rectifying the rivers in the plain to mitigate the impacts of drought, flood, saline and alkaline soil on the land productivity.

The technological breakthroughs related to agricultural production in the North China Plain generally fall into the following phases based on the characteristics of the saline and alkaline land in different periods and the status and effects of the different treatments.

(i) Early period of the founding of new China – 1960s

The state required irrigation ditches to be dug in the North China Plain in order to combat droughts in this region in the early 1950s. Due to a lack of forethought, although regional droughts were alleviated, problems of waterlogging and soil salinization were aggravated. This led to a situation of increasing yields in the first year, constant yields in the second year and decreasing yields in the third year in the new irrigation areas. The state then implemented water conservation projects, and built reservoirs in the North China Plain in 1957, but errors in the water-control guidelines led to increasing the saline land area from 1.87 million ha to 3.20 million ha in the Jiluyu Plain① during 1958 and 1961, in which farmers abandoned the irrigation channels to cut off the water. The severe floods in the Haihe River Basin in 1963 worsened the situation in the North China Plain.

With the droughts, floods and soil salinization unmitigated, the technological circle formed various but extremely different viewpoints, such as "agricultural reform", "water reform", "water net", "platform field" and "tube well project". However, no consensus viewpoint was achieved.

While the scientific community was busy arguing over flood management in the North China Plain, it suffered from a series droughts for three succes-

① The Jiluyu Plain is simply a large region located in the northeast of the North China Plain.

sive years in the late 1960s and early 1970s, which led to disputes over shallow or deep wells for drought management. Large amounts of human labor and financial resources were spent on implementing specific measures to manage droughts, though the effects were insignificant, or even reversed the desired effect, resulting in greater losses. After 30 years of poor drought governance, there was an urgent call for scientific theory and support for advanced technology to improve the production capacity and increase yields in the North China Plain.

(ii) 1960s–1980s

In the early 1960s, Changjiang Fan, the supervisor of National Science and Technology Commission, personally led a team to carry out scientific governance research in the North China Plain.

In 1973, Premier Zhou proposed that scientific research should be carried out on groundwater development and the integrated governance of droughts, flood and soil salinization using Hebei as a pilot zone. Yuanchun Shi accepted the difficult task, and established a research team in Zhangzhuang Brigade, the center of the alkaline soil in Quzhou County. Quzhou County was a poor county with low grain yields suitable for a pilot study on the integrated governance of droughts, floods, saline and alkaline soil.

Using soil survey mapping, long-term fixed-position observation points of water and salt dynamics, numerous interviews with farmers, and summaries of the experience of past governance in the county, Yuanchun Shi et al., developed the theory of "water and salt movement in semi-humid monsoon climate zone". This theory identified the complex relationships inherent among droughts, floods, saline soil, alkaline soil and evolution of their formation. The key points are:

- The coexistence and mutual interaction of the droughts, floods, saline and alkaline soil and saline groundwater are a set of natural phenomena related to regional water and salt movement under the semi-humid monsoon climate and the geological conditions of the flood plain, which are independent geographical landscape and ecosystem phenomena.
- The droughts, floods, saline and alkaline soils should be considered as a unified system, which must be managed with comprehensive governance measures rather than isolated governance measures. This is also the reason for the various unsuccessful management attempts in the previous 30 years.
- The comprehensive management of droughts, floods, saline and alkaline soil involves the scientific regulation and management of regional water movement (including precipitation, groundwater, soil water and its soluble salts), which will lead to the reduction in droughts, elimination of soil salinization and improvements in the agricultural ecological environment.
- The hub and lever for regulating and managing regional water and salt movement are to exploit and replenish shallow groundwater. A comprehensive governance program for agriculture and forestry water based on the characteristics of the North China Plain was carried out to meet

the need for integrated management and sustainable development, which started with the saline groundwater, using shallow wells and deep ditches as the foundation.

(iii) 1980s to the present

The development of China's grain production stalled during 1985–1987. To prevent severe nationwide food shortage problems caused by low food production and significant population growth, Zhen sheng Li led 400 scientists from 25 institutes of the Chinese Academy of Sciences (CAS) to undertake large-scale governance of medium yield and low yield land. The comprehensive development of land production occurred with the full support of CAS and local governments with support from other institutes of scientific research. The North China Plain was chosen as the study area and four provinces, Hebei, Shandong, Henan and Anhui, were the main agricultural development areas.

Their program achieved remarkable success in just a few years. In key areas, initially the low yielding hard hit areas around eight prefecture-level cities in the northwest Shandong, northern Henan, northern Anhui and Hebei's Cangzhou, the total grain yield in 1993 increased by 5.6 billion kg from 1985, an increase of 34.6% and an average annual growth rate of 5.81%. The average annual growth rate for the entire North China Plain region was 3.83%, while the national average annual growth rate was only 1.28% during the same period.

The state popularized the study area and achievements of CAS, which resulted in huge economic benefits for the prefecture-level cities, and also played a leading and promoting role in comprehensive national agricultural development. The achievements of CAS provided important technical support and experience for triggering rapid agricultural development in early 1990s, achieving the goal of a national grain yield of 500 billion kg by 1998.

This agricultural development program not only promoted grain production in China, but also indicated that the Chinese government had made significant advances in solving the problem of feeding and clothing the poor. China had achieved self-sufficiency in grain production.

8.1.2 Data and Processing

Climate data, land use and environmental data, crop and management data need to be processed and input into the model.

8.1.2.1 Climate Data

The meteorological data needed for this study came from the Chinese Meteorological Administration, and included data from 726 meteorological stations including daily average temperature, precipitation, average daily relative humidity, daily average wind speed, average daily solar radiation, daily minimum temperature, and daily minimum temperature from January 1, 1991 to December 31, 2000.

The original meteorological data were in text format, but the data required for this research is in GRID form. The conversion of the data were undertaken in ArcMap, using the following steps (Deng, 2008a).

- Select ADD X, Y in the DATA menu in ArcMap.
- Select the abscissa column and coordinates in the pop-up window.
- Convert the text data into a point file.
- Using the GIS interpolation tool, add the Albers projection coordinates though a Kriging interpolation of the meteorological data based on the latitude and longitude information for various meteorological sites.
- Generate the data in a GRID format, and further overlay it with the boundary map of the North China Plain to obtain meteorological data for the North China Plain.

The spatially disaggregated mean annual air temperatures, mean annual maximal air temperatures, mean annual minimal air temperatures, rainfall, wind speed, relative humidity identified the spatial variation for all these climate variables (Fig. 8.1).

8.1.2.2 Land Use and Environmental Data

(i) Area percentage data on Land Uses

The cultivated land use type and distribution data come from the land use dataset at a 1 km^2 pixel level developed by CAS. The 1:100 000 scale land use dataset was initially developed with data derived from the US Landsat TM/ETM images in the late 1980s and the 1990s. The 1:100 000 dataset covers all of China and used a self-designed digital human-computer interaction remote sensing extraction method with the land resource information in 1998. An additional digital field survey was carried out in 1999 to validate the accuracy of the dataset. This survey involved a cumulative coverage of more than 75 271 km, averaging about 2 509 km per province. In addition, more than 8 000 landscape photos were collected during the survey to further improve and modify the land use area percentage dataset (Liu et al., 2002; Gao and Deng, 2002; Liu et al., 2005).

The province and county level mapping and classification area summarization were based on the land use maps for all the provinces in the mid-1990s, using graphic cutting methods and area adjustment calculations. First, the digital land use maps of the provinces that met the design requirements were cut into regional maps with county-level units. The county areas were derived from the theoretical area of the 1:100 000 topographical maps framed with an international standard as the control area. The adjusted area of each county was then broken down into all the land use plots in the county. Finally, the areas of the different land use types in each county were calculated, and the areas of the 25 land use types in six land use categories including cultivated land, forestry, grassland, water areas, built-up areas and unused land in each province and the whole country were gradually added together (Liu et al.,

2004).

The dataset was comprehensively updated with the Landsat TM/ETM data as the data source, with the regions not covered by the Landsat data complemented with data from the China-Brazil Earth Resources Satellite 1 (CBERS-1). A total of 235 387 land parcels changed across the 32 provinces of China during the update process. From the dataset, we can identify the type and location of land use changes in China in the mid- to late-1990s, and understand the characteristics and rules that underlie the conversion among land use types. We carried out the same graphic cutting, area adjustment and subtotal calculation on the updated land use map of the late 1990s as we did for the mid-1990s map.

Based on the 1990s land use dataset with the Landsat and other remote sensing data as the data sources, we compared remote sensing images from the 1980s and the late1990s, and extracted information on past land use change.

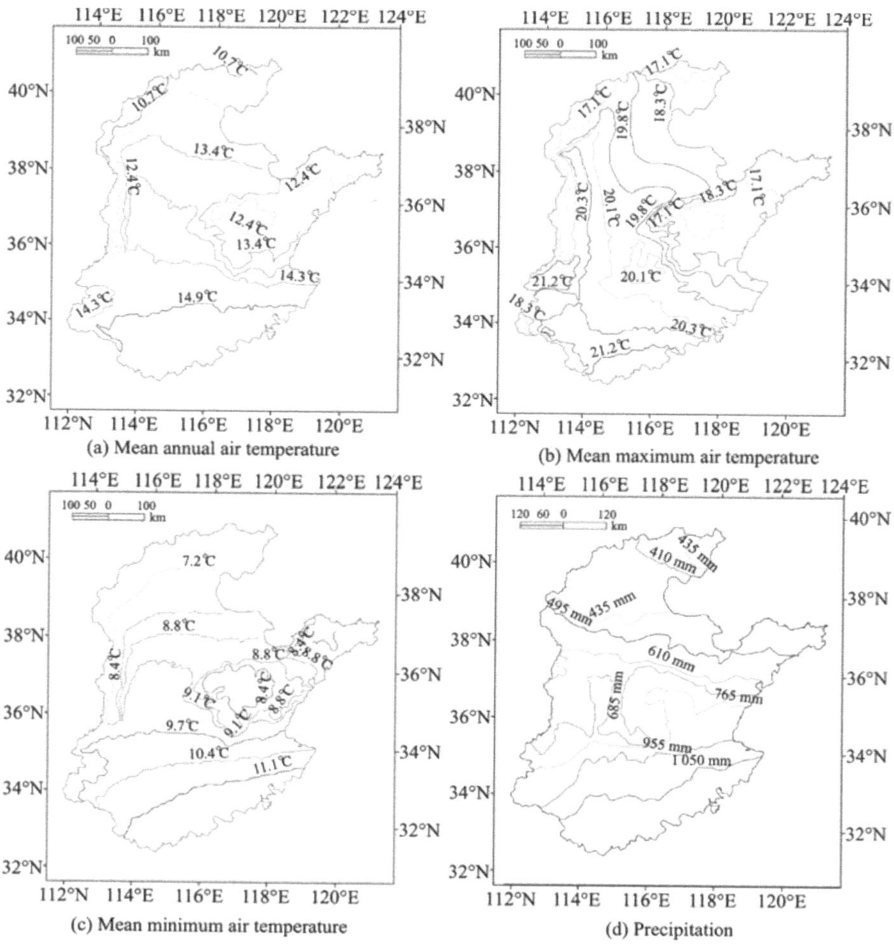

(a) Mean annual air temperature
(b) Mean maximum air temperature
(c) Mean minimum air temperature
(d) Precipitation

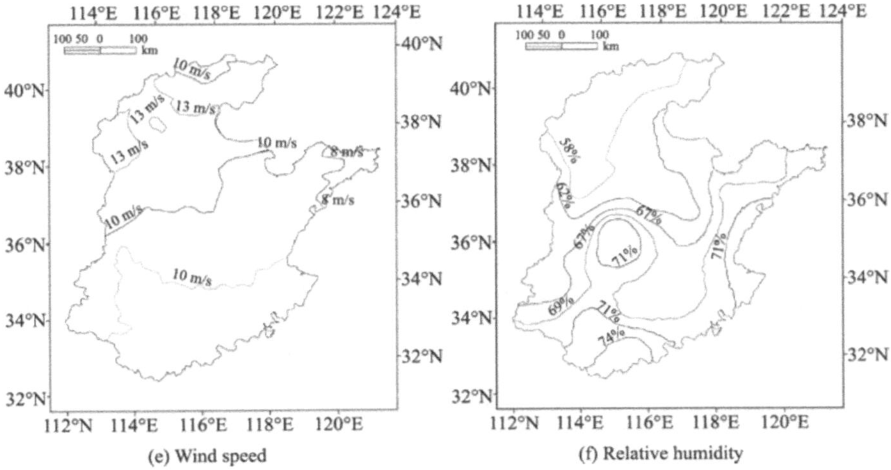

Fig. 8.1 Spatial variation of the relative humidity of the North China Plain in 2000.

Using the land use data from the late 1990s, we identified and sketched the regions of change, and annotated dynamic information codes on the land use type changes that reflected the land use types of the changed land parcels before and after the two periods in each county. Full coverage of the whole country was obtained. The same analysis also undertook the land use data from the 1980s, with 364 379 changed land parcels identified across the whole country, with a qualitative accuracy above 95% (Liu et al., 2002)(Fig. 8.2).

(ii) Soil texture data

The soil texture data were mainly extracted from soil texture maps from 1986 provided by the Institute of Soil Science, CAS, which reasonably and accurately reflects the geographical distribution of the different soil textures. These soil texture maps were drawn based on many soil particle analysis results (pipette method), using the Chinese soil texture categories as the standard. The 1:1 000 000 Chinese soil parent material map was used as the base map and the soil map of China drawn by Institute of Soil Science, CAS was used as a reference. The boundaries of the soil texture maps should be drawn based on the distribution of the soil particles to reflect soil particle composition and soil texture(Fig. 8.3).

(iii) Data on other soil properties

The soil is one of the important environmental factors that influence crop growth, and the quality of the soil can directly affect the model simulation results. The soil property datasets used in this study include the soil category and distribution dataset in the scale of 1:1 000 000, and the soil physical and chemical properties database. The 1:1 000 000 soil category and distribution dataset, compiled by the National Soil Survey Office, is created based on the second national soil survey of China using the *1:1 000 000 Soil Map of China* as the blueprint. It was digitalized, corrected and edited by Institute

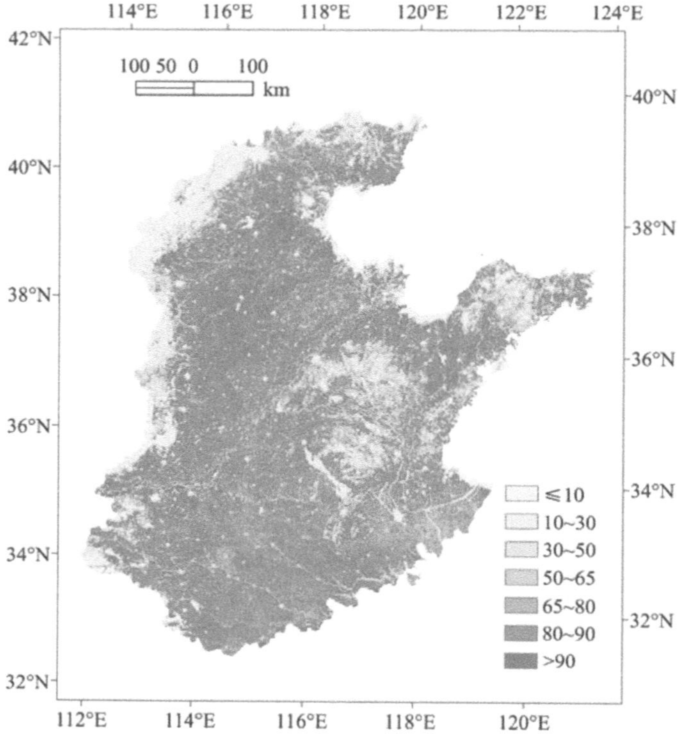

Fig. 8.2 Spatial pattern of cultivated land in 2000 identified by area percentage data.

of Soil Science, CAS, including 12 soil classes, 61 soil groups and 227 soil subgroups. From the soil category dataset, the Chinese Academy of Agricultural Sciences constructed a soil physical and chemical properties database from the *Chinese Soil Record 1–6*. The database holds soil physical and chemical properties based on the soil layer with the soil genus used to delineate the soil. The data include the depth of the plough layer, organic matter content, total nitrogen, total phosphorus, total potassium, C/N, pH, available phosphorus, and available potassium (Fig.8.4).

(iv) Topographic data

The topographic data used in this study include elevation, slope and aspect (Deng et al., 2008). The elevation map (Fig.8.5) was produced by the following procedures.

- Scan the topographic map of North China and save as the raster data image.
- Digitalize the image with the ArcMap software, and obtain a contour layer by extracting the contour lines and point elevation feature information (mainly peak elevations).
- Using the contour layer as the source file, interpolate the contour line

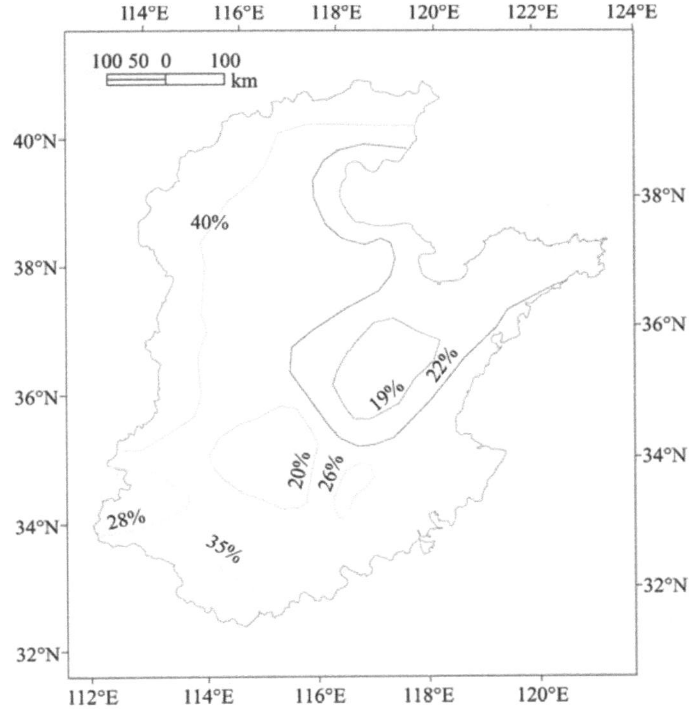

Fig. 8.3 Spatial variation of the soil texture of the North China Plain.

map into the GRID elevation map using the Kriging interpolation tool in the ArcMap software.

- Extract the slope and aspect using the "slope" and "surface" commands in the "surface" tool of the spatial analysis extension.

8.1.2.3 Crop and Management Data

(i) Crop growing period

The crop growing period, which considers the impact of the season on crop production, is one of the main parameters in the ESLP model. The definition of the crop growing period is the period during which the moisture and temperature conditions are suitable from plant growth to crop maturation. The crop growing period is an index that considers changes in the agro-ecological conditions including climate (FAO, 1982; Fischer et al., 2005).The impacts of climate, precipitation, evapotranspiration and climatic hazards during the growing period can be included to improve the accuracy of the model simulation. The length and distribution pattern of the crop growing period are the basis of agro-ecological zoning. Crops have developed temperature sensing features during the long process of adapting to temperature changes in their environment. A certain temperature is required for all crops to grow and develop normally, and the demands of different crops for temperature

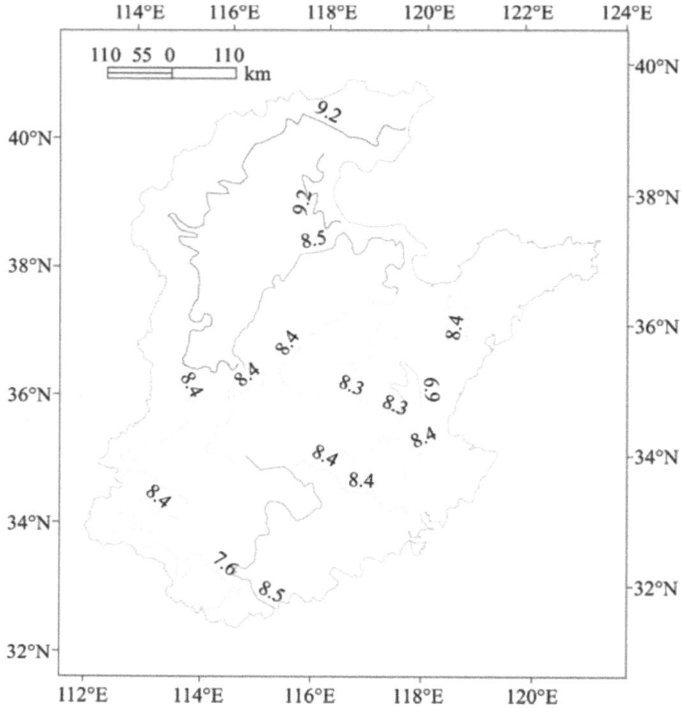

Fig. 8.4 Spatial variation in soil pH in the North China Plain.

vary during the different growing periods.

Thermophilic crops generally begin to grow from the first day with an average daily temperature above 10℃, which is the minimum critical temperature for sowing the early rice in spring, and to growing on or before the day an average daily temperature of 10℃ in autumn. Therefore, the period with average daily temperatures above 10℃ is important for dry matter production by photosynthesis, and can be called the active period of crop growth. The crop growing period was determined from the10-day average temperature in the North China Plain between 1990 and 2000, i.e., the crop growing period was taken as the period between the first and final 10-day periods with average daily temperatures ⩾ 10℃. The spatial distribution map of the crop growing period of the North China Plain based on the 10-day average temperature ⩾10℃ was obtained by calculation. The light-temperature productivity potential in different regions was then calculated based on the length of the growing period (Fischer et al., 2001).

(ii) Input level and management data

The input level and management data are mainly sourced from the Data Center of CAS, and partly from statistical yearbooks and field surveys. The irrigation coefficient is the ratio of irrigable cultivated land area to total cultivated land area in each county. The fertilizer quantity was obtained from

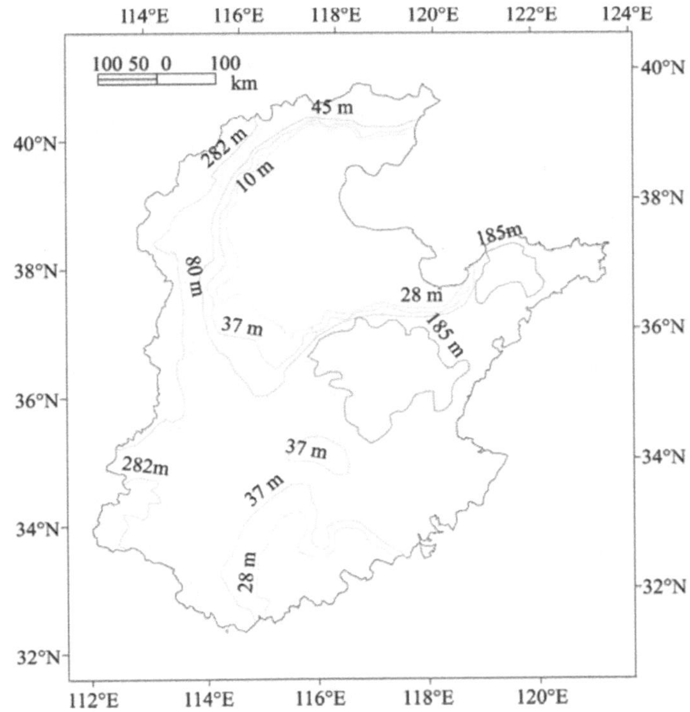

Fig. 8.5 Spatial variation in elevation in the North China Plain.

statistical data for each county. These data were saved in Microsoft Excel, and saved as a DBF table. The input level and management raster data were obtained by opening the county administrative division data and the DBF table at the same time in the ArcView software, selecting the county code column from the county administrative division data and the DBF table, then clicking "JOIN" to join the DBF file to the county administrative division data. The vector data were then transformed into raster data with the "POLYGRID" command in the ArcGIS software package.

8.1.3 Estimation of Land Productivity in the 1990s

Following introduces the estimation of land productivity in the 1990s, including features and changing trend of land productivity in the 1990s, as well we provincial land productivity during 1990s.

8.1.3.1 Features and Changing Trend of Land Productivity in the 1990s

Based on the annual data for 1991–2000, this research estimated the land productivity of the North China Plain in the 1990s. The estimation results show that there was some fluctuation in the land productivity of the North China Plain in the 1990s, which became increasingly significant over time (Fig. 8.6). For example, during 1996–2000, the minimum land productivity level in the North China Plain was 7 547.8 kg/ha in 1997, but the maximum in 1998 was 7 854.8 kg/ha. Although land productivity in the North China Plain peaked in 1998, it still showed an overall declining trend in the 1990s, due to significant fluctuations in precipitation and a subsequent drought in North China during the late 1990s. Land productivity in the North China Plain in 1997 and 1999 was significantly lower than that in other years because the precipitation was significantly lower than normal and the drought occurred widely in North China. For example, in 1999, the most severe drought of the century affected all of North China, resulting in the lowest land productivity level over four decades for North China (Fig.8.6).

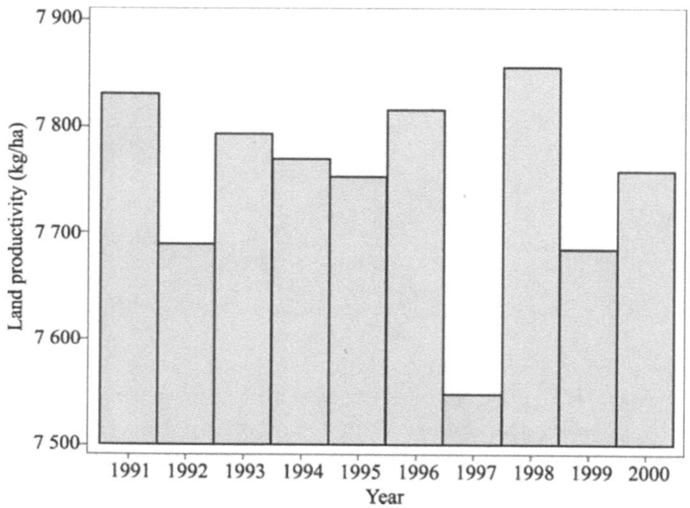

Fig. 8.6 Annual change in the land productivity in the North China Plain in 1990s.

8.1.3.2 Provincial Land Productivity During the 1990s

The land productivity generally declines from south to north in the North China Plain at a provincial level (Table 8.2), with the land productivity highest in Anhui being 9 378.3 kg/ha, followed by Henan and Hebei, being 8 581.2 kg/ha and 7 716.9 kg/ha, respectively. Beijing is to the north of Shandong and Henan, but its land productivity is relatively low, mainly because it is typical of urbanized regions, where cultivated land is often occupied by built-up land or abandoned. The land productivities of Jiangsu and Shandong are 6 709.8 kg/ha and 7 523.2 kg/ha, respectively.

There is a general decrease in the net land productivity from 1991 to 2000 in all the provinces in the North China Plain (Fig. 8.7). The net land productivity decrease in Hebei is 136.9 kg/ha, which is the province with the greatest change in the North China Plain, followed by Tianjin and Shandong, with an decrease of 99.0 kg/ha and 69.3 kg/ha. The land productivity of Jiangsu and Anhui decreased by only 10.1 kg/ha and 17.5 kg/ha during 1991–2000.

Table 8.2 Average land productivity in each province in the North China Plain during 1991–2000

Location	Land productivity (kg/ha)
Beijing	3 372.4
Tianjin	6 116.6
Hebei	7 716.9
Jiangsu	6 709.8
Anhui	9 378.3
Shandong	7 523.2
Henan	8 581.2

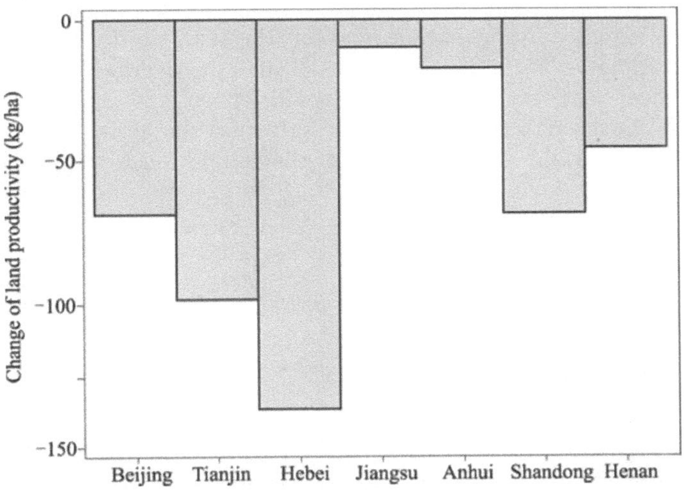

Fig. 8.7 Net change in land productivity by provinces in North China Plain from 1991 to 2000.

8.1.4 Validation of Land Productivity Results

The grain yield per unit of cultivated land in each county in North China in 2000 was collected, and linked to the county administrative maps, so that raster category data could be generated using the "POLYGRID" command in the Workstation module of ArcGIS. The grain yield per unit of cultivated land does not consider multiple crop indexes, which are taken into account during the validation process. The model calculation results are generally consistent with the statistical data from the perspective of the distribution of land productivity. However, the statistical values for county grain yield are the same for a whole county, while the model generates land productivity at the pixel level, which may lead to some discrepancies in the county region. To improve the accuracy of the validation, the Estimation System for Land Productivity (ESLP) model was used to summarize the land productivity of each county.

The county grain yield data for the North China Plain in 2000 was compared with the modeled average county land productivity in 2000. To avoid disturbance from abnormal factors, only grids with more than 50% of cultivated land area in the land use area percentage data were included in the validation of the model. For the statistical county data, to avoid the error caused by regions with a dispersed cultivated land layout or a small cultivated land area, only counties with a cultivated land area percent more than 30%, and with more than 100 cultivated land grids (equivalent to 100 km^2) were used. A total of 381 counties were included in the model validation. There is a significant correlation between the land productivity of the 381 counties estimated with the ESLP model and the average grain yield from the statistical data, with a correlation coefficient of 0.83. It can be seen from the trend analysis chart of the model results and the actual grain yield that the actual grain yield is about 39.1% of the estimation result (Fig. 8.8).

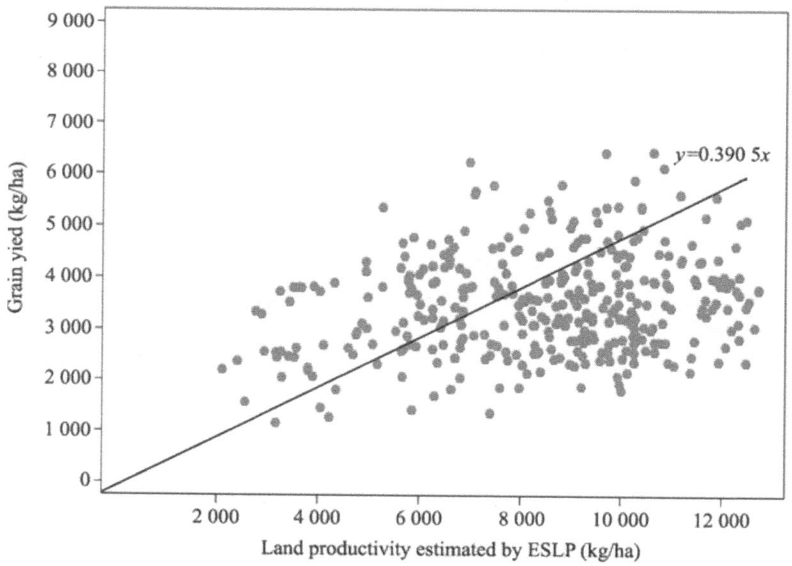

Fig. 8.8 Comparison of the estimated land productivity and the statistical grain yield at the county level.

8.2 Future Land Productivity

The change in land productivity change in the North China Plain during 2010–2020 was simulated with predicted climate change data, land use data and management data using the ESLP model.

8.2.1 Data and Data Handling

Processing and handling of climate adta, land use data and environment data and other data are introduced in this section.

8.2.1.1 Climate Data

The future ground climate data were sourced from the Intergovernmental Panel on Climate Change (IPCC) Data Distribution Centre (http://cera-www.dkrz.de/IPCC_DDC/SRES/) including daily average temperature, precipitation, daily average relative humidity, daily wind speed, daily average total solar radiation, daily maximum temperature and daily minimum temperature in 2010 and 2020.

Because the data provided by this website were in ASCII format, we transformed the data into text format using the PINGOs (Procedural INterface for Grib formatted Objects) software provided by the website (http://www.mad.zmaw.de/Pingo/pingohome.html), with the daily climate data for 2010 and 2020 saved separately to facilitate future data handling. The data for each weather station was then assigned corresponding latitude and longitude coordinates, with the longitude starting from the central meridian and from the Eastern Hemisphere to the Western Hemisphere with an interval of 3.75°, and the latitude starting from the equator and increasing to the north and south, respectively with intervals of 2.5°. The data from 418 weather stations were selected to cover the country based on the latitude and longitude range of China (from 4°N to 53°31′N, and from73°40′E to 135°5′E). The text file was added to ArcMap and vector point data were generated and then interpolated into grid data with the Kriging interpolation method. The grid data were further overlain with the boundary map of the North China Plain to obtain grid climate data for the North China Plain (Fig. 8.9).

8.2.1.2 Land Use Data and Environment Data

The land use area percentage data at the pixel level were obtained from simulations with the DLS simulation software. Soil texture, soil properties and topographic features are relatively stable, and would not change significantly in a relatively short period of time, the historical data were used (Deng et al., 2008).

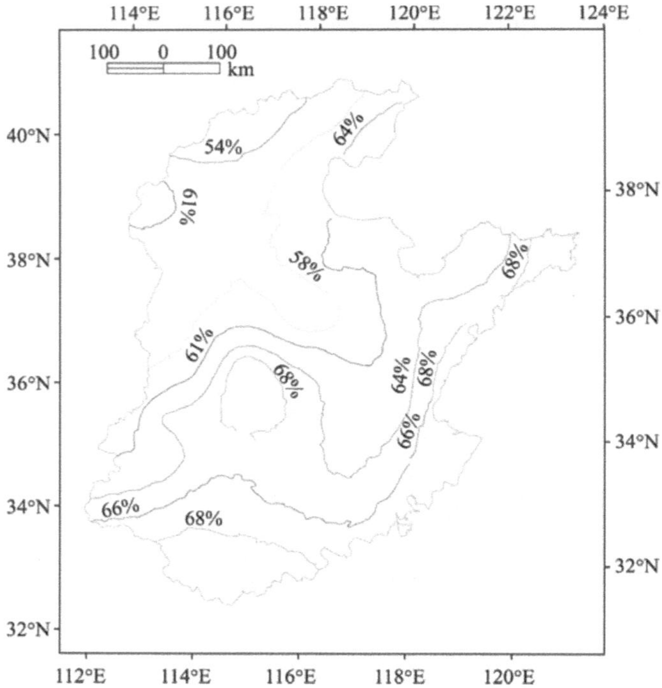

Fig. 8.9 Predicted solar radiation of the North China Plain in June 2010.

8.2.1.3 Other Data

Although the crop growing period fluctuates yearly, it will not change significantly in a short time, so the average crop growing period between 1991 and 2000 was used as the crop growing period for the forecast years. The input level and management data for each grid in the North China Plain in 2010 and 2020 were estimated based on a time series analysis of the input level and management data for 1991–2000.

8.2.2 Estimation Results for Land Productivity in 2010

The estimation results from the ESLP model show that the average land productivity in the North China Plain in 2010 will be 7 725.0 kg/ha, a decrease of 0.9 % from 2000. Considering the spatial distribution, the land productivity still shows a declining trend from south to north, without significant changes, except for Anhui where the land productivity changes are somewhat greater (Fig. 8.10).

In 2010, the land productivity of Anhui, Henan and Hebei is 9 357.7 kg/ha, 8 616.9 kg/ha and 7 778.6 kg/ha, respectively, and these are the

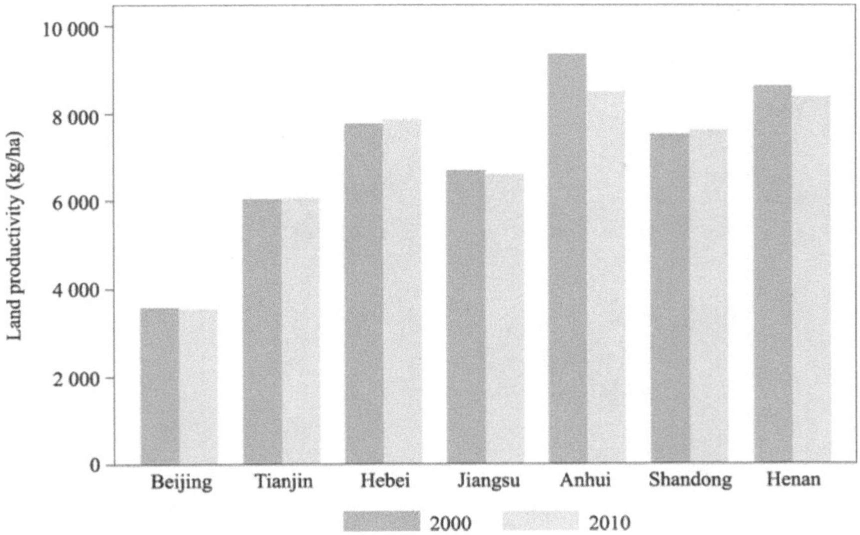

Fig. 8.10 Estimated land productivity of each province in 2010 compared with that in 2000.

top three provinces in the North China Plain. The land productivity then decreases in proper order of Shandong, Jiangsu, Tianjin and Beijing. In terms of the differences in land productivity between the provinces, cities, there is a trend of convergence in 2010. The gap between the highest and lowest land productivity decreases from 1 332.4kg/ha in 2000 to 640.1kg/ha in 2010, a decrease of over 50%.

The net change in land productivity of each province is greatest in Henan and Anhui with decreases of 861.7 kg/ha and 220.5 kg/ha, respectively. However, in Beijing, there was no significant change in the land productivity during 2000–2010 with changes in only 20.0 kg/ha. The land productivity in Shandong, Hebei and Tianjin increased by 101.7kg/ha, 84.5kg/ha and 59.5kg/ha in 2010 compared with 2000, respectively (Fig. 8.10).

8.2.3 Results of Estimation of Land Productivity in 2020

The results of the ESLP model show that land productivity in the North China Plain in 2020 increases by 0.2% in 2000, reaching 7 774.0 kg/ha. The spatial distribution of the land productivity in the North China Plain in 2020 is consistent with that in 2000 (Fig. 8.11).

In 2020, the land productivity of Anhui, Henan and Hebei is 8 884.8 kg/ha, 8 476.1 kg/ha and 7 836.6 kg/ha, respectively, and these are the top three provinces in the North China Plain. Beijing has the lowest land productivity

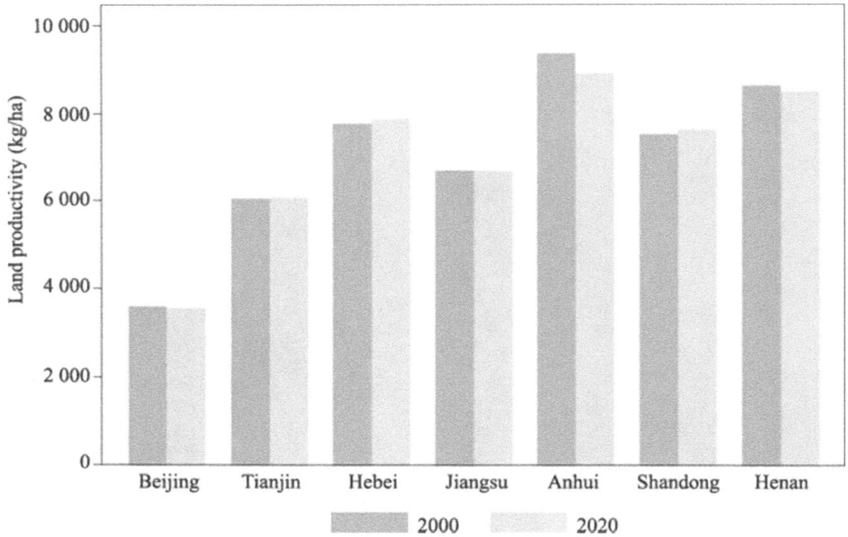

Fig. 8.11 Estimated land productivity of each province in 2020 compared with that in 2000.

at only 3 564.7 kg/ha. The land productivity between the provinces is slightly lower in 2020 compared with 2010. The gap between the highest and lowest land productivity is 5 320.1 kg/ha in 2020.

The maximum land productivity increase occurred in Anhui Province, with a net decrease of 472.9 kg/ha from 2000 to 2020, a decrease of 5.1%. The minimum land productivity decrease occurred in Beijing, at 14.5 kg/ha, a decrease of 0.4%. It can be seen that the net increases in land productivity in the North China Plain are seen in the provinces of Shandong, Hebei and Tianjin.

8.3 Impact of Cultivated Land Use Change on Land Productivity

There are various types and directions of structural change in land systems. The change in cultivated land and its relationship to land productivity are considered here. Land use change will be a focus of attention over the next 20 years, and research on the impacts of changes in cultivated land on land productivity provides a scientific basis for large scale land use planning and improving land productivity in China.

8.3.1 Simulation of Future Cultivated Land Use Change in the North China Plain

Methods for simulation of cultivated land use change and simulation results are listed bellow.

8.3.1.1 Methods for Simulation of Cultivated Land Use Change

The theory of simulation of land use change in the DLS model is used as the basis for this study with some improvements. Particularly, the regulation of spatial allocation and control of the land allocation institution with the predicted amount of land in each province and the percentage of cultivated land in each grid are amended. This research estimated the relationship between the binary dependent variables of whether land of a certain type exists and the spatially disaggregated driving factors, using the following estimation equation:

$$P_i = \frac{1}{1 + e^{\beta_0 + \sum_{j=1}^{m} \beta_{1j} C_{ji} + \sum_{j=1}^{n} \beta_{2j} T_{ji} + \sum_{j=1}^{o} \beta_{3j} L_{ji} + \sum_{j=1}^{p} \beta_{4j} I_{ji} + \sum_{j=1}^{q} \beta_{5j} D_{ji} + \sum_{j=1}^{r} \beta_{6j} X_{ji}}} \tag{8.1}$$

where P_i is the probability of appearance of a given land type by specific driving factors. C, T, L, I, D and X represent the climate, topography, geographic conditions, infrastructure, population and economic development, and policy changes and other factors, respectively; $\beta_1 - \beta_6$ are the regression coefficients for the six types of driving factors to be estimated (including lower level factors, for example, climate is a first level factor, by which there are influencing factors such as air temperature and precipitation). β_0 is a constant.

The two-dimensional data table that includes data for all dependent and independent variables was prepared in ArcGIS. A text file of spatial coordinate information was then input into the Stata software, and the relationship between structural land system changes and influencing factors was estimated using stepwise logistic regression (Kerr et al., 2003).

The driving mechanisms for structural change in the land use system model at a grid level were developed based on the spatial quantitative analysis method, and the influencing factors of large scale structural change in land systems in the North China Plain were estimated. The directions and effects of the impacts of driving factors are shown in Table 8.3.

8.3.1.2 Simulation Results of Land Use Change

The cultivated land area decreases by 2.73 million ha in the North China Plain from 2000 to 2010 and by 2.87 million ha from 2010 to 2020 (Table 8.4), showing an overall decreasing trend. The decreases in cultivated land are sharper in Beijing, Hebei and Anhui, with reductions of 33.0% from 2000 to 2010 and 41.7% from 2010 to 2020 in Beijing. The area of cultivated land in Hebei decreases the most, by 1.02 million ha from 2000 to 2010 and 1.06 million ha from 2010 to 2020. Henan is the largest agricultural province in China, and the decrease of cultivated land is relative small, only 0.19 million ha from 2000 to 2020. Through logical analysis, it can be determined that the decrease in the cultivated land area mainly results from the expansion of urban building land (Fig. 8.12).

Table 8.3 Effective coefficients of driving factors for land use change in the North China Plain

Variables	Cultivated land	Forestry	Grassland	Water areas	Construction land	Vacant land
⩾ 0°C accumulated temperature	—	32.008	—	—	—	—
Square of ⩾0°C accumulated temperature	—	-2.326	—	—	—	—
Precipitation	-2.584	-2.795	—	—	—	—
Square of precipitation	0.184	0.175	—	—	—	—
Elevation	0.694	—	—	-0.408	-0.594	—
Square of elevation	-0.086	—	—	0.083	0.063	—
Percentage of plain	0.159	0.085	0.057	0.426	—	—
Slope	—	-0.112	-0.073	-0.126	0.076	—
Content of clay	—	-0.537	-0.523	—	0.468	—
Distance to national highway	0.074	—	—	—	—	0.375
Distance to provincial capital	0.286	0.249	0.284	—	-0.239	-0.638
Population density	-0.094	—	—	-0.185	—	—
GDP	-0.083	—	-0.135		0.198	—
Agricultural inputs	0.878	0.653	0.785	0.763	0.276	—
Urbanization level	0.428	—	0.503	0.634	—	0.593
Car number per 1 000 people	—	0.208	0.494	—	0.306	2.975

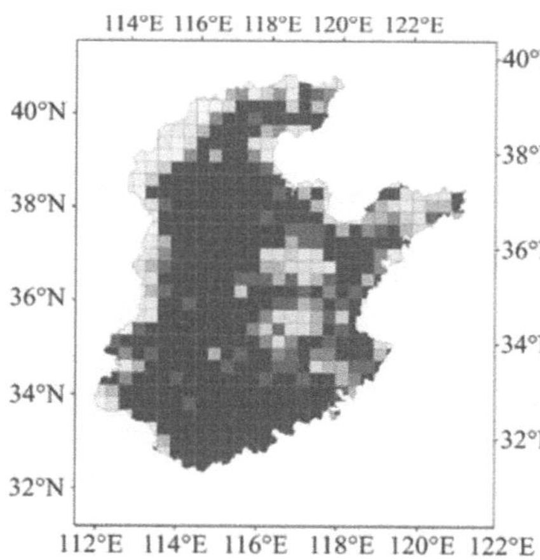

(a) 2000

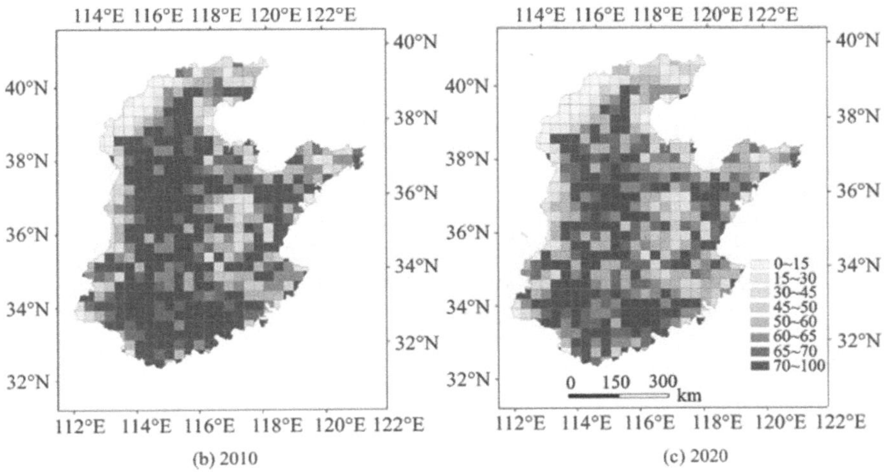

Fig. 8.12 Spatial patterns of cultivated land area which are identified by the area percentage grid data in 2000, 2010 and 2020 (5×5 km grid pixels).

Table 8.4 Cultivated land area in the North China Plain in 2000, 2010 and 2020 (10^5ha)

Location	2000	2010	2020
Beijing	43.34	29.05	16.94
Tianjin	52.06	47.67	42.94
Hebei	739.19	636.97	531.00
Shandong	531.30	484.77	436.55
Henan	630.47	563.68	491.86
Anhui	869.22	836.81	801.63
Jiangsu	481.30	473.27	462.27

8.3.2 Analysis of the Effects of Cultivated Land Use Change on Total Land Productivity

Analyses of affects of cultivated land use change on total land productivity mainly include affects of cultivated land use change on total productivity and response of cultivated land change to land production.

8.3.2.1 Effects of Cultivated Land Use Change on Total Land Productivity

To determine the impacts of land use change on land productivity, this study divided the contributions of the main variables influencing the land productivity, i.e., cultivated land area and land productivity per unit area to the total land productivity as follows:

$$\Delta A = A_2 - A_1 \tag{8.2}$$

$$\Delta AP = AP_2 - AP_1 \tag{8.3}$$

$$\begin{aligned}\Delta P &= P_2 - P_1 = A_2 \times AP_2 - A_1 \times AP_1 \\ &= (A_1 + \Delta A) \times (AP_1 + \Delta AP) - A_1 \times AP_1 \\ &= \Delta AP \times A_1 + \Delta A \times AP_1 + \Delta A \times \Delta AP\end{aligned} \tag{8.4}$$

As a result, the change in the total land productivity (ΔP) was divided into three parts: (i) changes caused by changes in land productivity per unit area (ΔAP); (ii) changes resulting from the cultivated land area change (ΔA); (iii) the change in the total land productivity under the joint effects of changing land productivity per unit area (ΔAP) and change in cultivated land area (ΔA).

8.3.2.2 Response of Cultivated Land Change to Land Production

Land productivity depends on the cultivated land area and the land productivity per unit area. The net decrease in cultivated land in the North China Plain from 2000 to 2010 is 27 300 ha. The newly reclaimed land is mainly located around the foothills of the Taihang Mountains with low productivity, while the high-yield farmland area in the eastern regions reduces significantly. Even with the extensive reclamation, the land production in the North China Plain decreases by about 1.6×10^7 metric tons. The land production varies in different regions due to regional heterogeneity of land use change and cultivated land fertility. For example, there is a decreasing in the land production in all the provinces due to the reduction of cultivated area (Fig. 8.13).

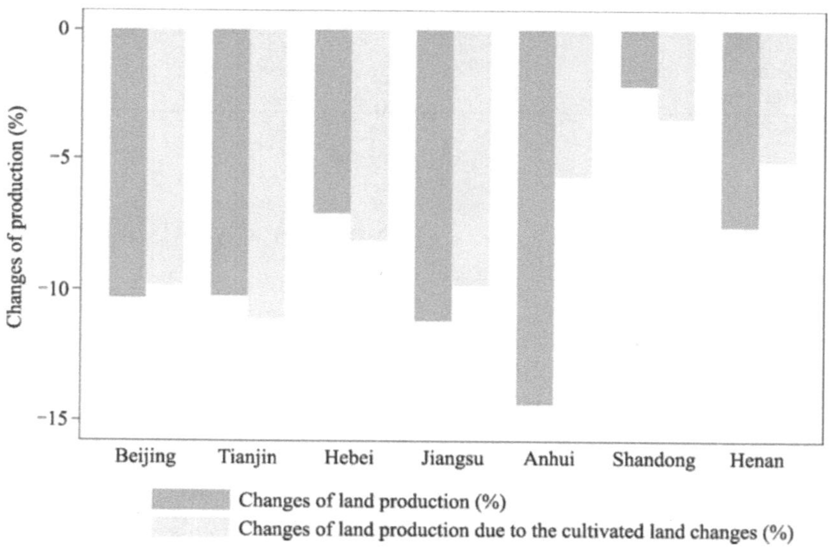

Fig. 8.13 Changes in land production in provinces due to the changes in cultivated land from 2000 to 2010.

There is a further large-scale transfer of land between 2010 and 2020, with the cultivated land in the North China Plain decreasing by 28 700 hectares. The rate of decrease of cultivated land increases further in all provinces compared with 2000, therefore, the land production of the land also tends to decrease further and the land production decreases by 3.3×10^7 tons. The changing rates in various provinces are significantly different from that in 2010; however, the changing trends are consistent. The land production decreasing in Hebei, Tianjin and Shandong is less than those caused by cultivated land change (Fig. 8.14). The contribution of cultivated land change, change in land productivity per unit area and their joint contributions to land production are quantitatively analyzed as follows.

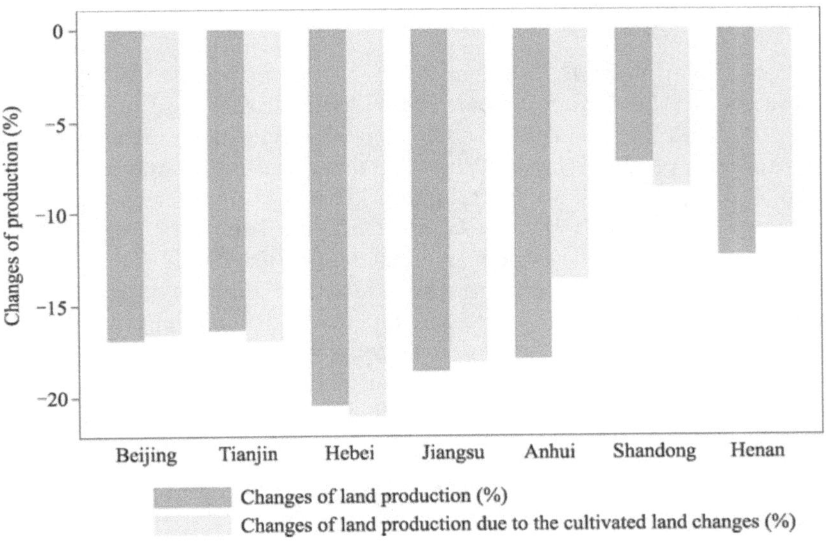

Fig. 8.14 Changes in land production by provinces due to the changes in cultivated land from 2000 to 2020.

From Equation (8.4), the change in cultivated land area in the North China Plain reduced the land production by 1.4×10^7 tons while the change in land productivity per unit area decreases the land production by 0.2×10^7 tons; the combined effect results in a reduction in the land production by 1.6×10^7 tons between 2000 and 2010 (Table 8.5). As described above, the cultivated land shrinking reduces the amount of decrease in the land production, especially in Hebei, Henan and Shandong. Although the increase of land productivity per unit in some area of North China Plain has a positive effect on the land production, the cultivated land not only offsets the increasing in the land production caused by the land productivity per unit, but significantly reduces the overall productivity of the land. Also there is a slight increase in the land productivity per unit area in Tianjin, Hebei and Anhui, but this fails to offset the changes in land productivity caused by the reduction of cultivated land area.

Table 8.5 Impacts of changes in cultivated land area and land productivity per unit on land production in each province in 2010

Location	Change in land production (10^5 tons)	Land production change caused by the change in land productivity per unit area (10^5 tons)	Land production change caused by cultivated land (10^5 tons)
Beijing	–1.3	–0.1	–1.2
Tianjin	–4.1	0.3	–4.4
Hebei	–39.0	5.4	–44.4
Shandong	–15.4	–1.9	–13.5
Henan	–40.0	–24.2	–15.8
Anhui	–16.9	10.0	–26.9
Jiangsu	–45.1	–14.6	–30.7

From Equation (8.4), between 2000 and 2020, the decline in cultivated land area in the North China Plain reduces the land production by 3.2×10^7 tons, and the change in land productivity per unit area decreases the total land productivity by 0.1×10^7 tons, leading to an overall decrease of 3.3×10^7 tons in the land production. The land production decreased by 102.4% compared with that in 2010 (Table 8.6), and decreased by 1.1×10^7 tons in Hebei alone, which is equivalent to 69.2% of the net national increasing during 2000–2010. From the statistical analysis, it seems that the cultivated land is the main reason for the growth in the land production. The impacts of the cultivated land are even more evident in 2010 compared with those in 2010, especially in Hebei, Anhui and Henan, where the cultivated land shows an increasing rate of decreasing productivity.

Table 8.6 Impacts of changes in cultivated land area and land productivity per unit on land production in each province in 2020

Location	Change in land production (10^5 tons)	Land production change caused by the change in land productivity (10^5 tons)	Land production change caused by cultivated land (10^5 tons)
Beijing	–3.9	0.1	–3.8
Tianjin	–6.5	0.2	–6.7
Hebei	–112.3	3.2	–115.5
Jiangsu	–25.6	–0.8	–24.9
Anhui	–50.2	–12.2	–38.0
Shandong	–55.5	9.9	–65.5
Henan	–73.7	–8.7	–65.0

8.3.3 Recommendations for Land Use Policies

China needs to formulate long-term and research-based land use planning and coordinate the development of agricultural and non-agricultural land. Compared with other countries, the degree of cultivated land used for non-agricultural uses is not high. China's future development depends on increasing the industrialization level, which will result in increased employment, income and productivity. This development will be accompanied by land use change, and moderate amounts of non-agricultural use of cultivated land are inevitable and the intentional suppression of this change will affect economic development. The focus should be put on formulating long-term, science based land use planning which balances agricultural and non-agricultural land uses.

In national land use planning, the land use plans for different regions should be different. Economic development is accompanied by the transfer of land from the agricultural sector with lower productivity to industry and service sectors with higher productivity (Li, 1999; Irwin and Geoghegan, 2001). However, the economic productivity of land varies greatly in different regions, and differences in the economic productivity of land are always greater than the differences in the land productivity. As the land is unchanging, there is a requirement for land use planning in different areas to reflect those differences.

Land use plans should aim to increase agricultural inputs and improve the comprehensive productivity of the land. The state should maintain the continual increase of investment into agricultural scientific research and technique extensions when promoting the reform of the agricultural science and technology system (Verburg et al, 1999; Verburg and Veldcamp, 2001; Verburg et al, 2004; Reenberg, 2001; Tanrivermis, 2003). There is also a need to improve the management of land with low and moderate yields while increasing investments into agricultural infrastructure (especially water conservation). These are fundamental measures for improving productivity of land to guarantee the security of grain and food supply in China (Rozelle and Rosegrant, 1997; Li, 1999; Haberl et al., 2001).

8.4 Summary

This chapter estimates the land productivity at the pixel level using the land system structural change scenario analysis function of the DLS model. The model was based on the natural, social and economic properties of national land resources, considering light, temperature, water and soil properties, input level and management and incorporating an ESLP model constructed using the GIS technique. Land productivity in the North China Plain between 1991 and 2000 was estimated using the DLS and ESLP models, and the land productivity change and its spatial heterogeneity in the 1990s were analyzed. Using the county grain yield data for the provinces in the North China Plain, the estimation accuracy of the ESLP model was assessed, and the correlation between the actual grain yield and the land productivity estimated based on the DLS and ESLP models was analyzed.

The models were then used to simulate the cultivated land conversion in

2010 and 2020, and the spatial pattern characteristics and regional heterogeneity of land productivity in those 2 years. The changing land productivity trends and their underlying reasons were analyzed by comparing the estimation results with the data for 2000.

This research shows that combining the DLS and ESLP models is an effective method to estimate the land productivity. Although there have been some interannual fluctuations in the land productivity since the 1990s, there was an overall downward trend. There will be different degrees of change in land productivity on 2010 and 2020 due to the influence of climate change and other factors. There will be significantly negative impacts on land productivity from land conversion, although the increase in grain yield per unit area offsets some of the changes caused by land conversion. It can be seen that to guarantee the national food security, it is necessary to control the land use change to some extent, increase investment, enhance scientific, technological and management levels, and enhance the grain yield per unit area. These research conclusions can provide decision-making support for developing land use plans and land resource management policies in the future.

References

Ash R F and Edmonds R L. 1998. China's land resources, environment and agricultural production. The China Quarterly 156 (Special Issue: China's Environment): 836–879.

de Koning G H J, Veldkamp A and Fresco L O. 1999. Exploring changes in Ecuadorian land use for food production and their effects on natural resources. Journal of Environmental Management, 57(4): 221–237.

Cai Y L. 2000. Problems of farmland conservation in the rapid growth of China's economy. Resources Science, 22(3): 24–28.

Deng X Z, Huang J K, Rozelle S, Uchida E. 2006. Cultivated land conversion and potential land productivity in China. Land Use Policy, 23(4): 372–384.

Deng X Z. 2008a. Analysis of Land Use Conversions. Beijing: China Land Press.

Deng X Z. 2008b. Simulation of Land System Dynamics. Beijing: China Land Press.

Deng X Z, Su H B, Zhan J Y. 2008. Integration of multiple data sources to simulate the Dynamics of Land Systems. Sensors, 8(2): 620–634.

Deng X Z, Jiang Q O, Zhan J Y. 2009. Scenario analyses of land productivity in China. Ecology and Environment, 18(5): 1835–1843.

Jonathan A, Foley R D, Gregory P, Asner, Barford C, Bonan G. 2005. Global consequences of land use. Science, 309: 570–575.

FAO. 1982. Assessment of land resources for rainfed crop production in Mozambique. Rome, FAO.

Fischer G. 1998. AEZWIN — An interactive multiple-criteria analysis tool for land resources appraisal. Interim Report, IR-98-051/October. Laxenburg, Austria, International Institute for Applied Systems Analysis.

Fischer G and Sun L X. 2001. Model based analysis of land-use development in China agriculture. Ecosystem and Environment, 85(1-3): 163–176.

Fischer G, Shah M, Tubiello F N, van Velthuizen H T. 2005. Socio-economic and climate change impacts on agriculture: An integrated assessment, 1990—2080. Philosophical Transactions of the Royal Society B—Biological Sciences, 360(1463): 2067–2083.

Fischer G, van Velthuizen H T, Nachtergaele F O. 2000. Global agro-ecological zones assessment: Methodology and results. Interim Report IR-00-064. Luxemburg, Rome, IIASA.

Gao Z Q and Deng X Z. 2002. Analysis on spatial features of LUCC based on dataset of land use and land cover change in China. Chinese Geographical Science, 12(2): 107–113.

Haberl H, Batterbury S, Moran E. 2001. Using and shaping the land: A long-term perspective. Land Use Policy, 18(1): 1–8.

Heilig G K. 1999. China Food: Can China Feed Itself? International Institute for Applied Systems Analysis (IIASA), Laxenburg, Austria.

Irwin E G and Geoghegan J. 2001. Theory, data, methods: Developing spatially explicit economic models of land use change. Agriculture Ecosystems and Environment, 85: 7–23.

Jonathan A, Foley R D, Asner G P, Barford C, Bonan G. 2005. Global consequences of land use. Science, 309: 570–575.

Kerr S, Liu S, Pfaff A S P, Hughes R F. 2003. Carbon dynamics and land-use choices: Building a regional-scale multidisciplinary model. Journal of Environmental Management, 69(1): 25–37.

Li X B. 1999. Change of arable land area in China during the past 20 years and its policy implications. Journal of Natural Resources, 14 (1999): 329–333 (in Chinese).

Lin G C S and Ho S P S. 2003. China's land resources and land-use change: Insights from the 1996 land survey. Land Use Policy, 20(2): 87–107.

Liu J Y, Xu X L, Gao Z Q, Zhuang D F. 2004. Recent land use change and its impact on farmland productivity in China. Remote Sensing and Modeling of Ecosystems for Sustainability, 5544: 295–300.

Liu J Y, Deng X Z, Liu M L, Zhang S W. 2002. Study on the spatial patterns of land-use change and analyses of driving forces in Northeastern China during 1990—2000. Chinese Geographical Science, 12(4): 299–308.

Liu J Y, Liu M L, Tian H Q, Zhuang D F, Zhang Z X, Zhang W, Tang X M, Deng X Z. 2005. Spatial and temporal patterns of China's cropland during 1990—2000: An analysis based on Landsat TM data. Remote Sensing of Environment, 98(4): 442–456.

Reenberg A. 2001. Agricultural Land use pattern dynamics in the Sudan–Sahel—Towards an event-driven framework. Land Use Policy, 18(4): 309–319.

Rozelle S and Rosegrant M W. 1997. China's past, present, and future food economy: Can China continue to meet the challenges? Food Policy, 22(3): 191–200.

Seto K C, Kaufmann R K, Woodcock C E. 2000. Landsat reveals China's farmland reserves, but they're vanishing fast. Nature, 406: 121.

Tang H J. 1997. Comparative study on methodology of land production potential. Beijing: Agricultural Use of Land Resources in Rural China.

Tanrivermis H. 2003. Agricultural land use change and sustainable use of land resources in the mediterranean region of Turkey. Journal of Arid Environments, 54(3): 553–564.

Verburg P H, Veldkamp A, Fresco L O. 1999. Simulation of changes in the spatial pattern of land use in China. Applied Geography, 19: 211–233.

Verburg P H and Veldkamp A. 2001. The role of spatially explicit models in land-use change research: A case study for cropping patterns in China. Agriculture Ecosystems and Environment, 85: 177–190.

Veldkamp A and Verburg P H. 2004. Modelling land use change and environmental impact. Journal of Environmental Management, 72(1–2): 1–3.

Verburg P H, Veldkamp A, WillemenV, Overmars K P, Castella J C. 2004. Landscape level analysis of the spatial and temporal complexity of land-use change. Ecosystems and Land Use Change, 153: 217–230.

Yang H and Li X B. 2000. Cultivated land and food supply in China. Land Use Policy, 17(2): 73–88.

Yu H N and Zhao F S. 1982. On the light and thermal resources and the crop potential productivity—Taking Luancheng county of Hebei Province as example. Acta Meteorologica Sinica, 40(3): 327–334.

Zhu C. 1964. Some characteristic features of Chinese climate and their effects on crop production. Acta Geographica Sinica, 30(1): 1–13.

Conclusions and Further Research

The environmental effects of the improper exploitation of land resources have become increasingly prominent, particularly with the aggravation of climate change and other global environmental changes. The dynamics and consequences of land system change as a direct reflection of the disturbance caused by human society in terrestrial ecosystems have been a focus of academic study. Land system change is not only closely related to human production activities, but also has an important influence on the biogeochemical cycles of the Earth's surface. These cycles directly affect the interaction between human society and the ecological environment, and can limit the sustainable development of society.

The simulation of the dynamics and consequences of land system change has been a key focus of the Global Land Project (GLP), but the commonly used models and methods still require further improvement. For example, the current models that simulate the dynamics and consequences of land system change do not have an overall methodology from analysis of the dynamics to the simulation of the effects, and the connections between the models lack feasibility. Problems with the current models include: a lack of explicit descriptions of the micro mechanisms in the dynamics analysis process; a lack of driving mechanism analysis at the individual grid level; and a poor macro effect analysis, making it difficult to use the research results to uncover mechanisms at the regional level. Given these problems, this book introduces a three-tier model to analyze the dynamics and consequences of land system change. The book explicitly illustrates the models' principles, function modules, installation and usage steps, and selects some key areas undergoing land system change in China as case studies to show the models advantages in the simulation of the dynamics and consequences of land system change.

1. Main Conclusions

(i) Land system change is closely related to human production and life, and also has an important influence on terrestrial and marine ecosystems. It is one of the key areas of land science and global change research. The research on land systems needs to adopt the processes and methods of systems science and emerging technologies to undertake comprehensive and in-depth explorations of the dynamics and consequences of land system change.

Research on the land use system is represented by the land use and land cover change (LUCC) research program, which is now complete, and the fledgling GLP. The LUCC achieved breakthroughs on aspects such as mechanisms of land cover change, the land use change mechanisms, and the construction of regional and global models. The LUCC research program was also responsible for developing relatively complete monitoring techniques, accumulating the original results of the driving mechanisms and environmental effects, developing analysis methods for land use change models, and accumulating large quantities of global and regional research data and information. Based on the global science research from the IGBP and IHDP, the GLP is attempting to promote the formation of a new global network to better understand the scientific issues related to land and the intersection of natural science, sociology and many other subjects. This network will make it possible for experts in various fields to participate in land system science research and decision-making, providing a foundation for research on land use conversions and its driving mechanisms.

(ii) The main directions of current models for land system structure, driving mechanism analysis, spatial allocation and effect assessment are to extract land system change processes at the grid scale, analyze land supply and demand balance at the regional scale, and analyze differences in the action of model variables at different scales. The dynamic analysis of land system change is an important prerequisite for effects assessment, which is a key focus in current land system studies. Although great progress has been made in land system research both in China and internationally, a complete methodology has not been created to analyze both the dynamic mechanisms and the consequent effects of land system change. The separation of research on the dynamic change in land systems and the simulation of effects lead directly to the inconsistent spatial resolution of parameters and different variable selection principles, increasing the gap between the dynamic analysis models and the effect models for land system change. The three-tier architecture model provides a complete procedure for the study of regional dynamics and consequence of land system change, and thus provides a complete methodology and analysis process for the study of regional land systems.

(iii) One part of the three-tier architecture model is the Computable General Equilibrium Model of Land Use Change (CGELUC) model. This considers the influence of regional industrial structures, trade environments and economic policies on regional land system change, and describes a framework with an opening balance and feedback system for analyzing regional land system change. The Computable General Equilibrium (CGE) model is used to analyze the influence of industrial structure, trade environment, economic strategies, institutional arrangement and other socioeconomic factors in a balanced economic system on regional land use structure. The structural change in land use is assumed to be the result of changes in economic decision-making and behavior due to market volatility and policy adjustments by introducing the price mechanism function. The CGELUC model can also simulate the structural change in regional land use caused by the constraints and impacts of policies by explaining the simulation results with models, and it can undertake studies on simulation, prediction, evaluation and analysis related to land use.

(iv) The foundation and prerequisite for the dynamic simulation of land system change are the analysis of restrictions on land use distribution at a grid level using the Dynamic Land System (DLS) model. There are two types of models for land use distribution at a grid scale: the explanatory linear model of land use pattern (ELMLUP), which is based on the driving factors of land use type distribution; the nonlinear model based on logistical distribution, which fully considers the indistinct relationship between land type distribution and driving factors. The features of the DLS model include: being controlled by external demands; considering the impact of neighboring effects; valuing the inherent suitability of land use types; controlling random interference factors; and having clear conversion rules. Therefore, the DLS model can be successfully applied in the dynamic simulation of land systems in terms of both the mechanism expression and the simulation results. The DLS model can simulate the spatiotemporal dynamic processes of structural change and pattern succession of land systems, and can export land system pattern succession maps at high spatiotemporal resolutions by establishing land use conversion rules and designing change scenarios.

(v) The Estimation System for Land Productivity (ESLP) model is based on the natural, social and economic properties of regional land resources, and integrates GIS technology to estimate land productivity at the grid scale based on effective radiation, temperature, water, soil, input level and operating conditions. It is a collection of several application programs including the assessment of land suitability, evaluation of land productivity and advanced applications, which use the stock of land resources as basic input information. The output information from the ESLP model provides decision-making reference information for the evaluation of land degradation, simulation of land productivity, assessment of population carrying capacity and optimal allocation of regional land use. There are many parameters and complex calculation processes in the ESLP model, so this book has integrated the ESLP model into a software system and introduced the required parameters and methods of data preparation for the processes of land productivity evaluation.

(vi) The case studies indicate that the three-tier model for simulating the dynamics and consequences of land system change can successfully simulate changing trends in the regional land system structure and estimate regional land productivity.

Overall, the three-tier architecture model is an effective tool, which explicitly simulates the dynamics and consequence regional land system change both quantitatively and spatially using models based on the land system. It has an unmatched advantage over traditional models for the simulation of regional land systems.

2. Further Research Prospects

In this book we have introduced a three-tier architecture model for the simulation of the dynamics and consequences of land system change by integrating research results from related fields, building models and developing software. The models, including CGELUC, DLS and ESLP, provide the basic tools for the analysis of dynamics and consequences of land system change and the implementation of related research on the global land science project.

The three-tier architecture model is being developed and improved, and its functionality for the analysis of the dynamics and consequences of land system change will also grow as it is used in more case studies. The three-tier architecture model will surely be improved as further mechanisms are identified and the selection of variables will also change with improved understanding of the interactions and links between land system change and natural and socioeconomic factors within the land system with the participation of more experts and scholars from different fields. In addition, with the development of remote sensing technology and different methods of Earth observation, the demands of the three-tier architecture model for data of high spatial and temporal resolution will be met, which will improve the accuracy of regional simulations with the three-tier architecture model. It can be assumed that the three-tier architecture model will be used more widely with the support of high accuracy and spatiotemporal resolution data and with the development of multi-source data fusion technology and spatial analysis technology.

Even the most rigorous mathematical model is only an approximation of reality, and cannot completely delineate actual processes of structural change and pattern succession of land systems because the future is continually changing. However, the three-tier architecture model can delineate the distribution of future probabilities as accurately as possible. It is probable that the simulation method provided by the three-tier architecture model will be developed and improved with the development of related spatial statistical theory, and it will begin to approximate natural laws when it predicts possible scenarios of the dynamics and consequences of land system change given proper scenario design.

It is important to note that the three-tier architecture model for the simulation of the dynamics and consequences of land system change provides a flexible interface for users so that the appropriate mechanism model can be selected to predict and analyze the regional land system change and its effects based on the characteristics of the case study areas during scenario analyses. The certainty of the output results increases because the three-tier architecture model has considered the complexity of land system change, its regional differentiation and its effects, providing more flexibility and freedom for users. It is necessary, therefore, for users to improve the accuracy of verification and sensitivity analysis of the estimation results when simulating land system change and its effects with the three-tier architecture model to ensure the a high precision of the simulation results.

In summary, the three-tier model for the simulation of the dynamics and consequences of land system change is still in the process of rapid development. The theoretical basis, methodological support, parameter selection and designs within the program are yet to be completed and expanded, and the conclusions obtained from the case studies at a regional level also need further verification.

Appendix 1 VBA Program of RAS Method

```
'RAS Macro
'Sheets("Sheet1").Select
1 Define the arrays and variables referred to in the RAS method.
'=============Define arrays and variables ==============
Static rn As Integer 'Row
Static cn As Integer 'Column
rn = 2
cn = 3
ReDim G(rn, cn)
ReDim A(rn, cn)
ReDim Row(rn)
ReDim Col(cn)
Dim ba As Double
ba = 1
'2 Import the initial matrix A0, row sum vector ROW, column sum vector
   COL, 'and intermediate matrix A00 from the corresponding region of
'Excel workbook "Sheet1".
'====Import the row sum, initial matrix and intermediate matrix====
For i = 1 To rn
      Row(i) = Sheets("Sheet1").Cells(i + 1, cn + 3).Value
         'cn+3 is the given column sum
      For j = 1 To cn
            G(i, j) = Cells(i + 1, j + 1).Value
            A(i, j) = G(i, j)
      Next j
Next i
'================Import the column sum==============
For j = 1 To cn
      Col(j) = Sheets("Sheet1").Cells(rn + 3, j + 1)'rn+3 is the given row sum
Next j
'3 Check whether the summation of elements in the given vector COL or ROW
     is 'equal with each other. If not, vector COL should be adjusted in proportion.
'========= Check whether the summation of elements in the given========
```

```
'=========vector COL or ROW is equal with each other==============
rsum = 0
csum = 0
For i = 1 To rn
        rsum = rsum + Row(i)
Next i
For j = 1 To cn
        csum = csum + Col(j)
Next j
'======= If vector COL or ROW is not equal with each other,=======
'========= adjust vector COL in proportion================
If csum <> rsum Then
        ba = rsum / csum
        For j = 1 To cn
                Col(j) = Col(j) * ba
        Next j
End If
'4 Calculate the RAS iterative process.
'======================RAS iterates==================
        iter = 0
Top:
        iter = iter + 1
        rdismax = 0
        cdismax = 0
'5 Use the multiplicator of column to multiply the intermediate matrix A00
    in the 'right, and calculate the column sum gap between the obtained
    matrix and the 'given 'matrix COL.
'Use the multiplicator of column to multiply the intermediate matrix in the
  right
For j = 1 To cn
        csum = 0
        For i = 1 To rn
                csum = csum + A(i, j)
        Next i
        If (Abs(csum) > 0) Then
                csum = Col(j) / csum
        Else
                csum = 0
        End If
        For i = 1 To rn
                A(i, j) = A(i, j) * csum
        Next i
'====Calculate column sum gap between the obtained matrix=======
'====and the given matrix===========================
```

```
        dis = Abs(csum - 1)
        If (dis > cdismax) Then
            cdismax = dis:
            cis = csum - 1:
            jmax = j
        End If
Next j
'6 Use the multiplicator of row to multiply the intermediate matrix A00 in
   the left, and calculate the row sum gap between the obtained matrix and
   the given matrix 'ROW.
'==Use the multiplicator of row to multiply the intermediate matrix in the
      left==
For i = 1 To rn
        rsum = 0
        For j = 1 To cn
            rsum = rsum + A(i, j)
        Next j
        If (Abs(rsum) > 0) Then
            rsum = Row(i) / rsum
            Else: rsum = 0
        End If
        For j = 1 To cn
            A(i, j) = A(i, j) * rsum
'==Calculate row sum gap between the obtained matrix and the given
        matrix==
        dis = Abs(rsum - 1)
        If (dis > rdismax) Then
            rdismax = dis:
            rdis = rsum - 1:
            imax = i
        End If
Continue: Next i
'7 Determine whether the iterations can be converged, and set the termination
   conditions of iteration, which include two aspects,
'First, the iterations cannot be infinite, here we set it as no more than 50,000;
'Second, the row sum gap or column sum gap between the result matrix and
'given matrix is small enough, here we set the error accuracy as 0.000001.
'==========Determine whether the iterations converge=========
If (cdismax > rdismax) Then
        dismax = cdismax
        Else: dismax = rdismax
End If
'===========Set the termination conditions of iteration========
If (iter < 50000 And dismax > 0.000001) Then
```

```
    GoTo Top
    End If
    If (dismax > 0.000001) Then
        Beep
    End If
    Cells(rn + 5, 1) = ba
    '8 Record the final result matrix obtained from the iterations, and export
      the 'structure to workbook "Sheet1" in the corresponding region.
    '============Record the final result matrix============
    For i = 1 To rn
        For j = 1 To cn
            If Row(i) = 0 Then
                Cells(i + rn + 5, j + 1).Value = 0
                Else: Cells(i + rn + 5, j + 1).Value = A(i, j) * ba
            End If
        Next j
    Next i
    Beep
Worksheets ("Sheet1").Activate
```

Appendix 2 SAM of Jiangxi Province in 2007

Table 1. Outputs of production activities

-	1	2	3	4	5	6	7	8	9	10	11	12	13	14	15	16	17	18	19	20	21	22	23
47	1135800.3	8525.3	0.0	891.5	183.1	1651957.3	137439.0	5470.4	110968.6	2441.2	0.0	115572.1	33.5	17.6	265.6	2431.0	37.5	160.1	0.0	73.0	84754.3	0.0	4.0
48	14984.8	24678.0	0.0	1145.3	3131.4	7102.1	1888.2	65.1	2245.3	2066.9	22867.0	41585.0	73456.0	82362.5	443.6	1207.4	1736.9	241.7	44.5	36.4	2195.7	0.0	207136.1
49	0.0	139.4	0.0	90.1	0.0	245.7	0.0	29.8	0.0	217.6	251120.0	37862.5	254.4	13.9	0.0	135.0	3.6	735.0	0.0	0.0	0.0	0.0	172.4
50	0.0	4713.4	0.0	56217.5	365.4	0.0	1.6	0.0	0.0	0.0	2803.7	45446.1	4604.6	486582.9	2070.1	1283.1	3703.8	5261.7	37.1	0.0	0.0	0.0	0.0
51	2540.8	572.2	0.0	455.3	68722.8	2865.8	7.9	19.5	29.9	4200.2	8.9	10030.5	47589.7	5104.5	409.8	292.4	89.6	20.2	5.4	220.9	11.4	0.0	77.7
52	493187.3	0.0	0.0	7.3	0.0	408552.9	532.3	141.6	58.3	429.5	13.5	10787.8	15.1	283.3	830.6	259.8	2.2	1436.6	16.9	7.6	0.0	0.0	0.0
53	844.7	4484.4	0.0	287.7	165.7	505.6	256110.5	119396.2	3044.8	323.3	67.5	9244.7	296.0	230.5	275.0	245.5	291.3	233.0	71.0	102.8	23.5	0.0	145.1
54	1244.3	1887.1	0.0	1687.3	471.0	1675.1	25457.4	71194.5	309.1	2032.4	144.8	2107.3	4296.2	1485.8	815.2	1194.5	1460.3	572.9	531.2	372.2	61.3	0.0	1848.4
55	13743.7	1000.8	0.0	594.7	184.8	1494.3	868.6	187.4	115167.0	928.2	80.0	2556.8	4026.3	671.7	449.3	1486.9	800.3	432.3	406.1	10354.5	4249.1	0.0	497.7
56	9312.5	1350.5	0.0	616.7	447.4	50699.6	2247.0	1097.3	5592.0	387201.7	224.6	39107.0	13916.7	1174.1	1224.4	3748.1	2348.8	2445.2	6806.4	14460.9	8664.4	0.0	2614.2
57	58422.1	3110.3	0.0	9666.2	5213.3	3484.3	1486.3	135.4	1426.4	2485.4	31866.5	19426.1	44561.5	48367.2	1692.8	5047.3	4014.4	3891.8	327.5	268.8	12762.5	0.0	6091.8
58	506259.2	6231.3	0.0	26428.8	20676.5	74922.6	48833.6	6435.1	47293.6	52463.3	10776.4	843767.2	63588.6	27952.3	8322.1	51904.5	35935.0	21964.0	11813.4	30953.1	22428.7	0.0	5974.7
59	11389.8	8236.4	0.0	3048.7	29564.1	16694.9	1220.0	267.8	504.7	709.4	389.4	19886.1	357952.1	25886.9	4806.7	8068.3	7013.4	26375.9	563.8	3311.6	1695.0	0.0	1387.5
60	1755.8	6864.2	0.0	36900.9	1368.1	2441.2	454.2	76.6	277.2	78705.9	15173.1	43258.2	78542.1	588513.7	99817.7	108641.4	69352.9	162120.4	4861.9	13782.9	2317.8	0.0	2815.0
61	25581.7	5157.8	0.0	3465.0	1952.1	9258.5	1347.9	248.2	8524.6	9458.8	1024.6	8582.9	26043.8	4691.5	119680.2	65758.2	27787.6	10402.6	1201.7	12753.4	26483.3	0.0	5481.1
62	42653.8	9736.1	0.0	23234.8	4453.0	10375.0	3640.9	389.8	14192.9	8964.6	3241.0	14143.5	18777.3	50439.1	14988.7	196041.4	123373.0	64485.2	1032.2	3518.5	608.1	0.0	40843.0
63	11376.3	1469.5	0.0	8593.5	942.2	1995.9	801.4	98.2	1467.3	223.5	706.3	1248.1	2876.5	3515.6	573.6	7155.2	433613.4	7829.9	75.7	1969.9	139.4	0.0	5469.5
64	1107.0	2678.2	0.0	3361.2	1765.3	3483.8	1392.6	199.4	892.5	982.4	1246.1	5730.8	8433.5	5089.7	2245.7	14952.5	17227.4	39925.5	3693.1	1415.8	280.5	0.0	46700.5
65	3704.6	631.2	0.0	813.4	302.0	1249.5	335.6	117.7	328.2	370.8	555.8	2234.9	1278.2	700.4	173.6	2875.8	24124.2	7557.9	115628.2	11356.2	41847.9	0.0	4163.6
66	947.6	985.4	0.0	1216.6	577.6	1948.3	571.0	157.5	376.3	3158.9	479.7	4467.2	2665.2	2008.2	974.6	9817.4	1325.9	613.9	198.6	18348.5	177.2	0.0	4676.6
67	4913.8	1572.6	0.0	644.8	1024.0	54221.5	369.4	1366.2	457.6	18746.3	4022.2	31756.4	30863.6	2764.1	948.5	23475.6	10358.9	13557.7	1340.2	13136.0	39537.7	0.0	674.3
68	628.6	0.0	0.0	269.6	146.0	840.6	3.6	0.7	0.0	5468.0	0.0	4061.0	16292.7	74988.3	0.0	25830.2	177.2	866.1	0.0	5873.1	0.0	0.0	1541.5
69	55527.1	30338.1	0.0	68199.8	9164.8	42140.3	14652.4	2414.0	15909.7	11241.8	7672.0	90767.2	124875.6	109306.2	13035.7	21336.3	30566.5	11571.9	2335.4	4052.3	3279.6	0.0	104382.6
70	0.0	0.0	0.0	78.6	0.0	348.3	116.7	4.5	166.3	237.0	463.2	1207.8	4070.4	2203.2	741.3	9.3	46.7	546.8	92.0	1.4	0.0	0.0	0.0
71	2069.7	1469.3	0.0	3595.1	211.6	10092.6	1783.6	656.9	1570.3	1792.1	243.5	8116.9	8012.8	6273.9	738.0	3495.3	2100.9	1426.5	481.2	1006.8	247.0	0.0	78411.9

Continued

-	1	2	3	4	5	6	7	8	9	10	11	12	13	14	15	16	17	18	19	20	21	22	23
72	12846.7	724.1	0.0	172.8	47.0	556.9	172.5	111.2	101.3	125.7	21.4	1666.0	2083.9	1967.8	93.8	190.0	1564.4	153.8	146.7	141.9	247.4	0.0	62076.6
73	180226.4	21031.1	0.0	21231.8	82003.0	122000.3	16770.5	8567.5	69618.5	43149.2	43611.5	130702.7	208748.0	148733.0	19590.6	44045.5	45437.6	19794.9	5469.4	11507.8	11711.6	0.0	79240.6
74	3071.5	85.9	0.0	65.8	160.3	745.9	114.1	103.4	428.7	532.7	55.2	1347.7	1762.6	298.8	52.1	516.9	254.5	151.0	168.3	589.4	31.8	0.0	693.8
75	19103.8	925.6	0.0	543.4	619.7	9855.3	688.0	725.3	3156.3	1553.3	367.4	3185.0	4544.1	990.0	1468.1	2466.4	1584.6	950.6	760.6	1208.4	147.3	0.0	3955.8
76	172451.4	10059.2	0.0	12168.2	16686.6	137386.0	39339.1	28946.0	54422.1	76411.2	43379.6	130407.4	61939.6	93704.9	23897.7	46200.6	44860.2	38187.4	14737.1	13200.5	18048.3	0.0	28487.5
77	19202.4	5432.6	0.0	1704.8	2953.3	23636.2	1925.3	3731.2	5797.8	6480.4	990.6	22035.6	21892.7	3360.3	2648.8	11273.3	6254.9	3785.0	2293.8	3013.6	1119.1	0.0	9697.5
78	66476.7	12225.8	0.0	20873.7	6026.5	50681.6	16368.7	7034.0	14072.9	21887.1	24148.5	70655.3	70008.9	49965.9	5902.1	24932.2	36485.5	14267.1	7128.8	8118.7	6680.4	0.0	76377.7
79	485.2	4.1	0.0	428.0	85.1	4692.3	621.6	248.4	2500.5	1491.9	17.6	1026.3	2374.1	887.2	1129.9	518.2	1176.6	380.8	280.5	33.4	349.5	0.0	0.0
80	8520.4	1028.0	0.0	5743.2	8115.9	53143.7	1423.2	2812.6	2928.8	8507.2	641.3	44560.3	11545.0	3064.9	3246.1	5924.6	29451.4	2779.3	1967.5	1456.5	321.2	0.0	1121.9
81	1.4	27.9	0.0	5.8	0.8	71.4	1.4	0.0	0.7	0.3	12.9	118.0	7.5	5.4	0.7	9.4	10.3	30.9	11.4	1.0	0.8	0.0	12.2
82	1108.5	104.1	0.0	401.3	2.1	3933.5	66.8	46.5	450.4	308.3	3082.8	3885.9	4100.5	3299.8	38.7	929.9	16688.2	1090.3	4266.6	817.9	1234.7	0.0	161.9
83	3637.9	53.8	0.0	337.0	50.6	1836.0	25.6	1.4	666.5	515.1	272.5	567.9	1078.0	1427.3	498.6	280.4	119.1	291.1	104.8	1753.3	5.5	0.0	679.0
84	16655.8	1428.7	0.0	972.6	129.5	7653.1	312.2	445.4	941.2	1394.2	218.3	7221.0	5712.3	1255.7	115.7	2291.6	3692.6	833.1	191.4	183.1	109.2	0.0	9410.0
85	829.0	257.4	0.0	238.2	15.1	339.0	12.7	19.9	31.5	112.5	66.1	286.5	417.8	211.7	68.3	200.9	377.7	81.4	54.1	83.6	39.0	0.0	427.9
86	8350.8	836.7	0.0	263.6	60.2	163.1	15.6	20.0	166.5	390.0	1855.7	2938.8	1047.7	1264.0	65.1	186.7	4667.1	52.7	10.6	107.6	0.0	0.0	347.7
87	3317.2	2562.7	0.0	541.1	959.7	9449.0	635.8	1629.9	2128.3	3088.2	319.6	9154.3	8678.2	1091.6	1142.4	2825.7	2163.0	1298.2	917.6	844.5	448.4	0.0	3882.9
88	45174.5	0.0	0.0	0.0	0.0	0.0	0.0	0.0	0.0	0.0	0.0	0.0	0.0	0.0	0.0	0.0	0.0	0.0	0.0	0.0	0.0	0.0	0.0
89	24221.3	229.0	0.0	46.3	16.1	34298.3	2844.6	134.8	2332.5	109.3	59.0	2627.1	214.2	87.2	25.1	118.3	282.1	40.3	56.3	40.0	1766.2	0.0	151.4
90	9528.0	81.0	0.0	12.9	4.0	13671.8	1135.7	49.5	924.1	31.9	11.8	1002.0	43.0	17.5	6.1	33.7	56.6	8.7	11.3	8.3	702.7	0.0	30.3
91	2582.7	33.5	0.0	10.2	4.1	3477.3	286.6	17.9	242.2	22.7	17.7	311.6	64.1	26.1	6.4	25.5	84.5	11.4	16.9	11.7	180.3	0.0	45.4
92	174.5	16.9	0.0	31.4	26.8	111.0	44.2	25.7	37.3	75.3	46.8	170.3	132.2	183.4	33.3	69.0	96.5	46.5	18.5	18.7	20.6	0.0	78.3
93	4933506.7	215266.9	0.0	90188.4	24561.3	156692.3	75045.2	40721.2	78722.2	84682.0	16830.6	193720.8	256563.9	158229.8	46544.3	146542.5	138734.7	53148.5	30652.7	52709.7	38794.7	0.0	175470.0
94	470355.8	27290.4	0.0	38828.7	39357.1	224569.6	18203.1	7417.2	51584.6	63732.7	18001.4	138262.6	142407.5	93167.3	20647.5	60817.2	72878.3	26199.6	22269.1	20884.4	5656.0	163164.5	373100.5
95	40357.8	0.0	0.0	0.0	0.0	0.0	0.0	0.0	0.0	0.0	0.0	0.0	0.0	0.0	0.0	0.0	0.0	0.0	0.0	0.0	0.0	0.0	0.0
96	23542.0	0.0	0.0	0.0	0.0	0.0	0.0	0.0	0.0	0.0	0.0	0.0	0.0	0.0	0.0	0.0	0.0	0.0	0.0	0.0	0.0	0.0	0.0
97	3363.1	0.0	0.0	0.0	0.0	0.0	0.0	0.0	0.0	0.0	0.0	0.0	0.0	0.0	0.0	0.0	0.0	0.0	0.0	0.0	0.0	0.0	0.0
98	0.0	7098.1	0.0	10228.4	2767.9	7174.8	1066.6	347.5	1555.5	2301.4	1626.1	8826.9	9421.3	7345.4	1103.1	3428.9	4378.4	1365.6	997.2	953.6	189.5	0.0	36065.8

Continued

-	1	2	3	4	5	6	7	8	9	10	11	12	13	14	15	16	17	18	19	20	21	22	23
101	212837.8	262132.6	0.0	43017.4	22903.4	221344.3	42615.2	26128.7	83257.7	56709.4	43611.4	271450.2	383399.4	212774.7	44991.7	102984.1	192937.7	64883.2	22620.7	52196.7	27742.0	0.0	417322.0
104	8679924.8	694767.8	0.0	499565.4	358588.2	3446078.2	721296.0	339454.8	706870.6	968461.3	554455.7	2459084.7	2135509.0	2313986.8	448838.9	1013503.7	1401727.7	614506.1	266714.9	317260.8	367310.7	163164.5	1799945.6
-	24	25	26	27	28	29	30	31	32	33	34	35	36	37	38	39	40	41	42	43	44	45	46
47	0.0	0.0	164351.3	7516.5	0.0	0.0	634.3	197044.7	0.0	1945.3	0.0	0.0	0.0	619.7	591.8	0.0	0.0	0.0	0.0	2649.0	1589.4	1059.6	1324.5
48	26468.8	19.1	20554.6	484.0	12.1	0.0	0.0	2470.7	0.0	6404.5	0.0	0.0	0.0	0.0	2458.4	0.0	0.0	0.0	0.0	0.0	0.0	0.0	0.0
49	12588.9	0.0	0.0	5451.3	0.0	0.0	0.0	6637.1	0.0	0.0	0.0	0.0	0.0	0.0	0.0	0.0	0.0	0.0	0.0	207.4	124.5	83.0	103.7
50	0.0	0.0	0.0	0.0	0.0	0.0	0.0	0.0	0.0	0.0	0.0	0.0	0.0	0.0	0.0	0.0	0.0	0.0	0.0	468.8	281.3	187.5	234.4
51	8.4	4.2	134417.2	20772.9	0.0	0.0	0.0	0.0	0.0	0.0	0.0	0.0	53.5	13.2	47.6	486.9	130.3	20.0	278.1	0.0	0.0	0.0	0.0
52	0.0	120.4	0.0	2251.5	0.0	0.3	718.3	251689.2	0.0	225.9	258.1	0.0	0.0	16.5	0.0	0.0	0.0	214.4	0.0	563.2	337.9	225.3	281.6
53	6.8	190.4	94.8	1416.8	477.5	0.0	4423.8	11287.7	268.8	789.5	27.0	11.1	0.0	0.0	45.8	0.0	0.0	394.1	0.0	340.3	204.2	136.1	170.2
54	595.4	352.6	24420.9	8766.5	1618.1	2598.0	3629.1	1799.8	988.8	1809.7	492.6	115.0	140.0	316.5	154.8	553.2	241.1	61.1	161.0	827.3	496.4	330.9	413.7
55	60.5	794.0	249815.4	5847.5	860.8	635.9	6410.8	740.3	5645.9	1672.0	5529.7	1.0	1335.1	330.4	1493.3	12146.4	3250.3	626.5	6938.8	607.3	364.4	242.9	303.6
56	619.8	635.3	34729.0	26974.3	4048.0	3048.5	14433.8	13051.6	53263.5	6939.8	19642.8	135.0	4166.0	2569.6	24307.0	40728.8	4361.6	51711.4	37612.6	187.8	112.7	75.1	93.9
57	921.5	333.5	195362.6	333266.8	3481.4	1707.3	48921.1	19378.1	12987.2	2814.3	2062.6	560.0	3025.8	2179.1	9481.0	8171.6	3746.9	4322.7	27659.5	0.0	0.0	0.0	0.0
58	645.7	4604.0	209825.3	44734.5	1507.7	275.7	5272.0	16550.0	6900.3	2080.1	14940.5	67.5	1598.2	413.8	2564.8	13152.0	185839.0	2370.2	7184.4	769.2	461.5	307.7	384.6
59	69.7	805.1	857035.0	16467.3	1220.5	0.0	1173.1	3751.6	0.0	13935.5	9563.4	0.0	1013.0	380.5	1075.1	9215.9	2466.2	378.5	5264.7	310.8	186.5	124.3	155.4
60	247.8	1606.9	714862.1	4751.4	0.0	0.0	29.6	78.7	0.0	1755.3	1879.2	0.0	91.4	2577.7	81.2	831.1	222.4	34.1	474.8	224.2	134.5	89.7	112.1
61	3021.1	677.6	287821.8	1899.0	169.0	504.4	1858.7	2105.3	1525.6	2983.4	6.0	1.1	471.4	116.7	454.9	4289.0	1147.7	176.2	2450.2	383.5	230.1	153.4	191.7
62	1221.6	5062.4	127963.6	5058.8	1987.0	1496.8	5479.2	1626.8	5072.7	5305.5	3948.1	0.0	2458.8	1005.5	14631.6	3438.8	255072.8	81.5	2641.6	7215.3	4329.2	2886.1	3607.6
63	254.5	1352.2	38267.1	202029.0	663.2	1432.0	33115.6	124.9	5662.2	2145.5	3990.7	0.0	180.8	47.6	6056.9	1644.7	440.1	4241.1	939.6	5447.6	3268.6	2179.0	2723.8
64	477.0	1525.8	259841.4	3308.9	363.5	12669.3	381.0	1543.4	2856.9	9321.3	204.0	4.9	1114.3	331.7	29055.5	10138.0	2712.9	14654.4	5791.5	1262.2	757.3	504.9	631.1
65	170.4	561.0	7819.4	8553.2	70.2	17774.3	2050.5	1287.7	2177.1	3499.4	1203.4	2.7	231.2	1082.0	7047.4	2172.3	539.5	96.2	1562.1	4249.4	2549.6	1699.8	2124.7
66	330.9	1115.4	24258.0	624.4	696.6	16403.0	1343.9	212.8	2849.5	2325.8	10841.2	61.1	1797.0	1286.0	1793.4	4246.7	429.1	719.0	3674.0	349.0	209.4	139.6	174.5
67	9.6	2052.2	14243.2	8716.3	0.0	200.3	0.6	999.9	948.4	0.0	742.5	0.0	0.0	0.0	1874.9	0.0	0.0	0.0	0.0	0.0	0.0	0.0	0.0
68	0.0	0.0	0.0	913.2	0.0	0.0	0.0	0.0	0.0	0.0	0.0	0.0	0.0	0.0	0.0	0.0	0.0	0.0	0.0	48.6	29.2	19.5	24.3
69	13514.6	70344.0	113163.7	23086.6	3775.5	39381.1	159929.0	52220.5	29855.0	4503.2	45063.7	2781.0	5310.5	2175.6	19755.9	63989.5	19933.1	16608.3	26624.7	0.8	0.5	0.3	0.4
70	731.6	0.0	0.0	49.3	3.3	0.0	0.0	5538.6	0.0	215.9	0.0	1.9	0.0	0.0	3.8	0.0	0.0	0.0	0.0	0.0	0.0	0.0	0.0

Continued

-	24	25	26	27	28	29	30	31	32	33	34	35	36	37	38	39	40	41	42	43	44	45	46
71	1370.8	8618.0	13791.8	3091.3	361.7	2690.1	19853.8	14501.3	7488.6	886.7	3433.0	310.6	1485.7	608.9	2463.6	31866.0	10688.1	4987.3	6869.9	0.8	0.5	0.3	0.4
72	17.6	125.7	219176.7	23217.2	3557.3	21103.3	60058.8	23901.7	23380.0	91008.9	26315.3	552.7	2418.5	722.6	56283.2	22003.4	5888.1	8387.1	92688.4	70229.1	42137.4	28091.6	35114.5
73	9617.8	4998.2	381529.4	532677.5	4386.9	6250.4	160203.6	21093.7	44674.1	6744.4	19745.9	1784.0	5728.5	4768.7	7637.9	30256.5	12902.2	11008.6	32993.0	553.0	331.8	221.2	276.5
74	404.8	68.0	3121.2	1554.0	213.5	724.8	5408.5	156.1	13172.8	349.9	3066.0	48.2	384.8	185.9	473.1	2827.9	435.3	1012.1	2662.4	0.0	0.0	0.0	0.0
75	362.1	647.7	15871.5	26941.4	2185.4	28027.1	82480.2	4479.0	40864.6	3583.5	11821.6	748.7	4554.8	1969.9	3383.7	32616.2	4291.4	8519.4	43245.8	0.0	0.0	0.0	0.0
76	3493.5	1721.7	336134.1	74578.9	20910.1	22669.2	349547.7	54058.5	14761.7	11953.9	13110.3	265.2	2137.3	8923.8	13249.2	11525.7	53613.2	9142.6	13592.4	1883.2	1129.9	753.3	941.6
77	2154.0	1506.8	148501.9	43737.1	1258.6	8076.9	68070.6	7161.7	48143.6	10889.6	12507.8	2530.2	6876.1	4775.8	9146.3	31683.9	6104.8	11372.5	61428.7	0.0	0.0	0.0	0.0
78	4373.3	7189.1	97991.3	181088.7	2799.0	46080.0	43821.4	39039.0	14713.2	67683.5	6465.0	8838.1	4757.6	1955.1	38022.6	23593.2	1787.1	16372.5	18525.9	4.3	2.6	1.7	2.1
79	93.6	0.0	587.9	1865.8	507.7	4438.3	40084.2	24444.4	43988.8	6241.1	259.9	17.1	0.0	0.0	52.1	0.0	0.0	0.0	0.0	602.5	361.5	241.0	301.2
80	686.7	210.5	50310.3	45319.2	3634.6	24005.0	57483.7	31120.8	53589.5	0.0	247774.4	442.2	2042.8	1279.6	6197.5	60101.3	1696.8	7073.4	19342.6	0.0	0.0	0.0	0.0
81	0.0	0.0	0.0	213.0	0.0	0.0	0.0	28.7	0.0	280.9	30.9	41039.5	0.0	0.0	0.0	0.0	0.0	0.0	0.0	0.0	0.0	0.0	0.0
82	19.4	475.0	21295.0	4097.4	0.4	85.9	38.5	0.0	267.0	58.8	0.0	0.0	38850.4	1364.2	12810.8	42465.0	10680.7	18118.3	64956.1	41.3	24.8	16.5	20.6
83	16.2	36.1	14737.8	8773.5	4.3	0.0	6174.6	11.3	0.0	574.1	0.0	0.0	66.1	1303.7	3.2	8586.4	13.5	7.6	0.0	676.2	405.7	270.5	338.1
84	1187.3	4123.0	12825.0	113862.4	306.1	2335.5	52714.5	3187.8	8669.3	16090.7	34610.6	294.2	758.4	442.9	2370.3	7149.5	1850.2	540.2	3929.0	49.3	29.6	19.7	24.6
85	116.5	142.5	3591.5	1595.0	0.0	383.3	2431.8	121.4	1586.3	267.6	175.0	29.8	709.9	122.9	522.8	3357.0	510.0	79.7	4503.8	0.0	0.0	0.0	0.0
86	7114.9	11.8	0.0	4528.1	0.0	8.2	380.0	344.2	2205.4	87.2	63.8	2282.5	5446.3	7606.1	13043.2	35890.7	19618.2	6573.4	30212.5	0.0	0.0	0.0	0.0
87	1047.5	689.0	22315.4	1317.3	0.0	1767.8	31156.5	2064.5	10514.0	0.0	521.0	1.7	3305.9	1070.6	3614.5	51144.4	34653.7	37248.3	23553.4	0.0	0.0	0.0	0.0
88	0.0	0.0	0.0	1658.2	291.2	0.0	0.0	0.0	1048.3	0.0	574.4	51.1	154.5	0.0	7.5	0.0	20.6	73.2	213.4	0.0	0.0	0.0	0.0
89	96.5	55.6	4147.7	1534.0	6.1	46.5	956.2	4120.9	246.6	213.5	364.9	27.0	500.4	133.7	340.9	1508.6	683.7	635.9	1293.1	0.0	0.0	0.0	0.0
90	19.3	11.1	1507.3	337.8	1.2	9.3	193.9	1636.7	49.3	50.7	73.0	5.4	100.1	29.3	70.6	301.7	136.7	127.2	258.6	0.0	0.0	0.0	0.0
91	28.9	16.7	566.6	429.2	1.8	14.0	284.2	423.7	74.0	56.0	109.5	8.1	150.1	37.6	99.8	452.6	205.1	190.8	387.9	0.0	0.0	0.0	0.0
92	8.5	11.7	458.2	166.0	6.1	26.2	117.6	61.3	43.6	26.8	46.5	6.0	5.3	4.0	25.9	42.2	57.8	17.5	42.1	0.0	0.0	0.0	0.0
93	48240.6	95484.9	1928084.6	693880.3	48063.2	99282.5	854170.6	137918.2	467933.6	172053.2	157872.1	18218.6	180017.1	114710.9	284991.7	992879.7	427905.6	210594.1	581062.1	21977.2	8193.5	2795.1	667.4
94	(28569.4)	59066.4	343257.6	324426.5	10371.8	287811.3	485193.7	256154.1	169713.1	472394.5	58629.8	11733.5	14199.2	8393.0	73240.2	91659.5	132549.6	(11976.3)	48439.2	5510.2	2054.3	700.8	167.3
95	0.0	0.0	0.0	0.0	0.0	0.0	0.0	0.0	0.0	0.0	0.0	0.0	0.0	0.0	0.0	0.0	0.0	0.0	0.0	0.0	577.4	91.9	22.0
96	0.0	0.0	0.0	0.0	0.0	0.0	0.0	0.0	0.0	0.0	0.0	0.0	0.0	0.0	0.0	0.0	0.0	0.0	0.0	1548.9	0.0	197.0	47.0
97	0.0	0.0	0.0	0.0	0.0	0.0	0.0	0.0	0.0	0.0	0.0	0.0	0.0	0.0	0.0	0.0	0.0	0.0	0.0	1290.7	481.2	164.2	39.2

Continued

-	24	25	26	27	28	29	30	31	32	33	34	35	36	37	38	39	40	41	42	43	44	45	46
98	2778.5	4509.0	138759.7	238081.1	3339.5	13325.5	15427.6	28688.9	13572.1	377311.0	2783.2	6062.4	105.4	244.7	1961.1	663.7	1905.0	1131.4	834.2	722.8	269.5	0.0	0.0
101	16421.7	42265.4	169822.4	143767.4	6252.3	3074.3	387772.0	117786.7	14406.3	62951.3	59405.8	3045.5	9605.4	7665.5	15698.3	506.7	5065.0	59574.4	116.1	5952.7	2219.3	757.1	180.8
104	133065.0	324139.8	7407231.2	3205678.1	129413.2	670362.8	3013828.2	1362644.1	1126107.7	1372429.6	780155.0	102084.5	307347.6	183781.5	668685.1	1658286.9	1213795.4	497520.9	1180408.0	137153.7	73885.9	44766.5	51199.3

* Negative in parentheses

Table 2. Outputs of Commodities

-	47	48	49	50	51	52	53	54	55	56	57	58	59	60	61	62	63	64	65	66	67	68	69
1	8679924.8																						
2		694767.8																					
3			0.0																				
4				499565.4																			
5					358588.2																		
6						3446078.2																	
7							721296.0																
8								339454.8															
9									706870.6														
10										968461.3													
11											554455.7												
12												2459084.7											
13													2135509.0										
14														2313986.8									
15															448838.9								
16																1013503.7							
17																	1401727.7						
18																		614506.1					
19																			266714.9				
20																				317260.8			
21																					367310.7		
22																						163164.5	
23																							1799945.6
24																							
25																							
26																							
27																							

Continued

-	47	48	49	50	51	52	53	54	55	56	57	58	59	60	61	62	63	64	65	66	67	68	69
28																							
29																							
30																							
31																							
32																							
33																							
34																							
35																							
36																							
37																							
38																							
39																							
40																							
41																							
42																							
43																							
44																							
45																							
46																							
101	94298.1	12004.9	154706.8	47212.7	74243.4	138902.6	20140.3	9644.6	34390.6	70252.4	34747.5	94770.7	331501.2	13515.3	67097.8	47044.8	70992.2	33225.7	11520.7	27834.0	28511.1	11282.8	175474.6
103	418783.7	183725.6	742798.8	338552.0	97622.9	72525.1	17301.9	413873.5	792.9	444132.2	366314.4	392283.8	100537.9	110255.7	275240.4	945064.6	382214.7	8972458.5	60490721.6	3561.2	5336.9	38.8	281931.4
104	9193006.6	890498.3	897505.6	885330.1	530454.5	3657505.9	758738.2	762973.0	742054.0	1482845.8	955517.6	2946139.1	2567548.1	2437757.7	791177.1	2005613.1	1854934.6	9620190.4	60768957.2	348656.0	401158.7	174486.1	2257351.6
-	70	71	72	73	74	75	76	77	78	79	80	81	82	83	84	85	86	87	88	89	90	91	92
1																							
2																							
3																							
4																							

Continued

-	70	71	72	73	74	75	76	77	78	79	80	81	82	83	84	85	86	87	88	89	90	91	92
5																							
6																							
7																							
8																							
9																							
10																							
11																							
12																							
13																							
14																							
15																							
16																							
17																							
18																							
19																							
20																							
21																							
22																							
23																							
24	133065.0																						
25		324139.8																					

Continued

-	70	71	72	73	74	75	76	77	78	79	80	81	82	83	84	85	86	87	88	89	90	91	92
26			7407231.2																				
27				3205678.1																			
28					129413.2																		
29						670362.8																	
30							3013828.2																
31								1362644.1															
32									1126107.7														
33										1372429.6													
34											780155.0												
35												102084.5											
36													307347.6										
37														183781.5									
38															668685.1								
39																1658286.9							
40																	1213795.4						
41																		497520.9					
42																			1180408.0				
43																				137153.7			
44																					73885.9		
45																						44766.5	
46																							51199.3

Continued

-	70	71	72	73	74	75	76	77	78	79	80	81	82	83	84	85	86	87	88	89	90	91	92
101	9556.4	0.0	0.0	34458.9	621.8	17014.5	58017.5	75813.4	7710.1	2697.9	38617.2	975.6	0.0	0.0	17237.5	145.0	2933.2	19035.7	0.0	0.0	0.0	0.0	0.0
103	6350.3	0.0	0.0	295540.8	117496.2	36289.0	490454.4	170057.4	216911.8	92690.7	8945.0	27386.6	0.0	0.0	16761.7	209385.4	36415.0	65622.0	0.0	0.0	0.0	0.0	0.0
104	148971.8	324139.8	7407231.2	3535677.7	247531.3	723666.3	3562300.1	1608514.9	1350729.6	1467818.1	827717.2	130446.8	307347.6	183781.5	702684.3	1867817.3	1253143.6	582178.6	1180408.0	137153.7	73885.9	44766.5	51199.3

Table 3. Outputs of other accounts

-	93	94	95	96	97	98	99	100	101	102	103	104
1												8679924.8
2												694767.8
3												0.0
4												499565.4
5												358588.2
6												3446078.2
7												721296.0
8												339454.8
9												706870.6
10												968461.3
11												554455.7
12												2459084.7
13												2135509.0
14												2313986.8
15												448838.9
16												1013503.7
17												1401727.7
18												614506.1
19												266714.9
20												317260.8
21												367310.7
22												163164.5
23												1799945.6
24												133065.0
25												324139.8
26												7407231.2
27												3205678.1

-	93	94	95	96	97	98	99	100	101	102	103	104
53							142237.5		0.0	33179.5	166647.9	758738.2
54							507253.1		0.0	80664.1	3325.0	762973.0
55							138667.2		0.0	59207.2	78346.6	742054.0
56							208414.1		0.0	18307.8	357376.7	1482845.8
57							14936.9		0.0	(4625.1)	1074.7	955517.6
58							395477.4		0.0	75000.2	28288.8	2946139.1
59							64648.0		0.0	30305.9	1019029.5	2567548.1
60							4078.1		0.0	21863.9	363690.2	2437757.7
61							29570.4		0.0	37390.1	36693.3	791177.1
62							8289.4		0.0	703487.0	183113.7	2005613.1
63							94404.4		0.0	531143.1	421039.7	1854934.6
64							125120.6		0.0	123064.2	8849750.7	9620190.4
65							167548.7		0.0	414316.5	59898219.0	60768957.2
66							46672.9		0.0	34027.0	136383.6	348656.0
67							32374.7		0.0	(5797.6)	89042.3	401158.7
68							0.0		0.0	4741.9	31722.2	174486.1
69							170256.8		0.0	82.1	602225.8	2257351.6
70							129503.4		0.0	(38.4)	2628.9	148971.8
71							64669.8		0.0	(9695.2)	0.0	324139.8
72							0.0		0.0	6465640.2	0.0	7407231.2
73							379156.2		3529.7	53913.5	465503.1	3535677.7
74							9614.6		0.0	0.0	190417.2	247531.3
75							321648.1		0.0	0.0	26625.3	723666.3
76							954528.2		0.0	183607.8	299146.7	3562300.1
77							648651.0		0.0	0.0	314707.8	1608514.9
78							0.0		0.0	415.9	114889.7	1350729.6
79							1114213.6		0.0	58741.7	152044.6	1467818.1

Continued

-	93	94	95	96	97	98	99	100	101	102	103	104	-	93	94	95	96	97	98	99	100	101	102	103	104
28												129413.2	80							1826.9		0.0	0.0	15276.4	827717.2
29												670362.8	81							42957.8		0.0	0.0	45565.8	130446.8
30												3013828.2	82							0.0		41193.2	4450.1	0.0	307347.6
31												1362644.1	83							0.0		63256.3	64324.8	0.0	183781.5
32												1126107.7	84							191381.7		125884.1	4801.9	52080.2	702684.3
33												1372429.6	85							841660.0		904971.2	0.0	96769.0	1867817.3
34												780155.0	86							196340.9		876347.2	0.0	22228.5	1253143.6
35												102084.5	87							89462.0		82659.4	0.0	126993.3	582178.6
36												307347.6	88							0.0		1131141.3	0.0	0.0	1180408.0
37												183781.5	89							0.0		50542.3	0.0	0.0	137153.7
38												668685.1	90							0.0		41595.7	0.0	0.0	73885.9
39												1658286.9	91							0.0		33751.1	0.0	0.0	44766.5
40												1213795.4	92							0.0		48569.1	0.0	0.0	51199.3
41												497520.9	93												14554325.1
42												1180408.0	94												4913914.6
43												137153.7	95												41049.1
44												73885.9	96												25334.9
45												44766.5	97												5338.4
46												51199.3	98												960718.2
47							1999382.1		175514.3	258274.0	3123484.8	9193006.6	99	14554325.1	4913914.6						0.0	666724.0			20134963.7
48							46591.6		0.0	(6566.5)	300981.0	890498.3	100												0.0

Continued

-	93	94	95	96	97	98	99	100	101	102	103	104	-	93	94	95	96	97	98	99	100	101	102	103	104
49							13187.7		0.0	20225.6	547877.1	897505.6	101			41049.1	25334.9	5338.4	960718.2	416269.0					7279031.9
50							0.0		0.0	45706.4	225360.7	885330.1	102							8767277.5		3033353.0			11800630.5
51							2238.8		0.0	(5261.0)	233969.0	530454.5	103										2450820.9		79297195.7
52							1754452.9		0.0	54910.9	674677.0	3657505.9	104	14554325.1	4913914.6	41049.1	25334.9	5338.4	960718.2	20134963.7	0.0	7279031.9	11800630.5	79297195.7	

* Negative in parentheses

Table 4. Code number of production activities, commodities, factors, institutions, capital accounts, account of other regions and the total

Code	Production activities
1	Agriculture, forestry, animal husbandry and fishing
2	Coal mining and dressing
3	Petroleum and natural gas mining
4	Metallic mining
5	Non-metallic mining
6	Food manufacturing and tobacco processing
7	Manufacture of textile
8	Garment leather, eider down and related products production
9	Wood processing and furniture manufacturing
10	Paper printing and stationery
11	Petroleum processing, coking and nuclear fuel processing
12	The chemical industry
13	Non-metallic mineral products industry
14	Metal smelting and rolling processing
15	Metal products industry
16	General and special equipment manufacturing
17	Transportation equipment manufacturing
18	Electrical, machinery and equipment manufacturing
19	Communications equipment, computers and other electronic equipment manufacturing
20	Manufacture of measuring instruments and machinery for cultural activity and office work
21	Other manufacturing industries
22	Waste scrap
23	Electricity, heat production and supply
24	Gas production and supply
25	Water production and supply
26	Construction industry
27	Transportation and warehousing
28	Postal and telecommunication services
29	Information transmission, computer services and software industry
30	Wholesale and retail trade
31	Accommodation and catering
32	Finance and insurance
33	Real estate
34	Leasing and business services
35	Tourism
36	Scientific research business
37	Comprehensive technical services
38	Other social services
39	Education
40	Health, social security and social welfare sector
41	Culture, sports and entertainment
42	Public administration and social organizations
43	Land conversion industry
44	Economic forestry conversion
45	Grassland conversion
46	Other types of land use conversion
	Commodities
47	Agriculture, forestry, animal husbandry and fishing

Continued

Code	Production activities
48	Coal mining and dressing
49	Petroleum and natural gas mining
50	Metallic mining
51	Non-metallic mining
52	Food manufacturing and tobacco processing
53	Manufacture of textile
54	Garment Leather, eider down and related products production
55	Wood processing and furniture manufacturing
56	Paper printing and stationery
57	Petroleum processing, coking and nuclear fuel processing
58	The chemical industry
59	Non-metallic mineral products industry
60	Metal smelting and rolling processing
61	Metal products industry
62	General and special equipment manufacturing
63	Transportation equipment manufacturing
64	Electrical, machinery and equipment manufacturing
65	Communications equipment, computers and other electronic equipment manufacturing
66	Manufacture of measuring instruments and machinery for cultural activity and office work
67	Other manufacturing industries
68	Waste scrap
69	Electricity, heat production and supply
70	Gas production and supply
71	Water production and supply
72	Construction industry
73	Transportation and warehousing
74	Postal and telecommunication services
75	Information transmission, computer services and software industry
76	Wholesale and retail trade
77	Accommodation and catering
78	Finance and insurance
79	Real estate
80	Leasing and business services
81	Tourism
82	Scientific research business
83	Comprehensive technical services
84	Other social services
85	Education
86	Health, social security and social welfare sector
87	Culture, sports and entertainment
88	Public administration and social organizations
89	Cultivated land conversion
90	Economic forestry conversion
91	Grassland conversion
92	Other types of land use conversion
	Factors
93	Labor
94	Capital
95	Cultivated land

Continued

Code	Production activities
96	Economic forests
97	Grassland
98	Other types of land use
	Institutions
99	Residents
100	Businesses
101	Government
	Capital account
102	Investment/Savings
	Account of other regions
103	Rest of world
	Total
104	Total

Index

F

G

H

I

J

K

L

M

N

O

P

R

S

T

U

V

W

X

Y

Z

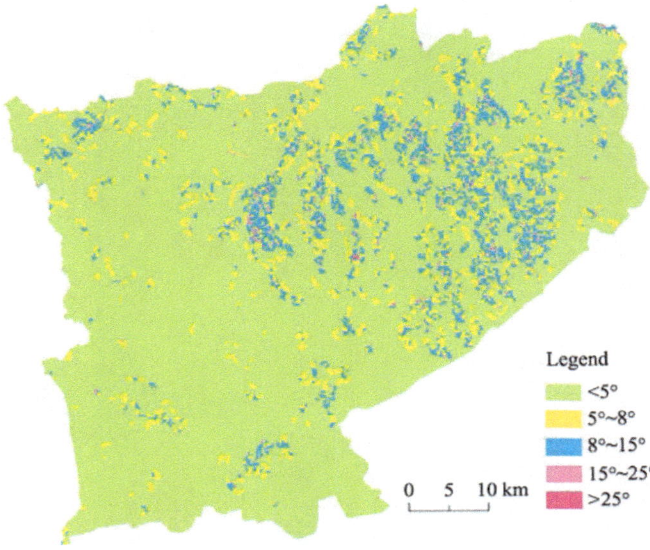

Fig. 7.8 Slope spatial heterogeneity map of the Taips League.

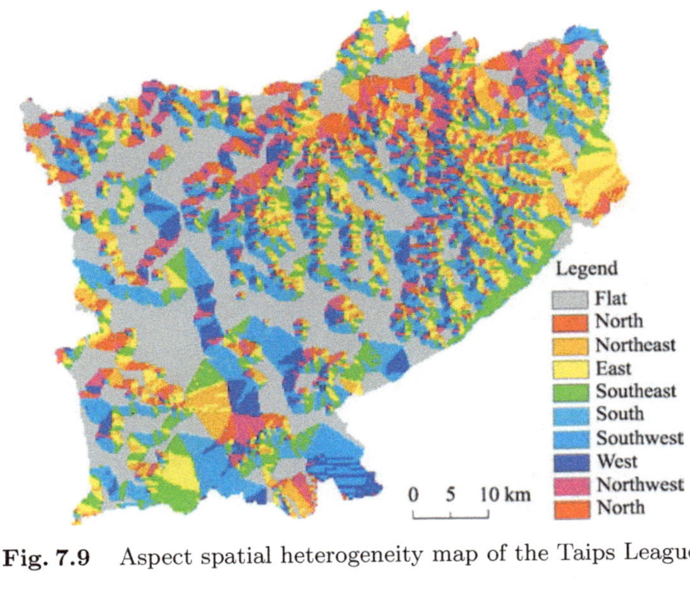

Fig. 7.9 Aspect spatial heterogeneity map of the Taips League.

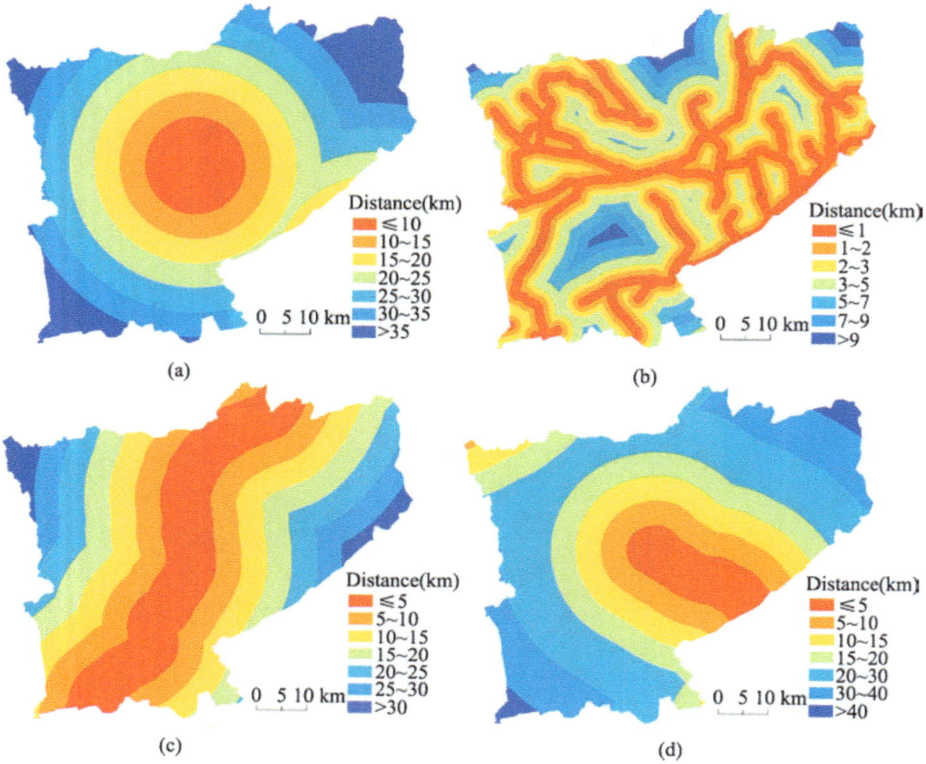

Fig. 7.10 Distance load on the 500×500 m grids of the Taips League.
(a), (b), (c), (d) are the distances to the centers of the county government office, nearest national highway, nearest provincial road and nearest county road, respectively.

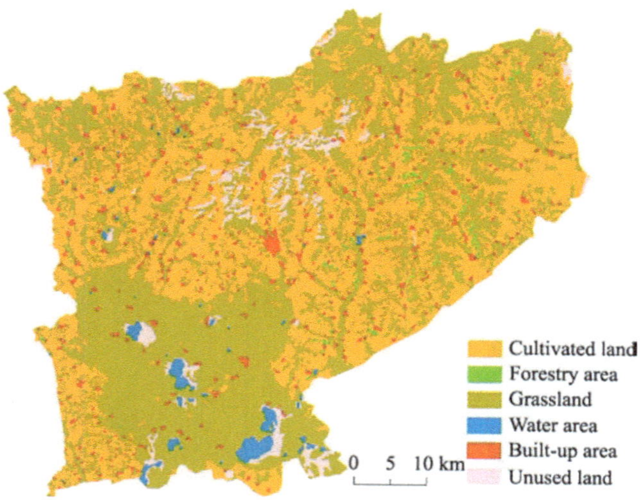

Fig. 7.11 Land use structure raster map of the Taips League in 1995.

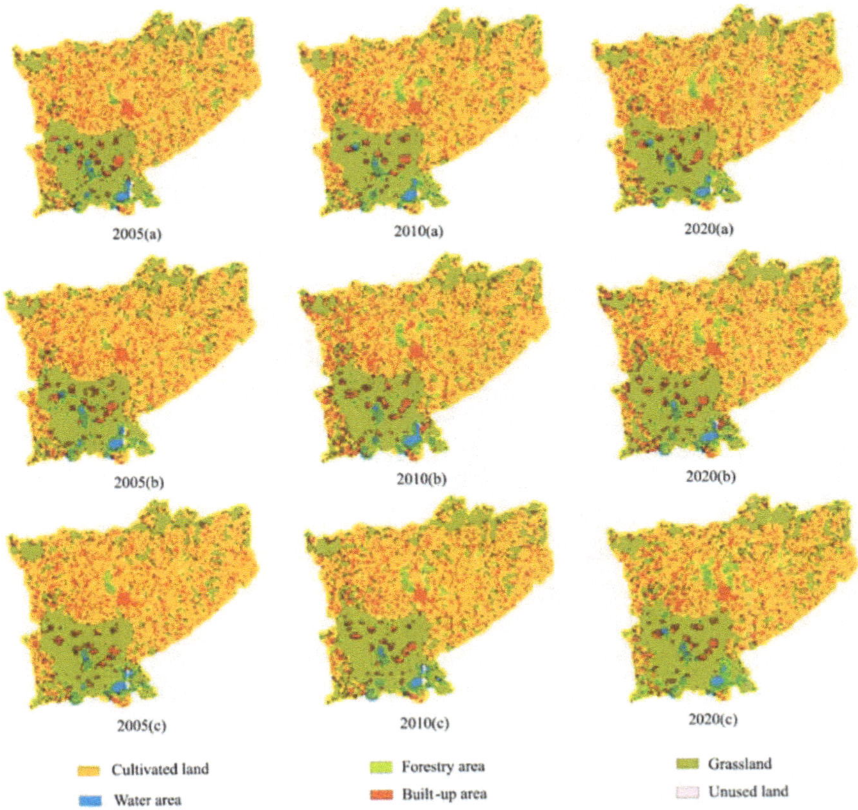

Fig. 7.16 Changing patterns of land system of the Taips League under the (a) baseline, (b) environment protection, and (c) economic priority scenarios.

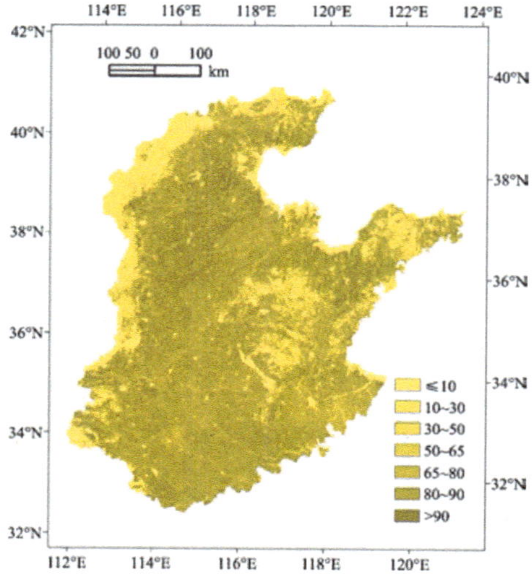

Fig. 8.2 Spatial pattern of cultivated land in 2000 identified by area percentage data.

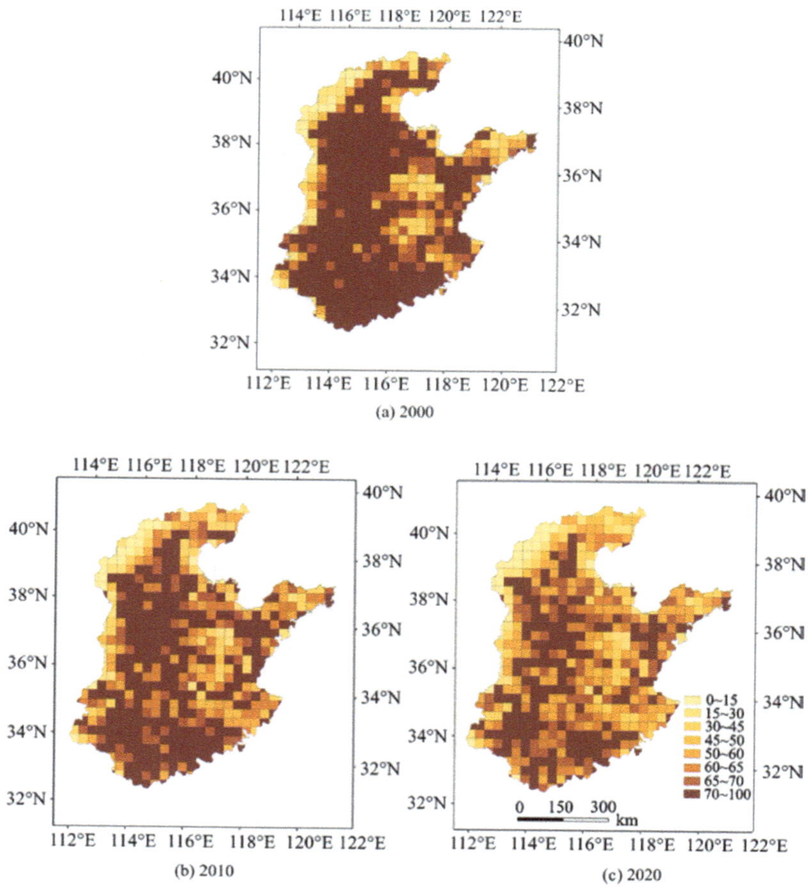

Fig. 8.12 Spatial patterns of cultivated land area which are identified by the area percentage grid data in 2000, 2010 and 2020 (5×5 km grid pixels).